Luck

Sunday Times bestselling author Freda Lightfoot was born in Lancashire. She always dreamed of becoming a writer but this was considered a rather exotic ambition. She has been a teacher, bookseller in the Lake District, then a smallholder and began her writing career by publishing over forty short stories and articles before finding her vocation as a novelist. She has since written over forty-eight novels, mostly sagas and historical fiction. She now spends warm winters living in Spain, and the rainy summers in Britain.

Also by Freda Lightfoot

A Salford Saga

Ruby McBride
The Favourite Child
The Castlefield Collector
Dancing on Deansgate

A Champion Street Market Saga

Putting on the Style
Fools Fall in Love
That'll be the Day
Candy Kisses
Who's Sorry Now
Lonely Teardrops

Lakeland Sagas

Lakeland Lily
The Bobbin Girls
Kitty Little
Gracie's Sin
Daisy's Secret

Luckpenny Land

Luckpenny Land
Storm Clouds Over Broombank
Wishing Water
Larkrigg Fell

Freda LIGHTFOOT
Luckpenny Land

CANELO

First published in the United Kingdom in 1994 by Hodder & Stoughton Ltd

This edition published in the United Kingdom in 2023 by

Canelo
Unit 9, 5th Floor
Cargo Works, 1–2 Hatfields
London SE1 9PG
United Kingdom

Copyright © Freda Lightfoot 1994

The moral right of Freda Lightfoot to be identified as the creator of this work has been asserted in accordance with the Copyright, Designs and Patents Act, 1988.

All rights reserved. No part of this publication may be reproduced or transmitted in any form or by any means, electronic or mechanical, including photocopy, recording, or any information storage and retrieval system, without permission in writing from the publisher.

A CIP catalogue record for this book is available from the British Library.

Print ISBN 978 1 80436 352 2
Ebook ISBN 978 1 80436 113 9

This book is a work of fiction. Names, characters, businesses, organizations, places and events are either the product of the author's imagination or are used fictitiously. Any resemblance to actual persons, living or dead, events or locales is entirely coincidental.

Cover design by Rose Cooper

Cover images © Shutterstock, Arcangel

Look for more great books at www.canelo.co

Printed and bound in Great Britain by Clays Ltd, Elcograf S.p.A.

1

1938

Chapter One

'Anyone would think I was asking to go on the streets.'

The stinging slap sent the honey gold hair swirling about her face, enveloping her burning cheeks in a wash of colour that for a brief moment lit up the shabby kitchen. Any ordinary face would have been hardened and cheapened by the cold light of the single Tilly lamp, but not this one. The girl's face was arresting, alive with the urgency of her request. There was strength in the way she firmed the wide mouth, resolution in the sweeping arch of the brow, in the smoke grey of the eyes fringed by a crescent of dark lashes above cheek bones that would hold their beauty long after time had wrought its damage.

But there was no one to be captivated by Meg Turner's youthful beauty here, certainly not her uncompromising father. Even her two brothers had withdrawn from the scene to a safer distance the moment supper was over, Dan to check the flock for any new lambs, Charlie reluctantly to clean out the sheds.

The remnants of the kitchen fire fell together with a small hushing noise. There was no other sound in the room, save for that of the rain that beat against the window. Outside, great waves of it washed down the hillsides from the high mountain tops, gushed into the overfilled beck and pelted onwards to the River Kent and the distant sea. They were used to rain in Lakeland and paid little heed to it, and the glowering skies seemed eminently suited to her mood. Meg wished she was out in it, letting it wash over her face and limbs, cleansing the pain and frustration from her as it so often did. The wind was rising, she could hear it whining in the great ash trees that lined the track to the farm and gave the name Ashlea to the place that had been her home for all of her nineteen years.

Inconsequentially, she remembered leaving a blanket loose on the line. She'd have to search for it in the bottom field come morning. Nothing that wasn't battened down would survive the helm wind that scoured these high fells. Though the wind could not penetrate the walls of the farmhouse which were four feet thick, solid enough to withstand the worst mountain weather, and keep her within, like a prisoner.

Meg began to clear the table with jerky, angry movements, swallowing the bitter tears of disappointment that threatened to choke her. She supposed the slap was no more than she deserved. She shouldn't have dared to repeat the rebellious statement she'd made to Dan earlier when he had caught her pulling pints at the Cock and Feathers.

'Get your coat on,' he'd bluntly told her. 'You're coming home with me.'

She hadn't been able to believe her bad luck, having deliberately chosen the inn because it was far from the market area of town where her father conducted his business. Not for one moment had she considered the possibility of her own brother choosing to drink there. But losing her temper would get her nowhere. Hadn't she discovered so a dozen times?

Nevertheless, since it had taken her weeks to find this job, she wasn't for giving in easily. 'I'll not,' she'd said, continuing to pull pints, feeling the excitement of defiance in the pit of her stomach.

When she'd tossed back a ragged abundance of honeyed curls from slender shoulders, an unconsciously sensuous act, not a man in the room would not have willingly championed her.

Only Dan Turner was not a man to take on lightly.

The elder of the two Turner brothers, his short stature belied the beefy power of him. In his tweed jacket and waistcoat, flat cap jauntily tilted to one side of his large bullet head, he looked even more intimidating than in his more usual working overalls. He had the typically round, handsome Turner face, broad nose and very slightly projecting ears. But unlike young Charlie, this brother seemed to wear a perpetual sneer, which drew up one corner of his mouth and flared the nostrils in a way that gave off a strong warning to leave well alone.

The farmers, recalling Dan Turner's expertise on the wrestling field, fascinated though they were by this little drama, had drawn back slightly, shuffling uncomfortably.

'You should be selling the eggs, not swanning around behind a bar.'

'The eggs are all sold. What's so terrible about a little job? You drink in enough of these places. Why shouldn't I work in one?'

'You know damn well why, because you're a woman! God knows what Father will say.'

'It's only Saturday mornings, for pin money.' She had spoken with calm assurance, desperately wanting to disguise the unease that filled her at mention of her father's reaction. 'You're not going to tell on me, are you?'

But he had.

Now the man at the head of the table glared at her with a cold fury in his eyes that made Dan's seem mild by comparison. 'How dare you speak like a loose woman at a Christian table? I'll wash thee mouth out with lye soap if I hear the like in my house again.'

Unrepentant, Meg returned her father's accusing glare, a show of bravado she did not quite feel in her young, fiercely rebellious eyes. 'I was only trying to make the point that it is a perfectly respectable public-house.'

'Palace of sin, more like! You should be grateful for a good home and food on your plate, not always be prating on after summat different.'

'It's not that, you know it's not,' Meg cried.

She longed to reach out, to touch the rigid figure, to seek some sign of affection, but knew such a gesture would be considered a show of weakness. They had never been a family to display emotion.

Life was grinding hard on these Lakeland fells, governed by the changing seasons with little time for sentiment. The year began in October when the rams were put to the ewes. Through the harsh days and long nights of winter the hardy Herdwicks and Swaledales survived on scant grass where they could find it, eked out occasionally by croppings of ash and holly. In March and April the flock was brought down ready for lambing. Later there would be the sorting, marking, dosing, clipping and dipping that marked the farming year until the autumn sales came and it all started again.

But Meg felt she had no part in this routine. Her life was spent almost entirely within doors, even more so since the death of her mother six months ago. Since then Joe Turner had fashioned an even tougher shell about himself. If Meg had never managed to penetrate that shell, even as a young child, how could she hope to do so now?

Worse, she no longer had her mother's protection. Without Annie's steady hand to calm him, who knew what her father might do? Joe Turner didn't approve of any show of independence from his women folk. He liked to know where they were at all times, and said as much, frequently.

As he was saying now.

'I'll not have you wandering round as if you had no home to go to and no proper work to do. If you're short of summat to do you can scrub the hen arks out.'

'I've done them.'

Meg felt the hot rebellion drain from her, and her shoulders slumped. What was the use? She could never win. She stared at her father and despite all her best efforts, she hated him. She hated his round, pugnacious face, the skin below the eyes loose and flabby, dragging the lids down at each corner. She despised the too large nose seeming to overpower the thin upper lip, drawn under slightly, to show a pair of expensive false teeth that grinned at him each night from his bedside table.

Meg knew all about honouring one's father and mother. It had been drummed into her at hundreds of unwilling visits to chapel over the years. But though she had willingly and lovingly done the latter there were shaming moments when she wished that it was her father lying in the cold earth and not her lovely mum. She longed for Annie now with a passion that brought a physical pain to her young heart.

'Are you going to tell me what it was all in aid of?'

Meg blinked the threat of tears away. 'Oh, for goodness' sake! I'm like stupid Cinderella in that daft fairy tale, and I won't stand for it any more. I want to have a life of me own. An *identity*.'

'Identity?' Her father's scathing tone made the word sound somehow not quite decent. 'Thee's my daughter, that's who thee are. What's wrong with that?'

Meg sighed, knowing he would never understand but unable to prevent herself from trying. 'I mean I've nothing that's just *mine*. No time to call my own, not a penny to spend that hasn't to be accounted for.'

'What do you need money for? Fol de rols, I suppose. Useless flibbertigibbets.'

Meg rubbed her forehead, which was starting to ache from the day's endless arguments. 'Don't talk daft.'

'Daft, am I? When have you ever gone short? Tell me that. You only have to ask.'

'That's just the point. Why should I have to ask? It's undignified, having to ask every time I need something.' Meg thought of her friend, Kath, who had a monthly allowance paid into her bank account, and knew a twinge of uncharacteristic envy.

'I'm your father,' Joe said stolidly, as if that explained everything. 'I hope I can keep my family without help from a slip of a girl.' Twin spots of colour lit the high cheek bones.

'But I want to do it. Mrs Blamire gets run off her feet and says she can't cope with all the cooking and serving on busy days, as she did when she was younger.'

'Mrs Blamire may do as she thinks fit, but no daughter of mine will work in a taproom. If women'd stop at home where they belong we'd soon cure the unemployment problem, you mark my words. Wilful, that's what you are, and it's time you learnt your place.' Dark brows met with the ferocity of his anger. 'You have the hen money. It was allus good enough for thee mother.'

But Meg wasn't for letting go easily, not now she'd got this far. In truth she didn't rightly know what she wanted but her confused mind desperately searched for something. She couldn't even put a name to it. Freedom? A purpose to her mundane life? Something beyond bringing in the coal bucket. She didn't particularly like the idea of working in a pub but it had been a job she could do, with money of her own at the end of it. The feeling had been a good one. And now it was gone and her father would never permit her to find another.

But somewhere, somehow, there must be a place for her. A place beyond this kitchen.

On her feet now, her small pert bosom rising and falling on shallow breaths of anxiety, she met Joe Turner's gaze with commendable courage and battled on. 'I'm not my mother. I can't take her place for you. Things have changed since her day. Women should have the same right to work as men do.'

'I can't believe I'm hearing this.'

The cold anger on his face was such that Meg quailed slightly and decided her to take a different tack. Deliberately she softened her voice. 'Cock and Feathers is a respectable house and I'd get up early and see to your breakfast before I went. I've plenty of time to sell the eggs and vegetables at the market before I start, and after I finish I'd see you all had a hot dinner to come home to. You'd never notice I was gone.'

Not entirely unaware of his daughter's burgeoning woman-hood, for the most part Joe chose to ignore it. But he certainly knew how to protect it.

'Thee would be open to all manner of lewd remarks from the scuff of the gutters that frequent such places. I hope I know my duty as a good Christian better than to let you. I'll hear no more about it. I have my reputation to keep up at chapel. What would they think? That I couldn't afford to keep me own daughter at home? It don't bear thinking of. Working in a pub indeed, where folk spend money they can't afford on demon drink. It didn't take long for someone to see you and tell our Dan, now did it?'

Meg opened her mouth to protest that Dan had gone in the Cock and Feathers himself for the purpose of drinking, but thought better of it. It would only make matters worse.

'Finish the washing up and get to bed.'

Joe's tone was stark in its decisiveness and he turned away to pull on the old mackintosh that hung steaming before the fire. 'And there'll be no dancing for you tonight. You'd best stop in for a bit, see if that'll get rid of your hysterics.'

Meg's heart plummeted and all her defiance fled. She could still recall the humiliation of being kept in for a whole month after she had once dared visit the Roxy Picture House in Kendal.

It had been her sixteenth birthday and she and her best friend, Kath Ellis, had ridden in on their bikes to celebrate by drooling over Humphrey Bogart. They had dawdled on their way home, stopping for a hot meat pie at the corner shop and arriving home later than promised. Their giggling happiness had soon been squashed. Joe Turner had reached for his belt and only Annie's pleading had saved Meg from a very sound beating. Even so, the punishment of being kept in for four long weeks had seemed severe and still rankled, nearly three years later.

Now it was all happening again. Only worse. If she was kept in then she wouldn't be able to go with Kath to the supper dance. More important, she would miss seeing Jack. The thought made her die a little inside. She had loved Jack Lawson for as long as she could remember and lived in hope that he would notice her one day. She'd made herself a new dress especially for tonight and now Jack would never see her in it. Hot tears stung the backs of her eyes as she fought for control.

'I'm not a child to be sent to my room.'

'You're behaving like one.'

'I'm trying to show you that I'm a grown woman who wants to start work instead of being skivvy to two idle numbskulls.' She dismissed her brothers with a flap of her hand. 'Why must everything be done for their convenience? Why have I no rights?'

'Because the farm will be theirs one day, not yours. Because they do all the work on it, not thee.'

Meg choked back the agony of unshed tears. 'That's not true. I work as hard as they do, harder. Our Dan only does what he has to and Charlie isn't interested in the land, you know he isn't.'

'He'll do what he's told. You all will. Now have done. I've heard enough.' Joe started to walk away but beside herself with the anguish of not seeing Jack, Meg snatched at his arm and pulled him round to face her.

'I won't stay in, I won't! And I won't skivvy for them two any more. They could do a bit more for themselves for a change. Fetch coal in for a start.'

Joe Turner went white to the lips, the spurt of flame from the dying fire reflected in the charcoal of his eyes. 'My sons have enough work of their own to do without taking on women's duties. Trouble with thee, young lady, is you don't know when you're well off. You've good clothes on thee back, food in thee belly. What more do you want?'

He set huge hands down upon the table top, hands that could bring a lamb from its mother as sweetly as butter, wring the life from a fat chicken or shoot a troublesome dog without flinching. He balled them now into threatening fists. A man who read his Bible nightly, he nevertheless considered it his duty to exercise discipline when it was needed. And this young madam was getting above herself.

'You let the lads do whatever they like, why not me?' She knew the answer so why did she torture herself by asking?

'I thought I'd made that clear.'

'It's clear you'd have liked me a lot better if I'd been a lad too.' Tears were standing proud in her eyes but she would not let them fall.

'Happen you'd've been easier to manage if you were. Just take a good look at yourself, madam. Eyes mad as fury. Hair all round your neck like a wild woman.'

'Would you prefer it if I had it all cut off? Then I'd look like a boy too.' She tossed back the wayward locks with a defiant twist of her lovely head.

'I'd prefer thee to act with proper decency.'

'If that is the only way to make you see me as a real person, and not simply as your serving wench then so be it.'

Snatching up the shearing scissors from the dresser Meg pulled her tangled hair down over one shoulder and began to hack recklessly with the sharp blades. Glittering golden tresses rained upon the scrubbed table top, curling and bouncing about with a life of their own.

Joe Turner reached for the shears but she danced away, evading him, and continued with her relentless massacre, forcing him to remain a helpless onlooker.

She might have continued on this self-desecration had he not slammed those same fists down upon the table, seeming to make the whole room quake.

'Enough! What would thy mother say if she saw thee acting so wantonly?'

Meg froze, tears brimming over at last from her clear grey eyes, making the room swim dizzily before her. *What had she done?* She stared at the bright curls falling away in her hand. He'd driven her to it. It was his fault. But she wouldn't let him see her distress. Against the greater tragedy of a desolate life, ruined hair seemed of small importance.

Meg gathered up the cut tendrils into her palm, and tossed them into the fire where they crackled and fired up. A lump came into her throat. She couldn't go to the supper looking like this, with half her hair cut off. What would Jack think of her now?

'Now thee will have to stop in,' Joe said with satisfaction, clearly reading her thoughts, and walked, spine rigid, from the room, his whole bearing making it clear that he'd had his say and won. As was only right and proper.

It took Meg the best part of an hour in her distress to finish the washing up, tidy the room and replenish the fire which had sulked itself black. When she had done, she refilled the big black kettle and set it back on the hob, so there'd be hot water for a mug of strong tea for her brothers when they got in. Then she took off her floral apron and hung it on the peg behind the pantry door before climbing dejectedly up the stairs to her room.

Hardly bigger than a cupboard tucked beneath the eaves right at the top of the house, it was at least her own. The only place where she could be sure of privacy.

Ashlea had been built some time during the early part of the eighteenth century. New by Lakeland standards, it was a typical, unprepossessing yeoman type building of grey stone with a slate roof and the traditional cylindrical chimneys. For all its plainness it had seemed warm and alive when her mother had lived in it, its homely rooms muddled and untidy with Annie's tapestry work, bottles for the lambs, and the usual boots and buckets of farming life.

Once the house had smelled of beeswax and lavender, over-laid by the strong tones of woodsmoke from the fire that burned constantly in the kitchen range. But Meg found she did not have the heart to reach these same standards. She could never rid her mouth of the taste of dust and unhappiness, as she coped with the cleaning of the five-bedroom house all alone, and the endless washing, ironing and cooking for four people.

It wasn't that she didn't try. Meg longed to recapture the scents of those lovingly remembered days. Of home-baked bread, the sharpness of bilberry jam and the tangy aroma of her mother's blackberry and apple pie. But her own efforts seemed poor by comparison.

So she loved her tiny hideaway high in the attic, the only place where no demands were made and she could be herself. From the window cut in the farmhouse roof she could see right over the stand of ash and rowan behind the farm to the heather-carpeted turf of the high fell, clotted with broom and juniper and punctuated with the grey rocks that resolutely burst out of the thin soil at every opportunity.

Now the rain and wind robbed her of the solace of this much-loved view and she fell upon the bed and lay on her back, determined not to cry. But despite her best intentions great fat tears rolled out of the corners of her eyes and ran down into her ears. She had chosen the wrong moment. Why had she risked spoiling the dance for an impossible concession? What had possessed her to be so reckless?

The thought of dancing with Jack Lawson made her stomach quiver with excitement. Now she wouldn't see him at all and he'd chat up some other girl.

She got off the bed to stand in front of the speckled mirror and confront the horror of her hair. One side was long as ever, rippling in waves over her shoulder. The other side was short, sticking out in a madcap sort of way like a halo. The oddness of it suddenly appealed to her sense of humour and she felt a giggle start deep inside. What would everyone say if she left it like this? They'd think she'd gone mad. The shortness of it seemed to exaggerate the devilish gleam of hot rebellion that still burned in her grey eyes.

The laughter started then, bubbling up and spilling over in great spurts of glee. And suddenly it didn't matter what her father did. She was young, wasn't she? Soon the dull days of winter and a cold spring would lighten into summer. There was still time to find some other way of escape. And she would, too. However much she might feel that she belonged here, at Ashlea, she wouldn't stay as anyone's skivvy.

What's more, if there was some way for her to go to the lambing supper, then she would find it. She must see Jack, she must. But first the hair. Meg opened a dressing table drawer and took out a pair of scissors. Short hair, Kath said, was all the rage.

–

It was Charlie who championed her, as always. He came in on a bluster of cold wind, banging all the doors. Dan and her father were upstairs getting washed and changed ready to go out and Meg was drying her hair in front of the fire. She had cut and washed it and now it sprang in short bouncy curls, a wild mass of golden colour about her head. She rather thought it suited her but was still self-conscious about it. Charlie sank wearily into a chair, telling her about the latest lambs to be born and put with their ewes in the barn for the night. It was a moment before he noticed her hair. When at last he did, an explanation had to be given and his young face darkened.

'He treats you as if it were still the dark ages instead of the twentieth century. Don't let him get away with it.'

Meg gave a rueful smile as she brewed tea and set a steaming mug in his hands. 'I think I already said more than I should. We had a real ding-dong.'

'He'll not keep me locked up. There's a war coming, you know. Hitler won't stop till he's got what he's after. All of Europe no less. While we fuss over the cost of building aeroplanes, German forces have taken over Austria. Where next? France? Poland?' His blue eyes came alight with fervour and he ran one grubby hand through hair only a shade paler than her own. 'I'll be one of the first to join up if war comes. You just see.'

'You're too young,' she laughed, rumpling his tangled curls affectionately, but he snatched himself away from her.

'Don't say that. You sound like Father.'

She was at once contrite. Charlie was not a natural farmer, being better with machines than the blood and gore that was an unavoidable part of country life. And Joe never let an opportunity pass to taunt his younger son about his squeamishness which hurt Meg as much as it did Charlie, for they were close.

'Come on, love, have a piece of gingerbread while I go and shut the hens up. It'll warm you. There might be more to lamb tonight and you'll need to cope alone with Father and Dan both going out.'

The hens were making those warm, contented chutterings as Meg slid down the door over the pop hole to keep them safe from unwelcome night visitors. She loved looking after the hens, sliding her hands under their soft bodies to capture warm eggs for breakfast, tickling them under their wings with powder to keep them free of mites. She loved talking to them as they scratched about, telling them her secrets, letting the peace of the night soak into her.

'Stay safe,' she warned them, hearing in the distance the bark of a lone dog fox.

The small animals were her province. Looking after the hens, and turkeys in season, feeding the pigs, milking the two cows that provided the family with milk, Meg enjoyed all of that. The animals made her life bearable. But she was not permitted to work with the sheep.

'Not women's work,' Joe said, when once she had asked if she might help. In such a way that she had not mentioned it again. The desire for purposeful work, an identity of her own, was challenged only by the greater need now to see Jack Lawson. Meg clasped her hands together and stared about her. The black mountains seemed to shield her, crouching closer as her eyes grew accustomed to the dark, attempting to pick out the familiar detail that scarred their smooth surface. 'Please help me to find the words to persuade Father to let me go to the dance.' She couldn't believe she had been so stupid as to risk missing it. 'I must see Jack, I must. And don't let there be a war.'

She'd heard talk of war a lot lately but never taken it seriously. 'Charlie's sixteen, young and headstrong. He thinks only of aeroplanes and adventure, do you see? Not the danger.'

Would Jack? If there was another war, then he too might be called up. Worry swamped her. Oh, she couldn't bear it if either of them went away. They might be wounded or killed. It made her go all sick and funny inside to think of it, and her own problems seem small by comparison.

Back in the kitchen she made a fresh pot of tea to warm herself, trying not to listen as Charlie chattered on about the latest aeroplane that would blast the enemy from the skies.

Her father came in, looking uncharacteristically smart in his setting-off suit smelling faintly of mothballs, firmly buttoned over his best waistcoat. But then nothing looked more polished than a farmer dressed in his finest. A man's pride would see to that. He wore his best flat cap, as he did for every occasion whether a birthing or a chapel function, the neb curling downwards from long wear, following the line of his thinned lips.

'I hear you and Meg have been having a bit of a set-to,' said Charlie, somewhat recklessly in her opinion.

'Aye, you could say that.'

'If you don't let her go tonight, everyone will want to know why. There'll be gossip. This dale is famous for it.'

'Pity folks have nowt better to do then,' he said tersely. But the point had been made. Joe Turner could not bear to lose face. There was a long pause while he considered, then he turned upon Meg. 'See you're quick about it then, if thee's coming. We haven't got all night. And splash thee face with cold water.' He indicated Meg's cheeks, hot from the fire. 'We don't want folks to know we've been having a few words.'

The remnants of her pride in tatters, her life in ruins, but the façade of family unity must be kept up. A tearing row passed off as a 'few words'. But Meg didn't care. The only thing that mattered was that she was to be allowed to go. She could fight her battles another night.

Chapter Two

The silence of the Lakeland night was profound as Meg followed her father and brother along the rutted lane to the school where the social was to be held. There was nothing to break the silence but the suck of moist earth at her heels, and the fast beating of her heart. Would Jack be there, as he had promised? She heard a rustling in the undergrowth and paused to watch the fleeting glimpse of the white rump of a roe deer, still clothed in its winter grey, as it blundered away from her.

'I'm so sorry to disturb you,' she whispered, moving more quietly still, afraid to disturb any other night creature.

There was no sign of Jack as she took one of the hard wooden chairs lined up around the walls of the main room in the school hall. A group of farmers' wives exchanged gossip at one end as they slapped margarine and potted meat on bread rolls, interrupted from time to time by the need to reprimand one of the younger children who were practising sliding on the candle-greased floor.

Her father and some of the other men had gone in to the meeting room next door to listen to a speaker, but in this hall a special licence had been obtained so there could be dancing.

Meg spotted 'Lanky' Lawson, Jack's father, so called because his stature was anything but. He was working the old wind-up gramophone and later, if pressed, she knew he would play his fiddle and they would all dance the old steps, the Cumberland Square Eight or the Ninepins Reel. Meg acknowledged his wave with a smile. He was a dear friend but this evening she was more interested in a modern waltz with his son. The kind of dance which meant Jack must hold her close.

Everyone seemed to be dancing. She looked about the room with a casual air, trying not to let it show that she felt conspicuous sitting all alone, or that she was looking for anyone in particular. Where was Kath? She had faithfully promised to come.

And then she saw them, dancing together, so carefree and good-looking.

They were dancing a quick step, a Tommy Dorsey number, and Kath seemed to be clinging just a little too closely to Jack's broad shoulders and he was laughing just a bit too much at something her friend had said. Then Kath looked across and saw Meg and at once abandoned her partner to come swooping across the polished floor on fashionable two-tone high heels.

She was wearing a little white embroidered jacket over a silk flared skirt in pillbox red. Nipped in at the waist with a narrow red belt, the jacket was trimmed with a row of tiny pearl buttons. She looked wonderful, a million dollars, and knew it.

'What *have* you done to your hair?' she cried, hugging Meg in delight. 'I love it. Oh, I shall have to cut mine too. Where did you get it done?'

'Where did you get those shoes?'

'Fun, aren't they?'

Kath swung her own sleek bob about as she talked and Meg had to laugh as her friend prattled on, happily recounting her own latest encounters with hairdressers, which were numerous. Kath was constantly changing her appearance. One week she was a redhead, the next a brunette. For the moment she was blonde and it suited her.

Meg felt herself relax, enjoying as she always did Kath's lively company. They chattered easily together with the familiarity of old friends, laughing at nothing in particular and understanding far more than was actually said.

'What happened about the job?' Kath asked, innocently recalling the tensions of the day.

Fortunately Meg was saved from answering this loaded question by the arrival of Jack himself who looked less enamoured of her new hair style. A frown drew two lines of displeasure above his straight nose.

'Don't you like it?'

'Not much,' he said bluntly.

'Thanks,' she said, disappointment blocking her throat with a rush of emotion. This was proving to be the most awful day of her life. 'Wouldn't you say that it makes me look more alluring and sophisticated?' she asked, daringly teasing, but he only shook his head.

'Personally I like long hair on a woman, more feminine.'

He was shocked by the change the hairstyle had made to her. With her hair long, never tidy, often dragged together with a bit of baling twine, she'd seemed like a young girl still. Now she looked like a woman. A sensual, mature woman. Long aware of her fancy for him, but also of his easy success with women, he'd thought he had plenty of time to play the field before he did anything about his feelings for Meg Turner. Now he wasn't so sure. Something had changed in her today, and if he was any judge, it wasn't just because of the new hair style.

'Jack and I have been showing the old biddies how it's done. But you can have him now,' whispered Kath, winking outrageously, and to her horror, Meg blushed.

But when he asked her for a dance she accepted eagerly, melting against him, unable to disguise her pleasure at feeling his arms about her. Pulling her close, he tucked her hand into his chest where she could feel the fast beat of his heart. Was he excited by her as she was by him? Meg longed to look up into his face, lean and hungry with teasing violet eyes, but dared not.

She had known Jack Lawson ever since their early schooldays together and had wanted him almost as long. He'd always seemed to favour the more feminine sort of girl, the kind who wore broad satin ribbons and didn't spend all their time climbing trees and damming up becks. He had never shown any interest in Meg Turner with her scruffy pigtails and scraped knees.

She hadn't seen him for some time after they left school. She'd heard he'd gone off to work in Preston for a while, on the docks. And then last backend at a shepherds meet, there he was, more handsome than ever with the same old wickedly teasing smile.

Since then she had come across him surprisingly often on the lanes and fields about her home when she was out walking. Though his father's land adjoined theirs, the houses themselves were a good mile apart. For a long time she had struggled hard not to read anything into these accidental meetings. Now hope rose hot and piercingly sweet in her breast.

They swayed together to the rhythm of the music. It was a Bing Crosby number, 'When the blue of the Night', and Jack crooned it softly against her ear, making little b-b-boom noises in imitation of the singer's style. The warmth of his breath tickled her lobes, making her shiver with a new awareness.

'Been on any interesting walks lately?' he asked, his voice no more than a velvet purr.

'Some. How about you?'

He grinned and pulled her away from him so he could look down into her face. 'Tend to leave the walking to the dogs, but maybe I should take it up again. Where do you go to get away from that lout of a brother of yours? Wouldn't care to cross him on a dark night.'

Meg giggled, knowing Jack was not the only one to be wary of Dan. 'He tries to be tough, like Father, but it's all show,' she said. 'If he bothers you, you'd best stay away.' And see if I care, her tone said.

The music finished and she walked away from him, burningly aware he was watching the sway of her hips in the new blue chenille dress.

He danced with Kath again and Meg wondered if perhaps she'd been a touch too casual. She should have given him more encouragement, tried to get him to make a proper date. She'd die if he didn't, she was sure of it.

Later, he took her outside. For a breath of fresh air, he said. Meg went willingly, heart thumping, aware that this was the usual mode of behaviour when a boy wanted to get to know you better.

The small schoolroom, a low, stone building that might have grown out of the rocky soil it stood on, was home to a few dozen children during the day and often commissioned into action as a social meeting point during the evening for the scattered farming community. Standing as it did in the middle of nowhere it was black dark all around, proving a great attraction for those wishing to try out a few undisturbed kisses. She'd noticed Kath make two or three well-timed exits, one of them, to Meg's great astonishment, with her own brother, Dan.

Now that it was her turn she felt quite sick with anticipation and excitement. What if she did something wrong, said something stupid? Jack was so sophisticated, with vast amounts of experience, while Meg felt simply gauche and juvenile.

He leaned placidly against the wall and lit up a cigarette. He offered her one but she refused. Somewhere an owl hooted. 'Your father wouldn't approve, I suppose?'

Meg managed a smile. 'I don't suppose he would.' She was tempted to take one, to prove she was her own person, but decided it would be childish.

His eyes were moving over her face and she put up a defensive hand to her hair. 'I could always grow it again,' she said, and his eyebrows lifted.

'For me?'

She wanted to fall into his arms and tell him she would do anything if he would only ask, but she smiled instead. Was he never going to kiss her?

'My father can be a pain too,' he said, sounding vaguely sympathetic. 'Always comparing me with my well-organised sister or pestering me to "put down roots", whatever they are.

And me with my whole life before me. What's the hurry? There's always tomorrow, I say.' Jack laughed then tossed the half-smoked cigarette away with a careless flick of his hand. Almost in the same movement he pulled her into his arms.

His lips were cold against hers. She could taste the cigarette ash, smell it on his breath along with the pint or two of beer he'd had earlier. But his skin was soft and warm and, oh, it was wonderful to feel herself pressed so close in his arms. She wanted to stay there for ever. His teeth grazed her lips and she felt a bolt of excitement so intense it shot right through her stomach.

'Hallo, everyone, having fun?'

Kath came bouncing alongside, one of the Jepson boys in tow, and Jack broke away with a laugh to light another cigarette. A cold wind from the fells brushed over her lips and with sinking heart Meg realised that the romantic interlude, if that was what you could call it, was over. And he still hadn't made a date to see her again.

The rest of her evening passed, as usual, with perfect decorum and at ten o'clock precisely her father took her home. Everyone else stayed on for the Conga and the Hokey-Cokey.

Meg flung open the back door and called for her young brother. 'Charlie, how many times do I have to call you?'

There he was, as she'd expected, expertly flicking cigarette cards against a row of them propped against the yard wall. With a sound of exasperation she marched over and gathered up the cards, tossing them angrily into the dustbin. He let out a howl of protest.

'What did you do that for, Meg?' He stood frozen, the next card poised between finger and thumb, bright blue eyes so affronted it was almost comical, had she been in the mood for laughing.

'You're too old for boys' games.'

'One minute I'm too young, now I'm too old. Make your mind up.' Too young for anything serious like marriage or war, and too old for games, she thought, feeling ancient as she remembered the awkwardness of being sixteen.

'Haven't I been calling you this last ten minutes?' She turned from him and started to snatch pegs off the washing line, the raw April wind whipping colour into her cheeks like a lash, turning her hands, still wet from a morning's scrubbing, all red and chapped. Washing always made Meg irritable and she'd not felt quite herself since the dance two weeks ago.

She'd got so touchy about not hearing a word from Jack Lawson that she'd even stopped taking her usual walk each afternoon, just in case she saw him and he thought she was chasing him. It was the silliest attitude to take, Meg well knew, but somehow she couldn't help herself. Unrealistically, she wanted Jack to seek her out, to court her. Though how he would dare venture on to Turner property without an invitation from the men of the household was a puzzle she hadn't yet solved.

Now, as if to chastise herself again for wanting something she couldn't have, she poured all her energy into work, unfairly taking her ill temper out on her young brother.

'Didn't you hear me shout that it'd started to rain and to bring in the washing before it got soaked? I think sometimes you've only sawdust between your ears. Just look at these sheets, all splattered with mud. You and your games.' Meg flung the spotted shirts and sheets back into the basket, hard put to keep the tears out of her eyes. It had taken hours to soak, scrub and starch them all. Now she'd have to start all over again.

'I didn't hear you.'

'You didn't listen. You only hear what you want to hear, you great lump.' She thrust the basket into his arms and pushed him towards the kitchen door. 'Did you fill the log basket like I asked?' She knew, of course, that he hadn't. It still stood in the middle of the slate floor where she had set it hours ago, waiting to trip up any unwary passer-by.

She spent the next two hours scrubbing the mud spots off the washing and setting it to dry on the wooden rack that hung suspended from the ceiling in front of the fire. Steam filled the small kitchen in no time, making her short curls cling damply to her rosy cheeks.

Then Dan came in, reminding her to take his boots to the menders and presenting her with a whole wad of socks to darn that had somehow got collected up in the bottom of his drawer. Meg bundled them in to her sewing basket, telling him tartly to take his own boots to the menders.

'You go to town more often than I do.'

'Well, it's not my job to darn socks.'

Meg bit back the desire to tell him just what he could do with his tatty socks.

She brought the logs in herself, Charlie having disappeared off the face of the earth, and by the time she had finished all the usual chores, and prepared liver and onions for the dinner, she was almost too exhausted to think straight. But she'd go out this afternoon, come what may. A breath of fresh air would do her good.

–

The wind had chased the rain away and a fickle sun had come out when Katherine Ellis saddled her pony to ride over to Broombank early that afternoon. There was an ethereal radiance to the light that turned droplets of water into sparkling diamonds on the newly sprouting fern heads, their tightly furled croziers like miniature shepherd's crooks. The air was rich with the resonance of damp earth and new grass, and that feeling of hope that is peculiarly discernible when spring comes to Lakeland, as if to celebrate having survived a hard winter.

'Come on, Bonnie,' she urged, 'stop blowing, then I can pull this damn girth strap tight.' Bonnie, being a slightly overweight fell pony of mature years, was not really Katherine's idea of a good mount. She would have preferred an Arab stallion or a fine roan. One who pranced and whinnied with excitement when she took her out, not stand on three legs with eyes closed, or drop her head to the grass verge at every opportunity, resisting any threat of exercise.

But Bonnie was an old friend and thus not easily discarded. Kath revelled in the freedom the pony gave her, even managing to stir Bonnie to a gentle trot if she squeezed her thighs against the pony's plump sides hard enough, though it might make her back and leg muscles ache.

She leaned forward and let the wind skim through her hair, knowing she should have worn a hat. Mummy was for ever telling her so. Just as she told her to wear a coat on a damp evening, or to take a torch and a whistle if she went over Kentmere. But Kath rarely listened to these words of wisdom. Where was the fun in life if you always did what was safe and proper?

Her mother was holding open the gate for her now, quite unnecessarily, at the end of the long drive that wound between jutting rocks to Larkrigg Hall where Kath had been born and in which she had been cosseted ever since as the unexpectedly late child of elderly parents.

The fine old house had once belonged to her mother's quarry owning forebears. Larkrigg Fell was pitted with the remains of a dozen old quarries, once worked for the blue-grey slate of the Silurian beds formed many thousands of years ago when Lakeland was young. The entire landmass had been pushed upwards by volcanic disturbance, fold upon fold of rock and earth with the most ancient rocks to the north. From these natural resources men had made fortunes, Rosemary Ellis's grandfather among them.

And she had largely spent it.

'You'll be back by tea time, won't you, darling? You know that Richard is coming over and particularly wishes to see *you*, not us old fogies.'

Kath flicked her crop against Bonnie's flanks, wishing the pony would speedily gallop away so that she could pretend that she hadn't heard the question. But Bonnie slowed down to nuzzle Mrs Ellis's hand, just in case she had a treat secreted in the pocket of her soft tweed skirt. Kath restrained a sigh and smiled sunnily.

'I'll do my best. But don't wait tea for me. You know how unpunctual I am.'

Rosemary Ellis watched her daughter until she was quite out of sight, a frown of concern upon her face. How difficult girls could be, particularly Katherine who had always shown a ruthless determination to have her own way. Perhaps it was because she was an only child and, as Rosemary was well aware, thoroughly spoiled by Jeffrey, that she seemed so wild and out of control. But she was young still, at eighteen, and there was plenty of time for her to mature. It was only that with Jeffrey being unwell and the future so uncertain, it would be lovely if she would settle down with some suitable young man. Richard Harper was ideal and from a good local family, his father likely to be Mayor of Kendal next year.

'We'll wait till five,' she called out in desperation, just as the pony's grey tail swished out of sight.

–

The whitewashed stone longhouse that was Broombank Farm came into sight as Kath rounded the last hill and Bonnie came to a halt without any prompting.

'Even the horse can read my mind,' Katherine said crossly, forgetting the countless occasions she'd ridden this way.

It was early yet for the blaze of gold which would soon surround the farm with an almost magical light, but the first spears of broom were already attempting to thrust through the thick green leaves.

Built as an Elizabethan manor farm, Broombank occupied three sides of a quadrangle though many of its buildings were now little more than ruins. Only its tall cylindrical chimneys stood proud, the narrow curtainless windows looking blankly out from thick stone walls that seemed to have shrunk in upon themselves with the passing of the years as if ashamed of the air of neglect. Kath knew that the inside was in an even worse state. It was hard to imagine the fine ladies and gentlemen who had installed the oak panelling and doors and whose initials were carved over the stone lintel taking too kindly to its present state. It was certainly not a house she would care to own. But it wasn't the building she had come to see.

'Let's see if he's in, shall we? Walk on, Bonnie.' The mare ambled forward readily enough knowing there might well be a mint humbug at the farm, if the old man was in. There was little Bonnie would not do for a mint humbug.

Jack came to meet them himself, just as Kath had hoped, as soon as they entered the farmyard. She stayed on the pony's back, sitting very straight to display her breasts to full advantage, and slanted a smile down at him.

'You're looking as devilishly handsome as ever on this glorious afternoon,' she said.

Jack Lawson rested one hand on the bridle and smiled back at her. 'And yourself.'

Four years older than Meg and she, Jack Lawson, with his black curly hair and sleepy violet-blue eyes, was the nearest thing to a rake that Katherine knew. A bit brash perhaps, just a little too full of himself, but one twist of that sensual lower lip and she could forgive him anything. Well aware that he belonged to Meg, or would if her friend had any say in the matter, still Kath could not resist testing her own standing with him. 'Show me a man and I'll wind him in,' was her favourite catch phrase. And, generally speaking, a true one. Jack Lawson was certainly a man who interested her but he was not proving an easy fish to hook.

'I was just giving Bonnie some much needed exercise and realised I hadn't seen you since the lambing supper.'

For all there was a coolness to the April breeze, Jack stood with his shirt sleeves rolled above the elbow, hands thrust in his trouser pockets, allowing Katherine ample opportunity to admire his muscles. He worked hard, so they were worth seeing. 'I've been busy. Why, have you missed me?'

Now she was thrown into a quandary. If she said that she had, it might make her look cheap. But if she said no, he'd wonder why she'd bothered to mention it in the first place. She decided to play it cool. 'Don't flatter yourself, Jack Lawson. It was nothing more than idle curiosity. Who else is there around here that isn't already half dead?'

They both laughed at that, aware of Kath's frustration with rural life and oft-pronounced intention of leaving the quiet fells to head for the bright lights.

'What about Meg? I thought you and she were inseparable.'

'So we are. When I can get her away from that sanctimonious old father of hers,' Kath agreed, sobering instantly. 'They do worry me, the Turner family. How on earth they managed to produce such a sweetie as Meg is quite beyond me. They are really quite dreadful with her.'

'You seem to find her brother amenable enough.'

She glanced down at Jack, startled for a moment as she remembered allowing Dan to take her outside at the supper. Something she had almost instantly regretted. He had smelled of beer and cow dung. She shrugged slender shoulders, a gesture that managed to look elegant even in the old green sweater she wore. 'He has a fancy for me, that's all. Not to be taken seriously. I can handle him.'

'As you can most men,' came the soft reply, and Kath glanced swiftly at him again, to see if he was just the teeniest bit jealous, but his head was down, concentrating on the horse. She looked at his hand instead, large and tanned, the skin rough and calloused from hard work on the farm, held flat now under Bonnie's soft muzzle. 'Not too many sugar lumps, they'll make her fat,' and they both laughed.

'Where are you off to?' he asked, as she gathered the reins ready to move on.

She walked the pony round in a circle, aware of his eyes upon her. 'Over Coppergill Pass. I often go there on a fine afternoon.' Hazel eyes regarded blue for a moment in silence.

'So long then,' he said, sounding very like a gangster in one of those new American movies she and Meg occasionally went to see in Kendal.

Kath urged Bonnie into action and with an airy wave of a hand trotted out through the gate Jack obediently held open for her. He stood watching her go, eyes on the delightful up and down motion of her rear as rider and pony headed off up the lane. It was the neatest little bottom he'd seen in a long time and he almost regretted not offering to go with her.

—

It was late afternoon before Meg set out, striding away up the fields towards Brockbarrow Wood. More a copse than a wood, the stand of trees stood high on the fellside, flanking the sides of a small mountain tarn, dark and skeletal against the glistening water. It was her favourite place even when the wind cut through like a knife. But today spring was in the air and her heart felt uplifted by the freedom of an hour out alone where she could sit and think without fear of being disturbed.

No one saw her go, not that she'd have cared if they had. She was entitled to a break she told herself. Meg loved walking and was never afraid to be alone. She had often thought it would be good to have a dog at her heels, but the only dogs the farm owned were working animals that belonged to her father and her brother Dan. They were treated well as there was nothing more important to a good shepherd than his dog, but they were never allowed into the house and spent their time in the yard or barn when not working. Meg felt she would like to have a dog beside her at all times.

'One day I shall,' she announced to the empty landscape, mentally adding it to her list of requirements for a happy life. As soon as I have a job, whatever that might be, and a place of my own. And Jack, she added silently. How any of these dreams would be achieved she had not the faintest idea but the determination was strong in her.

Meg continued upwards, her rubber boots slipping sometimes on the sharp stones. Above her the track narrowed and split into a dozen such sheep-trails, named 'trods' years ago by the Vikings who first populated these fells. The Herdwicks would later lead their lambs up them to the summer grazing, allowing the youngsters not a moment's rest in their eagerness to reach the heights. Today the fells were bare and quiet and she loved the silence, feeling it heave into her heart and push away all the unpleasant thoughts and niggling worries. A skylark soared, tearing up into a blue-grey sky in a frenzy of song, a winter migrant from a colder land. Meg called up to the small brown bird, assuring it that she would watch where she put her feet and not disturb its eggs.

'I wouldn't expect anything else from you.'

She stopped dead in her tracks, looking all about her for the source of the deep, disembodied voice.

'Jack?' she said, half hoping, half fearing. He stepped out from behind a rowan on the fringes of the copse above her and, leaning against it, grinned down at her, turning her stomach to water.

'Come on, slow coach. About time. I'm bored sick with trekking up this path to wait for you.'

Her heart leaped into her throat, soaring as surely as the skylark's song.

It no longer mattered that she'd near worn herself out with the washing all morning or that at the end of this wonderful afternoon she must return to a dour, taciturn father and two selfish brothers. He had come at last. And here, on this fellside, she felt suddenly wanted and alive.

They sat together under an old ash tree, leaning against its silver-grey bark. Meg was so overwhelmed at finding him waiting for her she could think of nothing to say. But she relished the warmth of him beside her. He smelled of tangy soap and fresh damp earth, and something she could only describe to herself as masculine.

'Have you really? Been wanting to see me, I mean,' she asked, unable to resist knowing the answer.

'What do you think?'

She turned to him, half accusing. 'You never said. How was I to know?'

'I would have thought it was obvious. Most girls would have guessed.'

'I'm not most girls.' Meg had no intention of having him think her easy. She knew all about such girls and she wasn't one of them. All the same she trembled inside when he shifted his position, moving his body closer.

'What do you expect me to do? Call on your dad?'

'No. I don't blame you for being wary of Joe. And Dan!' The words started to tumble out, covering the sudden shyness which was so ridiculous with a boy she had known all her life. 'Maybe Dan and I might have got on better if it hadn't been pumped into me from the moment we were old enough to toddle about that the farm was for the boys.'

'What would you want with a farm?'

'I'd like the chance to decide for myself,' she said. 'Can't you see what will happen? Dan will marry and I'll be the spare part around the place, the unmarried sister.' She shivered. 'It doesn't appeal, thank you very much.'

Jack shrugged. 'So leave. Do something different.'

'How? My father won't even let me go to town on me bike,' she complained. 'It's archaic.'

Jack made sympathetic noises but he wasn't really listening. He was watching the rise and fall of her breast beneath the pale blue blouse she wore. It strained enticingly against the buttons. A girl turning into a woman and she didn't even seem to notice. Jack wasn't sure whether it was Meg's innocence or her unconscious sensuality that so appealed to him. Either way it had come as a surprise to him since he usually preferred more sophisticated meat.

But however Joe Turner might try to keep his daughter a child she was very much a woman, and the ache in Jack's loins told him that he wanted her. And what Jack wanted, he usually got.

Chapter Three

'Keeps you short of money, does he?' Jack considered putting his arm about Meg's shoulders but she looked so fierce suddenly, he decided against it. He would content himself this afternoon with letting her chatter. There was plenty of time, after all.

'Money? I've none at all. How can he be so against women working when he has me labouring like a slave from dawn to dusk? How can he pretend to be so pious when everyone knows he's the biggest shark of a moneylender around these parts?'

'He's a fearsome character right enough, your dad. I know Sally Ann Gilpin is scared sick of him.'

'Is she?'

'They've been having their troubles lately. Her dad has been ill. Left them a bit short, I reckon.' Jack's eyes fastened on Meg's mouth, small and moist, a pink tongue darting excitedly over her lower lip as she talked.

'I see.' Meg was sad about that since she liked the Gilpin family, and strongly disliked an old friend being scared of her father. 'How did you hear?' What she really meant was, when did you see Sally Ann? She felt a spurt of jealousy that Jack had talked to a pretty girl, and hated herself for it.

Jack was too busy gazing at the white column of her throat to notice the sharpness of her tone. 'I don't remember exactly. Her mam is having a real hard time of it, though.'

'I can imagine.' The women who lived in the row of cottages up by the quarry and were forced to avail themselves of Joe's money lending service in order to survive the week, had every cause to fear him. Nobody got behind with their payments with Joe Turner, not if they wanted to avoid trouble.

'Why do women always get the rough end of the stick? I've been trained to keep house since I was three years old. Not so the boys, who were somehow excused anything that smacked of woman's work. But it's going to change, I tell you. I can only take so much and one of these days…'

Meg felt the anger drain out of her, becoming intensely aware of the warm weight of Jack's body beside hers. What was she doing wasting this precious time together talking about her father? Jack moved a little, his thigh brushing hers and it was as if she could scarcely breathe, as if her lungs were bursting, squeezing inwards, pushing a pain deep down into her groin.

She was aware too of Jack's breathing, of its strangely uneven quality, that it became less and less pronounced. She felt him turn towards her and knew instinctively that if she looked at him he would kiss her, but she could not move. Much as she longed to feel the warmth of his lips move over hers, her body was stuck fast to the tree, her hands curled tight into the clumps of grass at her side.

'Meg?'

That was all he said. Her name. So softly questioning it was like a caress. Then his hand came up to her neck and she turned her cheek into it, lifting her face to his as if to the warmth of the sun. She had waited for this moment for what seemed like a lifetime and Meg closed her eyes and gave herself up to the joy of it without hesitation.

The kiss roughened and deepened, and then moved on to explore the warm curve of her throat and the sensitive hollows below her earlobe. She rubbed her cheek against the roughness of his coat collar, loving the feel of it against her silky skin. Happiness burst inside her like the opening petals of a new flower.

Meg gasped when she felt his hand move to her breast. She wasn't ignorant. Brought up on a farm, she was well versed in the mechanics of life and had filled in the gaps with Kath long since, giggling behind the barn with one of those books in plain brown wrappers Kath had sent for. But theory was one thing, practice quite another.

His fingers were growing more adventurous since she'd done nothing to stop him and were now busily engaged in unbuttoning her blouse. Did she want him to carry on further? She felt flustered, not wanting to appear silly and naive.

He had found her nipple, pert and hard beneath her hand stitched camisole, and she gasped with pain and pleasure as he took it between his lips. 'Jack,' she whimpered, half in protest, half drowning in sensation. Even as she spoke, her body arched, instinctively craving for more. Wanting him more than she could say.

He pulled her down so that she was lying on the grass and she could sense the excitement rising in him. Something hard and pulsing was pressing against her leg. It seemed to make the pain worse.

'Come on, Meg, come on,' he murmured, then eased open her mouth with his tongue so she couldn't have answered him anyway, even if she'd known what to say. His tongue flickered between her teeth and curled about her own, thrusting, dancing, teasing, demanding. Despite herself she was catching his excitement, felt it run through her like liquid fire. She thrilled to his kisses, revelled in new sensations she'd never known before, responding to his passion without restraint.

'You want me, don't you?' he asked, letting her breathe for a minute as he nuzzled into her neck.

'Oh, Jack', was all she could say, a tremble in her voice. She was confused, filled with a racing desire to find out what it was her young body craved, even as some small part of her preached caution and held her back. Yet how could it be wrong if she wanted him to do these things to her? She felt dazed and weak, the longing to surrender almost beyond endurance.

His hand was on her leg now, sliding softly beneath her skirt, over her bare thigh. Then with a shock of breath in her throat she felt his hand creep beneath the leg of her cami-knickers. Very quickly she caught his hand with her own.

'Please, Jack, no.' But he wasn't listening, she felt him shudder against her, press the hardness of his body ever closer, and she remembered reading in the brown paper book how you shouldn't lead a man on. Was that what she was doing? Being a tease. He was saying something, whispering in her ear.

'It's all right, Meg. I can use something. You'll be quite safe.' A warm, melting sensation flowed through her veins, making her want to let him slide right inside her. The sigh of the wind through the old ash trees above seemed to shelter them, whispering secrets still to be understood; the slip-slap of water from the tarn beyond lulled her so that she could barely drag open eyelids heavy with love. Safe? *Use* something? What was he talking about? And then it came to her, why her inner voice cautioned, what it was she must be kept safe from, and she began to wriggle. 'Give over this instant,' she cried, pulling herself free. 'Me dad'll kill me if I get into trouble.'

'I wouldn't hurt you, Meg, you can trust me,' he crooned, still busy at her breasts. Dammit, he thought, I went too fast.

'How do I know that?' They broke apart to stare at each other, eyes glazed, cheeks flushed, breathing ragged, and for a moment she thought he was going to be angry with her for stopping him but then the mischievous smile came back to his face.

'What do you look like,' he said. And then Meg started to giggle because it was true, they must look a proper mess.

She pushed him gently away to sit up, smoothing down her skirt, fluffing out her hair, unaware just how enticing she looked with pink cheeks and lips bruised and softened by love making. 'We should have taken a bit more care.' Oh, but she didn't want to take care, she didn't!

'I will in future, Meg. I'm sorry if I scared you.' He kissed her nose, thinking if he could get this far the first time, a second chance should be even more interesting.

To Meg, the implication that there could be a future for herself and Jack Lawson made her gasp. She'd never known such joy in all her life: to feel so loved, so wanted. He must love her, mustn't he? Not only because he obviously wanted her so badly, but because he hadn't minded at all when she'd stopped him.

'You do respect me, don't you, Jack?' she asked, a touch of uncertainty in her voice, in case she had lost him by such wanton behaviour, but he only chuckled.

'Course I do, Meg. I've told you. I wouldn't be here else.'

Her mother had told her long ago that a boy never respected you if you let him go 'all the way'. Yet if she stayed here much longer, gazing into his violet blue eyes with their long curling lashes, she'd throw respect to the four winds and let him do what he would with her.

'I must go.' She got quickly to her feet, and was delighted when he did the same, putting his arms about her once more as if he couldn't bear to let her go.

'You're not angry with me, are you?' There'll be another time, he thought, plucking a piece of grass from her hair.

'No, course not. Why should I be?' They kissed again, softly now, with no urgency in it, and she knew it was all right. Life was suddenly wonderful and her heart was racing with happiness. Meg's only experience of love and romance came from her rare visits to the cinema, or flea pit as Kath called it. A diet of glossy sentimentality and cultivated passion filled with vows of undying love lightened by jokey wisecracks, always with a happy ending in the final reel.

'Will I see you tomorrow?' he asked, and when she hesitated he persisted. 'I must see you, Meg. I'm not made of stone, love.' He'd called her his love. The delight of being wanted as those screen goddesses were wanted, was so delicious that Meg, as many a woman before her, felt suddenly heady with a sense of her own power. Reaching up, she wrapped her arms about his neck and kissed him good and hard.

'Will that keep you happy till I can get away again?' she asked, and turning from him, started to run down the hill.

Her feet flew over the coarse grass, slipping and sliding down the hillside with the wind in her hair and exhilaration in her heart. Her father was waiting for her when she got home, complaining that his supper wasn't ready. He said nothing more but his silence was heavy and accusing as he riddled the coals in the grate and then banked it up for the night. He sent her up early to bed just as if she were a child and not a grown woman. But Joe Turner's disapproval couldn't touch her now, and she was glad to escape.

Meg undressed slowly and running her hands over her breasts before pulling on the flannel nightgown, she wondered if she was beautiful.

That night, in the secret darkness of her bed, she relived those moments over and over in her mind and knew with a shaming weakness that she hadn't wanted Jack to stop, not at all. Would she have let him go further if there'd been anywhere more suitable than a copse of ash trees by a small mountain tarn? She didn't know, but curiosity was strong in her and the thought did not go away that life with Jack Lawson would be a good deal more exciting than waiting on her crabby old father and brothers.

—

They met regularly after that. In the mornings Meg would race through her work, humming happily to herself. Most afternoons found her slipping out the back door and striding off up to Brockbarrow Wood, heart pumping as she waited for Jack.

She knew Joe watched her, often with dark brows drawn into a dour frown, but he never spoke about her change of humour and she never enlightened him. In her view, it was none of his business who she went out with. Besides, it was too soon to have their growing friendship examined by her grasping father. Joe would be sure to put the very worst connotation on it and start asking what Jack could offer as a prospective son-in-law.

Meg knew he wouldn't want to lose her from the farm, not yet. He maintained that her job was to look after him until he retired, or Dan married and brought a replacement housekeeper to the farm. By which time Meg reckoned she would be well past thirty and quite grey with age.

But she couldn't help telling Kath about meeting Jack at the copse, though she said nothing of the hot kisses or the furtive fumblings. These were secrets best kept to herself.

'You want to be careful,' Kath warned. 'Jack has had loads of girl friends.'

'Oh, I know he's experienced,' Meg said. 'But he wouldn't take advantage. I trust him.'

Kath looked disbelieving. 'So long as you don't get any silly ideas about him, Meg. Like falling in love and marriage.'

Meg took Kath's warnings with a very large pinch of salt. What young man didn't sow a few wild oats when he was young? And Jack was older than herself at twenty-three, nearly twenty-four, so of course he'd had a few girl friends. But she meant to be his last. The thought of marriage with Jack filled her with delight. Even so, instinct warned her that there had to be a greater purpose to her life. She understood this somehow, deep in her heart.

So although the two girls shared their thoughts and dreams, Meg had no intention of letting even Kath into this one. Not until she'd sorted out her own thoughts on the subject.

'Heaven forbid,' she scoffed. 'And spend my life in a kitchen?' Both girls giggled, content with each other, as they had always been. Meg resolved then that until she had discovered what that something was, and had achieved it, she would not allow Jack Lawson to get so far with her again. It was too risky. But she would go on seeing him, as often as she could manage.

There was a late snow the next day, blocking the lanes and filling the shady sides of the stone walls, burying the sheep who had sought shelter. Her father and two brothers were kept fully occupied bringing them in, often discovering the bedraggled, crow-picked bodies of newborn lambs, destroyed before they'd had time to taste life.

Meg too worked flat out as the snow created its usual chaos and extra work. Clothes to be dried, hot meals provided at all hours of day and night without a word of thanks. And on top everything else, the orphan lambs to be fed at frequent intervals throughout the day and night and kept warm by the kitchen range until they were strong enough to survive outside without a mother.

Worse, the snow meant that she couldn't get out to see Jack. Through the long claustrophobic days that followed, confined to the farm, Meg dreamed of the warmth of his lips against hers, the feel of Jack's fingers threading through her hair and the sigh of the wind in the ash trees as it washed over them, wrapping them in an almost mystical enchantment.

A week passed, and another. Was Broombank cut off too? she wondered, and began to worry about Lanky. She had known him all her life and loved him almost as a father. There had been times when she'd wished he was. Meg knew that the old man hadn't been well recently and would appreciate one of her home-made pies. And so, as soon as the lanes were passable, she decided not to wait for the thaw. She would go anyway.

—

There were fox prints deep in the snow as Meg trod steadily upwards, leaving a trail of her own beside them. The thorn bushes were shrouded with white, showering the lane with yet more pristine crystal flakes as she brushed by. In her hand she carried a basket in which reposed the pie, deep and rich with gravy. There was also a small cheese, and a pot of her best raspberry jam. Lanky Lawson, being a widower with only Jack at home, had few comforts these days. So even if the food was not up to her mother's standards, it would be welcomed.

The mountains glittered brilliantly in the morning sun, fallen rocks like glass marbles at their feet. Great banks of snow were still piled high at each side of the lane, alternately melting and freezing as the weather changed. Progress was proving difficult with her booted feet skidding and skating on the frozen puddles one moment, and the next knee deep in a drift. But she meant to get through, no matter what.

Stomach churning with excitement, she wished she'd thought to bring some lipstick with her, or a dab of Boots 711 Cologne to put behind her ears. In her old raincoat and wellington boots she looked a bit too plain and well scrubbed. But the anticipation of seeing Jack grew stronger with every step, making her hurry so that by the time she finally reached Broombank she was sticky and flushed with the effort.

The farmhouse, with its projecting wings and dilapidated barn, saddened her. Its once white walls, roughcast to better withstand the weather, looked grey and pockmarked. To think this had once been one of the biggest and best sheep farms in the district with its two hundred and fifty acres of intake land and six or seven hundred more on the fells above. But with his son away so long in Preston, old Lanky had lost heart.

Meg greeted him with a cheerful smile when he opened the door, trying to prevent her eyes from sliding past him to see if Jack was home.

'Eeh, now then,' he said, looking pleased. 'Thee's a grand sight on a cold day.'

She hugged the old man, kissing his too-thin cheek. The scent of St Bruno flake tobacco, wood smoke, and something indefinable that might have been animal feed clung to his parchment skin, like old leather against the softness of her lips.

Horny hands gripped hers with a strength that always surprised her, coming from such a small man.

'Come in and warm theeself,' he said, pushing the door closed behind her. 'There's a bit of a fire going.'

Moments later she had her hands cupped about a hot mug of cocoa, toasting her toes in the great fireplace which was wide enough, Lanky said, to take a horse and cart should you have one handy. No doubt the ladies of Tudor England spun their wool within its embrace, and wove the hodden grey clothing Lakeland was famous for. They would bake their oatcakes, known as clapbread since it was clapped flat by the palm of a hand, on the huge griddle that hung from the ratten hook in the centre of the huge chimney. Another hook held the great black kettle that now steamed and spat hot water into the flames as Lanky moved it to one side so she could feel the heat. The andirons still stood in the hearth but they did not hold in place a huge log on this cold day as they might once have done. Instead, an insignificant wood fire burned in an old iron basket, giving off very little heat and a good deal of smoke. It was no wonder that Lanky still kept a scarf looped about his neck, tucked into the vee of his waistcoat.

Lanky Lawson, for all his name, was a small, slight man with trousers that hung on braces from armpit to glossy boots, making his legs look like a pair of brown liquorice sticks, a bit frayed at the bottom as if someone had chewed them. And over it all he wore an old saggy tweed jacket that he declared 'had an easy fit to give him room to grow'.

'I'm right glad you came,' he said. 'Always did like a pretty woman to gossip with.'

Meg was at once sorry that she hadn't called more often recently. Her mother had been a frequent visitor with home-made titbits, Meg often accompanying her. Annie had loved Broombank with its spacious old grandeur crouching low in the rolling hillside.

Through the low oak door that led into the back dairy Meg could see the stone sink filled with dirty pots and plates. What was Jack thinking of to let them pile up so? She'd see if she couldn't tactfully deal with a few of those before she left.

There was no sign of Jack himself anywhere, which was a blow. Perhaps he was out looking for lambs, she reasoned, an endless job in this weather. Stifling the disappointment of missing him, she set the pie to warm on the trivet.

'How's Connie keeping?' she asked. Much in evidence from the many photographs that stood on the wide oak dresser, Connie rarely visited Broombank these days. There she was as a schoolgirl in pigtails, looking plump and serious. And on her wedding day, stoutly pleased with herself as well she might be. A sour-faced spinster for years, she had surprised everyone by marrying in her mid-thirties only a year or two ago.

'Oh, as busy as ever with her new house in Grange-Over-Sands,' Lanky replied, equally enough. 'She's a grand lass, if a bit pernickety. Coming home to see me soon, she says.'

Meg had heard this promise many times so took little notice but it saddened her to see the old man alone so much in his neglected house. Untidy and unkempt, it offered little more warmth and comfort than an empty cow byre. The thought came to her how much she would love to see it reborn, a loving home and working farm once more. She could see herself at one side of this great hearth and Jack at the other. The thought made her heart race with excitement.

'We used to have great hams hanging from the rannel balk when my wife was alive,' Lanky told her, following her gaze and referring to the thick beam that ran the length of the kitchen ceiling. 'We'll not see the like again.'

'You might. If your family produces lots of grandchildren for you to feed.'

'Nay, I doubt it. Jack's not about to rush into marriage, so far as I'm aware.' And when she flushed, confused by the meaning of his words, he gave a little chuckle, but not to mock her. He was thinking how her sweet beauty lit up his dusty kitchen and recalling how his own pretty Mary had once done just the same. Mary might not have been his first choice but she'd been a good wife to him all the same and he was not sorry that it wouldn't be long now before he saw her again. Till then he'd enjoy what time he had left, no complaining, and try to put things in proper order, as he should. If he could just work out what sort of order would be best, he'd feel better, he truly would.

Lanky insisted Meg stay and enjoy a bite of supper with him and how could she refuse? For once she had nothing particular to hurry home for. Father was out on some business or other. Dan had been asleep in the fireside chair snoring his head off when she left, and Charlie, as usual, was fully occupied with his aeroplane models, books, and cigarette card collection. Besides, there was always the hope that Jack might return home at any moment.

When they had a fair portion of the pie, she ventured to ask: 'Is Jack out with the lambs?'

'Nay. He's gone off down town. Claims he gets claustrophobia if he doesn't get away for a bit every now and then.'

'Oh.' Her disappointment was keen, and Jack still hadn't appeared by the time Meg had to leave. But she managed a smile as she put on her coat.

'I'll come again, Lanky, and bring an apple pie next time.'

'Just fetch theeself lass, that'll do. I'll walk part way with you. Give me chance to look over the sheep. There's still one or two left to lamb.'

–

The two walked companionably together along the boundaries of the top field, instinctively watching for any sign of a ewe going off on her own, or turning round and round as she sought a place to drop her lamb. The silent presence of the sheep, jaws grinding, incurious eyes staring, always filled Meg with a quiet calm. There were the Swaledales, pale and square, and the Herdwicks with their dark, barrel-shaped bodies, faces dusted with the same hoar frost as the coarse grass at their feet. Only these sheep could best survive the bleak conditions on the Lakeland fells.

'Do you remember when I insisted on buying that pet lamb off you when I was about ten?'

'Aye, I do that. You could have had it for nowt but you wanted to play at doing business, all proper like. You fed it with a bottle and it followed you about like a dog for a year or more.'

'I remember you even gave me the lucky penny to go with it. Just as if I'd bought it at the auction.'

'Aye, well, it's a custom that goes right back to the Norsemen. Brings bad fortune if you don't give something back. Always remember that, Meg. And that li'le lamb thrived, a good friend to you.'

She tucked her arm into his, feeling a flood of warmth for this old man who had made a small girl feel important and happy for a while.

'Till Father sold it.'

'Aye. He would.'

'I loved it, and cried buckets when one morning I found it had gone. Didn't speak to him for weeks afterwards.'

'I dare say. You were nobbut a lass.'

'No room for sentiment in farming,' he said. 'Sheep aren't pets and women shouldn't meddle with matters they don't understand.'

'A pet lamb is different,' Lanky said, with the kind of understanding that had always made her love him.

They reached the stile and started to climb over. Amber eyes glowed in the swinging light from the storm lantern and Meg smiled at the sheep, as if to reassure them.

'Sorry to disturb you, ladies.'

'They don't mind visitors, so long as they only have two legs.'

It was then that Meg noticed one of the Herdwicks in a far corner did not look right. She pointed it out to Lanky. It didn't take an expert eye to guess the problem. Even as Meg watched the ewe went down and lay grunting on the grass. From the hind quarters peeped a nose, no feet, just one small black nose. Lanky knelt on the frozen earth beside the ewe to examine it, prodding and probing with expert fingers, then to her great surprise stood up again.

'What would you do then?'

Meg stared at him in consternation. Wasn't he going to help the ewe? Its distress now was most apparent. Was he waiting for Jack? She looked about her hopefully, but only the sheep stared back, a little restless now as if sensing trouble.

'Why are you asking me?' The chill of the night made her shiver as it seeped into her bones.

'You're a farmer's lass. You should know.'

The ewe was starting to strain in her attempt to rid herself of the lamb which was locked fast in the passage, tied up in its own straggling legs. It might well strangle itself, and its mother, at any moment.

Meg stared helplessly into Lanky's eyes and saw the challenge in them. Was he testing her? *Surely he didn't want her to deliver the lamb?* She became aware that he was speaking to her again.

'You see to this one whilst I check on the rest. There's another over there might well be in a similar state.' And he walked away, leaving her alone with the poor trembling ewe.

For a moment Meg was paralysed with fear.

Her father's words echoed in her head like a litany. 'Farming isn't woman's work. Don't interfere in matters that don't concern you.' But Joe wasn't here now. No one was. Not even Lanky who was attending to one of the other ewes. He must trust her or he wouldn't have left her alone. Perhaps it was this that gave her the much-needed confidence, or else she could not help but respond to the anguished appeal in the animal's eyes.

It came to her then in a moment of startling clarity that she did know what to do. She'd heard enough talk, watched enough births, if only from a distance, to have a pretty good idea how to go about it.

Setting down the lamp some safe distance away, knowing there was no time to waste, Meg took off her coat and rolled up her sleeves. As she made her preparations a calmness came and the fear left her.

'There now, young lady, don't you worry, I'm here to help.' The ewe rolled its eyes, baring its teeth in a silent scream of despair. If she did something wrong, if she lost the lamb, or worse, the mother, how would she ever live with herself? And Joe would half kill her.

'All right, all right, hush now, hush.' Meg put all thoughts of her father from her head. She didn't think of Lanky, nor even of Jack. There was a job to be done and she was the one to do it. Her one concern was to help the distressed ewe.

It was almost as if she had been waiting for this moment all her life. The stillness of the night held and shielded her in its silent embrace. The rime of frost glistened but Meg no longer felt the cold.

Talking quietly all the time, she moved with a natural instinct. Holding the sheep firmly, but gently, she pushed the lamb back inside the mother, calming her as she did so. Meg found she needed to use more effort than she'd expected and anxiety gripped her, making her sweat despite the minus eight temperature. Sorting out the tangle of front feet from the small pointed head took longer than she'd hoped but at last she had them both tucked neatly beneath the chin in the correct position ready for birth, and with a little more urging they came sweetly forward and the tiny body slithered out on to the ice-frosted grass on a sigh of relief from herself as much as the exhausted mother. The lamb shook its raggedy ears and almost at once tried to get up.

Moments later a second lamb followed. Twins were rare with hill sheep so it would have been particularly tragic to lose these. The ewe turned her head to nuzzle them, making pleased little grunting sounds in her throat, and started at once on the task of cleaning each one in turn with her long black tongue. Meg sat uncaring of the cold on the freezing snow and watched the lambs as they circled their mother, and finally start to suckle. Tears rolled down her cheeks.

'There now,' said a voice in her ear. 'I knew you had it in you.'

'Oh, Lanky. I can hardly believe I did that. It was so wonderful.'

'Tha did well. I'll get 'em inside now, for their first night on God's good earth.'

The lanes held that empty silence of a snow-filled landscape on the walk home, with only the squeak and crunch of ice beneath her wellington boots. Meg was glad of the lantern that Lanky had lent her. Its glow lit her way but made the vastness of the scene seem infinite and unreal. But she was not afraid. The empty mountains, the whispering trees, held no threat for her. This was her country and she loved it. The birth had been the most moving experience of her life, and it had told her exactly what she wanted to do with it. She wanted to be a sheep farmer. The very best in the district.

Chapter Four

Following that spring day Meg expected, in some way, for life to change, but it continued very much as before, only now she had a goal to work for, an aim in view. It made her feel good and warm inside.

And even more glorious, she was seeing Jack almost daily. Though she took great care not to let her feelings run away with her again. He occasionally objected to the boundaries she set even as he kept to them.

Meg hugged to herself the memory of that night in April, one she'd come to think of as an almost mystical experience that had firmed her decision on what she wanted to do with her life. It seemed so obvious now. As if the knowledge had been there all along but she hadn't recognised it. Just because her father wouldn't let her help with the sheep at Ashlea didn't mean she couldn't work on another farm. And the best of it was that Jack was a farmer already. She began to fantasise about what it would be like if they married. They would be equal partners in the running of Broombank. Jack wasn't old-fashioned like Joe, he was young and modern and would expect his wife to share everything, and if she were that wife, she'd be only too happy to do so.

Meg visited Broombank regularly and took great care with her appearance, for didn't she want Jack to love her?

She would dive behind the barn to tidy her hair or rub the smuts from her cheeks the moment she saw him approach, making Lanky chuckle. But she didn't care. It made it an extra special visit when they could work together, as if they were man

and wife already. These were good times for Meg but sometimes Jack complained she spent too much time with Lanky
and not enough with him.

'I like you to myself,' he would say, stroking her hair which
she was growing to please him. 'You are my special girl and I
want you to stay that way.'

Jack's girl. Oh, it sounded so good.

'Then will you kiss me?' she would ask, and he was always
ready to comply. Life was perfectly wonderful in Meg's estimation. Nothing could possibly spoil it.

When spring ripened into summer they might walk over
to Patterdale by way of Angle Tarn. As wild and lonely as
anywhere in the Lake District, there they would marvel at the
sight of a golden eagle dipping in the wind, or hares quarrelling
furiously for no apparent reason. Then they would plunge into
the water together, ice cold after the warmth of the sun. But
no amount of sweet talk would persuade Meg to swim without
a costume.

'Prudish little miss, aren't you?' Jack teased and Meg could
only admit to her shyness and hold fast to her ideals, however
much she might wish otherwise.

'Don't you trust me?'

'Of course I trust you.'

'Then prove it.'

Slapping water at him, she would laugh and swim away as
fast as she could, thinking that perhaps it was herself she didn't
trust. Will he get bored with me, she worried, if I keep him to
such firm boundaries?

It was easier when they swam in their very own Brockbarrow
Tarn and Kath came with them. Though Meg regretted the
loss of intimacy on these occasions, she felt safer in an odd sort
of way, knowing that Jack wouldn't press her too much with
company present. And the three of them always had plenty of
fun together.

Sometimes they would walk for hours up Bannisdale or
along part of the old Roman road of High Street then follow

the ribbon of water that gushed down into Longsleddale where they would take off their shoes and paddle their tired feet in the fast-flowing river by the low bridge, squealing like children. A perfect end to a perfect day.

Meg, knowing herself lost to Jack's charms, ached for the day when he would declare his love for her openly. He was a cautious man, as farmers often are. Oh, but she was lucky. Any number of girls would envy her having Jack. She could afford to wait.

—

Joe Turner, not having been born yesterday, as he was fond of saying, was well aware that something had changed in his daughter. He had his suspicions what the reason might be, though nothing had been said between them. He tried to work out a way to winkle the truth out of her, but she kept things close to her chest did Meg. It annoyed him sometimes how like her mother she was, always singing and smiling to herself as if she knew something he didn't.

He'd never been entirely sure what went on in Annie's head, for all she'd made herself out to be a good, obedient wife. There'd been many a time, particularly in the early days, when she'd managed to speak volumes without opening her mouth. Now this little madam was behaving in just the same way. Keeping secrets. And he wouldn't have it, not in a house where he was master.

Love, if that was what was ailing her, had caused enough trouble for the Royal family with the King running off and marrying that Mrs Simpson. Joe would have no such nonsense at Ashlea. Duty and the needs of the farm came first and last in the lives of his own family if he had any say, which of course he did.

When she wasn't wandering over the countryside goodness knew where, Meg was forever giggling and chattering with that Ellis girl, telling secrets he shouldn't wonder, as silly young girls tended to do. Joe didn't like secrets. Above all things, he liked to keep control in his own hands.

So one day he followed her and was surprised to find her land up at Broombank.

Now what would she be doing up there day after day? He asked himself, and came up pretty quickly with the answer. Jack Lawson. Plain as the nose on your face. Now there was a turn up for the book. Something he might well be able to use to his advantage one day. When the time was right. Joe was so pleased with his discovery he almost sang as he walked home, but remembered in time to keep his usual taciturn expression. Always the safest.

Visitors to Ashlea were rare. Farmers, not having much time for socialising at home, tended to confine their gossiping, which they loved, to their gatherings, meets and markets. The women-folk had their own list of busy chores which kept them at home just as firmly. So Meg was surprised to have a visitor one day in early summer. She was alone in the house, her father having gone to make arrangements with Lanky for the coming clipping. Dan and Charlie were out in the fields.

The day was sunny, ideal for a bit of gardening, washing curtains and baking a fresh batch of scones. Feeling well pleased with her efforts Meg quickly fed the new growing calves then awarded herself a well-earned rest in the sun. She was sitting with her feet propped on an upturned bucket when Sally Ann Gilpin, the seventeen-year-old eldest daughter of the Gilpin family of Quarry Row came knocking at the farmhouse door.

She was a plump girl with a round smiling face. Meg remembered her from school as always wearing hand-me-down clothes a size too small, and she had changed little over the years, as untidy now as she had been at twelve. Kath, who of course had gone to a private girls' school in Carlisle, had never been a particular friend of Sally Ann's but Meg liked her. Sally Ann had a good warm heart.

'Is your pa in?' she asked now, hugging a buttonless cardigan about an ample bosom.

Meg explained that he was away and she wasn't sure when he'd be back. 'Dan's in the top field. I could call him for you.'

'No, it's all right,' said Sally Ann, too quickly. 'I can call again.'

Meg smiled encouragingly at her. 'He'll be in shortly, for his tea. Stay and have a cuppa with me and a bit of a crack. It's not often I get a chance for a gossip with another female. Surrounded by great clods of menfolk I am, and I haven't been out for days.' Meg laughed and Sally Ann, eyeing the scones on the kitchen table, quickly agreed.

'That'd be grand, ta.'

They went inside while Meg brewed a fresh pot of tea and buttered several scones. She carried the tray out so they could sit in the sun, Sally Ann trailing silently behind her. But the small tea party proved to be a disappointing failure. Her one-time friend, perched uncomfortably on the edge of her chair, seemed lost in thoughts of her own and all Meg's efforts at cheerful conversation fell flat. Finally she recalled how Jack had told her that Mr Gilpin had been unwell.

'How's your dad? I hope your ma's managing all right.'

The girl swallowed a mouthful of tea, seemed to choke upon it and quickly set the mug down as she broke into a fit of coughing. Meg waited patiently for the spasm to pass.

'Dad isn't too good as a matter of fact. His leg was smashed by a boulder that ran loose in the blasting and he's had to give up quarrying. He gets a bit of labouring here and there. Doctor doesn't think it'll ever properly mend, not that we've had him up recently. Doctors cost money.'

Meg looked shocked. 'But surely your dad was insured, with the quarry?'

'Oh, aye, at least he paid his penny a week for a while, only it don't last for ever.' Again she swallowed a mouthful of scalding tea as if wanting to soothe away unpleasant memories. 'And there's not been much spare cash about with Dad off sick for so long.'

'No, there wouldn't be.'

'That's why I'm here, if I'm honest,' Sally Ann admitted, her voice so low Meg could scarcely hear her.

'You're wanting to borrow some money off my father, is that it?'

Sally Ann looked up at her with haunted eyes. 'Well, your pa's already helped us out a time or two. I was wondering if he'd give us more time to pay.'

Meg regarded the girl for a moment in compassionate silence. Unable either to read or write, Joe Turner was nevertheless frugal and adept at saving money. And if he could make that money work for him by lending it out at a good rate of interest, nothing pleased him more. He kept track of every penny owed him on tally sticks which he kept in a sacking bag hung behind the pantry door. One for every client. He never made a mistake and Meg had seen grown women weep as they begged for more time to pay, and him just turn and walk away. It sickened her sometimes but it was infinitely worse to see it happen to a friend.

'He never likes extending the loan period. I do know that. Is there no other way you can get the money?'

Sally Ann looked bleak. 'I earn what I can at the Co-op shop and we're very careful. But Mr Shaw says he has to cut me hours from next week so I won't be able to pay so much back. And the little ones are needing boots for their feet, not new ones you understand, but teacher says they can't go to school without. The house we've found, well, hovel more like since we had to leave Quarry Row...' Sally Ann rolled her eyes as if trying to make a joke of it... 'needs a coat of distemper if only to kill the bugs. We can't go on like this much longer.' Her voice broke, betraying her resolution to remain calm.

Hearing her friend's problems filled Meg with shame. She was in the depths of despair any day she missed seeing Jack, agonising over where he was and who he might be with. Only when she was with him was she truly happy. Jack was also growing more ardent, his hands seemed to be everywhere and she worried about how much longer she could control him. She loved him so much and she did want him, she did truly. Only she was afraid of what might go wrong if she gave in. Meg thrilled at the new excitement that had come into her dull life, delighted that at last someone cared, but it worried her all the same.

Yet really it shouldn't, she told herself, not in comparison with Sally Ann's lot.

'I'll call and see your ma. We've more vegetables here than we know what to do with. And I could spare a bit of milk and eggs now and then, for the little ones.'

'Oh, she'd be made up.'

'I wish it could be more.'

'Just tell your pa that I…' Footsteps sounded across the yard and Sally Ann stopped speaking, clamping her lips together as Dan swaggered towards them. Meg poured her brother a mug of tea, buttered a large scone and handed both to him without a word.

He settled himself with a sigh on a low stone wall and looked across at the two girls seated on kitchen chairs before him, brown eyes speculative while he consumed his tea.

They talked for a while of inconsequential matters, mutual friends they knew who had married or given birth recently and various members of Sally Ann's large family. At last Meg turned to Dan with an enquiring smile.

'Do you know what time Father will be home? Sal has come to see him on a matter of business.'

Dan gave a grunting laugh as if she'd said something amusing. 'Women don't know owt about business.'

'That's not true,' Meg refuted stoutly. 'Women aren't given the chance, that's all.'

Dan glowered at his sister, bristled brows twisted in scornful mockery. 'You think you're so smart.'

'Maybe I am.'

'Smarter than me, a humble farmer, I suppose?'

'Most people are smarter than you. I certainly work as hard as you, great lazy lump that you are, and don't pour money down me throat. What Father would say if he found out that's what you do, I don't know.'

'You're going to tell him, are you? Miss-Goody-Two-Shoes.'

'No, I'm not the tell-tale round here. Stop trying to pick a fight, Dan, and just tell me what time Father'll be home so Sally Ann knows whether it's worth her while waiting.'

Clearing her throat, Sally Ann spoke up, perhaps thinking to stop this argument before it got quite out of hand. 'It's only about the loan.'

'Well now, if it's to do with money lending, I'm the one you want to see, not me father.'

'Oh, but it was Mr Turner that I dealt with last time.'

Dan was setting down his mug as he got to his feet. He looked impressive at full stretch, a well-built man it was true, but handsome when he made the effort to adopt a more pleasant demeanour. And all too aware of his own power.

'Well, you can deal with me now. Father leaves much of that side of the business in my hands these days.'

'Since when?' Meg asked, startled.

Dan ignored her. 'He has enough to do with the farm, he says. These financial matters are often left to me.' He smiled at Sally Ann.

A year or two younger than herself, Meg thought Sally Ann looked suddenly old and haggard, and she was filled with pity for her. Dan had never been known for his caring personality. Rather the reverse. He had been the kind of child who pulled wings off butterflies and hated anyone to best him. She reached out a hand instinctively to reassure the other girl.

'What do you know about finance? You couldn't even learn your multiplication tables.'

'If you're so clever I dare say you think you could run this whole farm better'n me?'

'You don't run it. Father does.'

Dan's face went red. He hated the idea that he must wait till Joe died before he had any say in running Ashlea. 'It'll be mine one day. Then you'll have to do what *I* say.'

Meg was so infuriated by this high-handed bullying the words were out before she had checked them. 'Maybe it'll be mine and not yours, who can say?'

'Huh, that's a laugh. Father'd never leave it to you.'

'He might, if I proved I could look after it better'n you,' she protested, then quailed at the grimace of pleasure that came to his face.

'You? Run this farm? A woman?'

'Yes, me, a woman.'

'I'd like to see you try.' Dan jerked his head towards the empty field and the smooth green fells beyond, where could be seen moving flecks of sheep grazing. 'If you're so wonderful, let's see you fetch some of the sheep down for the clipping. Go on, I dare you.'

She could tell him not to talk so daft. It took three men with dogs to walk the several hundred acres of open fell and bring down the hundreds of sheep that belonged to Ashlea.

Perhaps it was the mocking laughter on his face, or his heartless bullying of poor Sally Ann. Or the fact that he had ruined her one chance of earning a bit of extra money by getting her in trouble with her father. Or Meg remembering all too vividly that night in the snow. She had told no one, not even her family, of that night, and neither it seemed, had Lanky. Perhaps because of that experience Meg felt certain she was capable of so much more and had a sudden longing to prove it.

'All right,' she said. 'You're on.'

Dan turned away, a sneering laugh on his lips. 'Don't talk soft. There's only two places where women should be. At kitchen sink, or in bed.'

That did it. Meg tossed her bright head, curls bouncing with boundless energy, grey eyes meeting her brother's with a challenging glare. 'Right. I'll bring some of your damn sheep in. See if I don't.'

And leaving them standing open mouthed, she recklessly set off alone, up the fells.

–

Drops of water sparkled in the sunshine on firm brown flesh. Two bodies, now entwined, now swimming and diving, ducking and leaping, girlish laughter mixed with the more gruff teasing tones of the man who pursued her carried upward on the still warm air.

Not for this girl any sense of shyness or undue modesty. Her body was carefully toasted to a coffee and milk colour and she held no inhibitions about showing it. She knew her breasts were firm and full, her waist narrow over the seductive swell of girlish hips. Her legs were long with slim ankles and highly arched, pretty feet. She buffed the skin at night till it was smooth as silk, nurtured with creams and lotions. Now she gasped with delight as the ice-cold tarn water flowed upon it, swimming as briskly as she could to keep her blood flowing.

'Come here, damn you!' Jack was after her in a second. When he caught her she wrapped those long brown legs about his waist, shaking wet hair back from her face. He buried his face in it, capturing her breasts with his hands. 'God, you're beautiful. You're like a drug I can't leave alone.'

'Why should you leave me alone?' Slanting hazel eyes regarded him with open provocation. 'When it's so good.'

'Oh, it's good right enough.' It was so easy to penetrate her here in the lake. He grasped her hips and pulled them down hard against him, making her scream and shiver with ecstasy as he plunged upwards into the soft warmth of her. The experience was intoxicating, addictive.

Later, when they lay spent on the cropped grass, gazing up at speckled sunshine glistening amongst the green leaves of an old oak, he swore softly through gritted teeth and she laughed. 'Don't tell me you want it again, so soon?'

'No, witch, leave me alone. Why do I feel so damn guilty?'

Kath smoothed a languorous hand over the broad chest and down the length of his flat stomach. 'I can't imagine. It's not as if you're engaged or anything, is it? You're still a free man.'

He pushed her hand away and sat up. When she was touching him like that he couldn't think clearly. 'Meg seems to be making plans.' He couldn't understand how it was that matters were moving so fast between them. She'd have him buying a ring soon if he didn't watch out, and he hadn't yet decided yet if that was what he wanted. Nor could he quite bring himself to give her up.

Kath sighed deeply, closing her eyes against the sun and enjoying the heat of it on her bare skin. 'Nonsense. Tell her not to. Life is too short for plans.'

'She spends hours at the farm with my dad. Keeps talking about farming. I think she's more besotted with the sheep than me.'

'I wonder why.'

He gazed down at Kath's nakedness and felt himself start to harden again. 'Meg would certainly never lie here with me like this.'

Kath's eyes sparkled with a taunting challenge as she watched his discomfiture worsen. She licked drops of water from her upper lip and saw him groan in fresh agony as his eyes followed the movement. 'Well, there you are then. Nothing to worry about. She's happy with her sheep and I'm happy with this. No plans. No ties. Come here. Let me make you a happy man.'

–

Trying to fetch the sheep down on her own was, Meg discovered, the craziest thing she had ever attempted in her life. And it was all Dan's fault for stirring her up into anger.

Some of the greedy ones followed her, hoping for extra feed, but if she attempted to herd them in one direction they quickly panicked and set off at a gallop the opposite way.

She had run and stalked and circled wide, blocked up gateways, called, begged and even cried, but had known all along that it was useless. And all the time she was aware of Dan watching her from the house, laughing fit to bust, she shouldn't wonder.

In the end she realised she was in danger of risking injury to the precious stock and sat on a boulder shaking with fatigue and anger, letting the tears of humiliation and ruined pride fall.

What a fool she was always to rise to Dan's jibes. Why couldn't they have an easy relationship, like she had with Charlie?

Just because she had helped one sheep bring a lamb into the world didn't make her a farmer. Because she knew how to give a dose of treacle and egg white to cure its ills, didn't mean she could catch the animal in order to issue it. Sheep were not half so stupid as they looked, she decided.

Meg gazed about her at the majesty of the mountains that rose above the lower slopes of the fells and felt humbled. Patches of shadow, like giant grey sheep, were being chased over the barren fell by brilliant swathes of light. And on the ridges beyond, the remains of last winter's snow formed skeletal faces, warning people to tread with care. It put her in awe of the task of caring for heedless animals in such a setting. She was mad. She must be to let a little knowledge go to her head. Perhaps Dan was right when he said she was too sharp for her own good.

Alone, here, on the mountainside, she made a private vow that whatever she needed to know, she would learn. Deep inside her was an ache Meg knew must be satisfied. Nothing to do with love, or Jack, or even her family, though they made her more aware of it.

This was something to do with the search she had been engaged on all her life, with that night in April, and with the destiny that she had found on that night. She drew the sparkling air deep into her lungs and felt better for knowing nothing could touch that secret part of her.

In the end she was forced to swallow her pride and return to the farm. Dan crowed with pleasure at her embarrassment and her father mockingly reminded her he had said all along that shepherding was man's work.

'I could do it,' she told them both, shame and humiliation adding unusual beauty to her rosy cheekbones. 'If I had a dog to work with. Even you couldn't do it without a good dog, you know you couldn't.' But neither would admit such a thing so Meg held her silence for the rest of the meal. Only Charlie seemed to be on her side.

'I think Meg had guts to try. I couldn't bring the sheep in on my own.'

'We know that, you great clod,' said Joe, masticating slowly. 'Nor would you have thought to try. Shut your face and eat your food.'

It was when she was washing up and Joe was settling by the fire with his pipe that the subject of Sally Ann Gilpin came up.

'What do y'mean, she came to see me? Why has no one thought to tell me.'

'I'm telling you now.' Meg took off her apron and hung it behind the door. 'Dan sorted it out, ask him. I'm off for a walk.'

'No, you're not, madam. I want to know by what right thee put her on to our Dan without speaking to me first.' Joe started to tamp down the tobacco with a yellow-stained finger as if trying to dampen his rising temper along with it.

For once Meg was surprised to see her elder brother wriggling with discomfort.

'It was only a small matter,' Dan muttered. 'Sal Gilpin needs to reduce the weekly payments for a little while, that's all.'

'That's all?' The voice was ominously soft. Joe Turner had learned that a quiet tone injected far more menace into simple words. He stared unblinkingly at his son. 'Under what conditions did you agree to her reducing the weekly sum?'

'Conditions?' This from Meg who was anxious to provide Sally Ann with a defence at least. 'What more can you ask for? If she pays less each week it'll just take longer to be paid off, but you'll get your money in the end, and no doubt extra interest.'

Dan nodded eagerly. 'She'll call here regular to pay it, every Friday.'

Joe stood up to face his son, his body quivering with unspent anger. 'Didn't she tell you that I called at her house each week along with my other regular clients? Thee has no right to change the arrangements behind my back.'

Meg looked from one to the other, dazed by the tension that had sprung up so quickly in the small kitchen. 'For goodness sake, what does it matter how you get your money? She'll do her best. Calm down, Father.'

'Don't thee tell me to calm down, madam. This is my farm, and I'm in charge of it.'

'You're in charge of everything, it seems,' Dan said in a rare show of rebellion. 'When do I get some rights? And some wages?'

'Why would you need wages? I don't charge thee any keep.'

'I'm not your whipping boy. You keep saying you'll retire. But you won't, I know you won't, and how can I ever think of taking a wife with no money coming in to keep her?'

Such an unusually long speech from Dan silenced Joe for a whole half minute. He chewed on his pipe and considered. 'It's come to a pretty pass when a man's own son is after stepping into his shoes before he's taken them off. Thee could allus go and work for someone else if tha's dissatisfied.'

Dan subsided into his chair, his rebellion spent.

'I'm the moneylender in these parts, not you, you daft ha'porth. I'm the one that feckless women come running to when they find themselves out of money by Tuesday morning and need my coin to get them through the week.'

Meg found she couldn't let that pass without defending her sex. 'Women run out of money because their husbands don't give them enough. They drink it.'

63

'Very likely, but where would those poor women and bairns be without me, I ask you?'

'It's not their gratitude you enjoy, it's the profit you make out of them. Where would you be without those same poor women paying interest through the nose every Friday when you collect your coin back at the quarry face?'

'I'm not a charity, miss,' Joe roared, losing his calm again. 'Is it my fault if some chaps can't hold on to what they earn?' He pushed his face close to his daughter. At fifty-nine the years of toil, of being out in all weathers, had left their mark, worsened by lines of bitterness set there by a sanctimonious determination to make life as difficult for himself as possible. As if by doing so he could be brought closer to his elusive God. What he suffered, he felt duty bound to make his family suffer likewise.

'Times are hard, don't you forget that. A bit more gratitude wouldn't come amiss. Sally Ann Gilpin at least never complains about her lot – she does summat about it. You don't know what it is to be without food to put on the table. When have you ever gone hungry, tell me that?'

How could she dispute such logic? Meg knew she was fortunate. They may be short of cash, and not keep so fine a table as Kath's family, but they never went hungry like the Gilpins. She felt diminished, as she always did when her father turned the attack upon her. 'I was only meaning to speak up for Sally Ann,' she said.

'Aye, well, happen she can speak up for herself.'

On top of her foolishness of the afternoon Meg felt she had failed to defend her friend. Perhaps her father was right and she was selfish, ungrateful and greedy, with, as Dan said, too high an opinion of herself.

But if that were so then why did she feel deep inside that the name of the emotion she experienced so strongly was not greed but ambition? Not selfishness but self-esteem. She wished with all her heart that she could work it out.

Chapter Five

On the last day of September 1938 Chamberlain was boasting of 'Peace for our time'. Czechoslovakia and later Britain herself would have cause to doubt this statement but for now appeasement was all. It seemed to Meg that similar political efforts were being made in the Turner household.

She was determined to have no more arguments with either her brother or her father. Life was otherwise too perfect to let them spoil it. Sally Ann called regularly at the farm every Friday to pay what she could and there seemed to be no further trouble there. Meg wished with a deep longing sometimes that Jack could be as easily welcomed. If only she could pluck up the courage to tell her father about him, but she never managed to.

Though Jack sometimes complained she spent too much time away from him, she loved him all the more for that little show of jealousy. Meg too preferred it when they were together but she also enjoyed helping Lanky.

She wanted Jack to come with them all to the Merry Neet which was a favourite social event. It took place in the backend of the year so that any sheep that had strayed in bad weather, or through a gate left carelessly open, could be checked against the Shepherd's Guide and their rightful owners take them safely home. Meg loved these traditional get-togethers.

In the old days horse racing would often follow the serious business. Nowadays it might be hound trailing or Cumberland and Westmorland wrestling, both of which were favourite pastimes of her brother Dan.

There was a great fire at the inn to toast toes and cheerful faces. It burned so fiercely that after a while caps were removed, brows mopped and chairs eased back. The trestle tables were as packed with plates of hot pot and tankards of ale as the floor was with dogs. And everyone was expected to do a 'turn' as they sat and smoked and drank and chatted into the small hours.

The chairman in charge tonight was Lanky, and he volunteered to 'get the ball rolling' with a rendition of 'The Bonnie Sheep' on his fiddle.

Several other people sang songs while the shepherds beat time with their sticks, the dogs with their tails, and Meg and Charlie sat laughing together on the wooden settle in the corner, not taking part but feeling privileged to be allowed to join in with the merriment. Oh, but how she wished Jack were here. He'd sulked when she'd insisted on coming tonight, wanting her to go with him into town.

'You'd love it,' she'd urged, kissing him softly on the mouth. 'Why won't you come with me?'

'You'll be the only woman there.'

'No, I won't.'

'What would your father say?'

'We don't have to tell Father about us. You're entitled to come with Lanky.'

But he refused, so she'd come with Charlie instead, and was glad.

There were no women shepherds, of course. How she would love to be the first. But several of the wives had come.

And then cries went up for the gurning to start. A popular local sport it might be, nonetheless she was astonished to hear Joe volunteer. She watched him stick his round head through the horse collar, known as a braffin, and start to pull and stretch his lips and cheeks into the most horrendous face. All the farmers stamped their feet and roared with laughter. Meg couldn't believe this was her own, stern-faced father who was performing so outrageously. How could he be so unfeeling towards her, yet the life and soul of the party with his friends?

'Nay, Joe,' cried one, as he let his face relax into a grin. 'Give over, that's worse.'

He was declared champion gurner of the night and was so well pleased with himself he told them a lively tale of losing two sheep from the back of his van and chasing them all round town, which had the farmers almost falling off their seats with delight.

'Why isn't he like this at home with us?' Meg asked Charlie, but her brother only shook his head, equally bewildered.

'Because he isn't happy there,' came Lanky's voice from behind her. 'Not since your mam died. Come up and see me tomorrow. I've got summat to show you.'

She stared thoughtfully at her father and wondered if she knew him at all.

-

Meg finished her chores and walked up to Broombank as promised. She took her time, enjoying the softness of the autumn breeze which failed to shift the phosphorous cloud that clung to the mountain tops. Dundale Knott rose up at her left as she walked, looking like a lop-sided cottage loaf with a knob on top and a large slice of it cut away, leaving a sheer drop to a bubbling beck below. She found Lanky mending broken walls.

'You look busy,' she said.

'Thee'll not catch me laikin,' he said, meaning lazing about doing nothing. 'I've summat to show you. Hold on a minute while I finish this bit.'

He laid all the stones out on the grass and then it was like watching him put a very complicated jigsaw puzzle together. He never picked up the same stone twice, just slotted each one together perfectly. Meg did what she could to help, learning all the while.

'It's nowt much, just summat to say thank you.'

'Thank you for what?'

'For helping an old man.' He grinned, showing gaps in his teeth. 'But mainly for your company. Why a young girl like you should waste her time with an old chap like me, I don't know, but I'm right grateful for it.'

'Oh, Lanky.' Meg put her arms round him and gave him a big hug.

'Go on. It's in t'barn. See what you think.'

'But don't we have to put the cam stones back on top of the wall yet? Can't it wait?'

'No, it can't. Our Jack'll help lift these big stones. They're too heavy for a young lass, and an old man. Go on. Get away with you.'

He was clearly as eager with his surprise as a young boy, and, laughing, Meg ran down the slope and pushed open the great door. The barn was packed from floor to ceiling with hay as it always was at this time of year. Nothing else that she could see. Except the dogs, of course, who slept in a corner. There was a gap in the bottom of the door so they could move in and out of the barn at will on the ends of their long ropes. There was Tess, Lanky's old collie, and her two sons, Ben and Rust. She stared at them now, a sudden wondering idea coming to her.

Meg turned to look questioningly at Lanky. 'Tess hasn't had more pups, has she?'

'Nay, she's past it now. But Rust is young enough to risk with a change of master – or mistress.'

'Oh, Lanky.' She was stunned for a moment by his generosity. 'You can't. He's your best young dog. You can't give him to me.'

'I can do what I like, I reckon, with me own dogs. He needs someone young to tackle him. And Charlie says you'd like one.'

Meg grey eyes were shining. 'Charlie would say that. He saw me make a proper clown of myself trying to do something clever without one.'

Meg looked at the dog. Most of him was black, the colour of all Border collies, but the rest was rust, as if he'd been left out in the rain too long. Hence his name. He was standing in front of her, feathered tail out straight, one brown ear erect, the other black and flopping over. Feet foursquare, eyes bright and alert with a question in them. 'He understands. He's weighing me up. Can you see it in his eyes?'

'Oh, aye, he's not daft is young Rust. Lie down, lad.'

The dog obeyed instantly, falling softly to his belly, velvet eyes fixed upon Lanky's face. 'He'll make up for the loss of the pet lamb, eh?'

'Oh, Lanky. He's much better.' She could feel tears in her throat.

'You'll have to keep him fastened to you for a while till he gets accustomed or he'll keep coming back home to me.'

'Oh, I will. I will.' Meg held out the back of her knuckles for the dog to sniff, talking softly as she knelt beside him. 'I'll take good care of you, boy. You and me can be friends. Would you like that, eh?'

Tongue lolling from the side of his grinning mouth, he gazed at her, then up at his old master.

'Aye, lad. Go on. It's all right.'

Reassured, the dog nosed the hand, indicating he'd be happy to have it stroke him. Meg obliged. Then she remembered what Joe had done with the pet lamb, all those years ago. 'Can I leave him here for a while though, just till I've made it right at home?'

Lanky smiled. 'Not told Joe yet then about your efforts in the sheep department?'

Meg lifted anxious eyes to his. 'No. I will tell him. In me own good time. You won't…'

'Nowt to do wi' me. But that cur will need training. He's young yet, coming up to twelve month. I'll teach you to whistle.'

And so he did. Meg spent hours practising the signals in quiet corners, finding it far more difficult than she'd imagined. And twice as many hours encouraging Rust to round up the ducks and hens in Lanky's yard without setting them off in a flurry. Only when he had served a long apprenticeship, and obeyed her every command, would he be permitted near sheep.

All of this had to be done in complete secrecy from her father and brother, so Rust stayed, for the moment, at Broombank. But Meg meant to have him with her as soon as she had spoken to her father. There was so much now that she had to talk to him about, the prospect was chilling and exciting all at the same time.

–

Meg's peace ended one day in October. It was one of those quiet, still days only found in autumn. The leaves of the Lakeland woodlands were a paint palette of russet, gold and terracotta. A fat yellow sun that never seemed evident in August now turned the cooling lakes to a blinding sparkle of light. Dew-spangled cobwebs knitted the thorn hedges and, high above, swallows and martins bossed and ordered each other into massive groups ready for their flight south.

The weather was unseasonably warm, almost balmy, and Meg and Jack had walked to their favourite place in Brock-barrow Wood. As usual she had responded eagerly to his kisses, but this time he objected to the set boundaries and there was a particularly undignified tussle. Meg was forced to slap his exploring hand away, cheeks flying flags of hot scarlet.

'What kind of girl do you think I am?' she demanded to know, feeling disappointed and somehow guilty all at the same time.

'You're turning into a prude.'

'I'm not. I've told you I'm...'

'Yeah. Keeping yourself on ice. Well, maybe I don't want a woman with ice in her veins. It's hot blood that warms a man, Meg.'

Meg flushed. 'You know how I feel about that. I don't want to take any unnecessary risks.'

'Oh, come on.' He stroked her leg, making her shiver with longing. 'What's so wonderful about settling down, I'd like to know? Make's a man boring and middle-aged before his time.'

'It needn't.'

'Don't expect too much from me, Meg. I am what I am.' Dark brows crashed down over violet eyes, and he got quickly to his feet. Then thrusting his hands deep in his pockets Jack strode briskly away, leaving her alone on the cold grassy slope where a moment before she had been warmly clasped in his arms. 'Let me know when you decide to be a real woman,' he tossed casually over his shoulder, his frustration finally spilling over into temper.

Meg thought of running after him but his broad back looked so furious and unapproachable that she let him go. An action she later regretted.

She spent several miserable days hoping he would come round and ask forgiveness for his ill temper. But he didn't. Nor did he meet her in their usual place each afternoon in Brockbarrow Wood.

Meg's despair deepened. Perhaps she was wrong to hold herself back. Should she take the risk? She did love him, but any talk of marriage had always come from her, not Jack. Surely that only meant he was waiting till she was twenty-one?

In the end she decided to seek advice about her dilemma, and who else was there to ask but Kath? It didn't seem quite right to talk about such personal matters, even to a dear friend. What went on between herself and Jack was their affair after all. But Meg was desperate to know what she should do, for she was so afraid of losing him.

'We'll walk as far as Whinstone Gill,' Kath declared, determined to enjoy the warm sunshine. A deep cleft cut in the rock, the two girls loved to scramble along the gill, sometimes as far as Whinstone Force, a gushing waterfall that burst out of the rock face from a network of underground mountain streams.

Kath had been out riding and her cheeks were flushed by the wind. She wore jodhpurs of pale cream cord and a shirt that was very likely silk clinging to firm uptilted breasts. By comparison Meg felt frumpish in her old sandals and cotton frock, and foolishly naïve.

Nevertheless she decided there wouldn't be a better opportunity and, screwing up her courage, she put her question. 'Can I ask you something?'

'Goodness, this sounds serious.'

'I suppose it is.'

'Ask away.'

'Have you ever, you know, gone all the way?' Meg's cheeks fired up with embarrassment.

Kath stared at her, startled for a moment. 'What did you say?'

'I was only wondering what it was like, if it was as good as all the romantic stories say? And if there's a really safe way of doing it?' she rushed on, finishing in a fluster of heated confusion.

'Safe?'

'Yes. To stop – you know – babies.'

Kath was stunned. 'Didn't your mother tell you? I mean, haven't you and… Oh, my God.' This was the last thing Kath had expected to hear and she wondered for a moment how to cope with it. Meg's attitude to sex had always been less down to earth than her own, though they'd discussed it openly enough between them on many occasions. But not this, she'd never expected this.

'You really don't know? I thought you and Jack…'

'That's just it. He wants to.'

'But you don't?'

'No. Yes. Oh, I don't know. The thing is, will I lose him if I give in?'

'Or will you lose him if you don't?'

Meg stared at her friend in consternation. Trust Kath to spot the nub of the problem right away. 'Something like that.'

'Would it matter very much?'

Meg flushed. 'Yes, of course it would matter.' Jack wasn't the only one to suffer. No matter how hard Meg tried not to think about it, as her love for him grew so did her need to demonstrate that love. Completely. 'I daren't risk getting pregnant and it would be just my luck to catch on first time. Father would throw me out instantly, if only to save his face at the chapel.'

'Funny, isn't it?' Kath agreed. 'How it's always the girl who is blamed, when it takes two to make a baby?'

'And how do I know that Jack would do the decent thing by me? It has been known for the man to walk away and deny the child is his. Not that I think Jack would be so cruel but, oh, it doesn't bear thinking about!'

She wished they didn't have to wait till she was twenty-one to marry. She wished they could go right this minute and live at Broombank and she could help him run the farm. Then they'd live happily ever after. Meg did her best to explain all of this to a suddenly silent Kath.

'So do you think I should – let him, I mean? Would he still respect me, still marry me?'

Kath and Meg had always been close ever since childhood. With few other girls their age living in the area, they'd been almost like sisters. Kath certainly loved her as a sister, but that hadn't stopped them being rivals, not ever, just as real sisters were. Now she felt, not guilt exactly but as near to it as Kath's selfish, careless nature could get. It came together with a great wave of protectiveness towards her more innocent friend. Kath chose her next words with care. 'I didn't realise he was so important to you.'

'Of course he's important. I love him. I've always loved him.'

'I thought that was just schoolgirl stuff.'

Meg's eyes widened. 'No. It might have been once, but not now. And he loves me, I know he does.'

Kath turned away quickly, unwilling to meet the certainty in Meg's clear grey eyes. She climbed up on to the top bar of a wooden gate to give herself time to think, swung one elegant, smoothly jodhpured leg as if they were discussing nothing more important than whether it would rain tomorrow. 'Jack's a rolling stone. He won't stay here.'

'He will. He loves Broombank. He's settling down nicely. He would have left long since otherwise, wouldn't he?'

'You know he's no good, don't you? Never has been. He's had any number of girls.' Kath gave a little laugh, sounding oddly uncertain in her resolution to say what she must. 'He would once have been termed a libertine and a rake. Can't you just see it in those come-to-bed eyes?'

Never in all their long friendship had the girls had a really serious row. But Meg could feel the hot anger stirring within her and knew that at any moment she was about to spoil that good record. She bit down hard on her lower lip. Kath was her best friend, only showing that she cared about her as she'd always done, but Kath didn't understand. She didn't understand at all. For the first time in their relationship, Meg felt superior to her more confident friend.

'He might have been once, when he was younger, but not any more,' she carefully explained.

Kath's heart sank as she looked at Meg's earnest expression. Why hadn't she seen what was happening, put a stop to it earlier? How could she have been so blind? But then why couldn't Meg see that Jack would never settle down? Not in a million years. Certainly not with a quiet little mouse like Meg, however resolute she might pretend to be underneath that meek and mild expression.

'Jack is only kicking his heels,' Kath gently pointed out. 'Waiting for the right opportunity to leave Broombank and the Lake District for the great wide world beyond. Can't you see that?' She could understand that need in him. Didn't she have it herself? There was genuine anxiety now in her plea. 'Don't get caught up with him, Meg. He'll only break your heart.' But the warning was months too late.

Meg was listening appalled. 'How can you be so cruel, Kath Ellis? You don't know him, not as I do. You don't know what it's like to love him.'

Kath swung down from the gate and started to walk away. Shielding her eyes from the direct glare of the sun so that it was impossible accurately to read her expression she looked back at

Meg. It was a long moment before she spoke again. 'No,' she said, 'I don't suppose I do.'

--

'Nay, gentlemen – that price won't do. People are trying to make a living here. Put your hands in your pockets and dust off your money.'

Laughter rippled among the throng of farmers who crowded the auction ring viewing the crop of ewes on sale. Some sat on planks, others leaned on the railing set up to prevent sheep from straying, though what chance they would have in that crowd was hard to reckon. Joe Turner was amongst them, standing next to his old friend and arch rival, Lanky Lawson.

The auctioneer's jokes lightened the tension among the sharp eyed, tweed–clad farmers. Sometimes one would thrust out a horny hand to feel the hind quarters of a sheep, checking her fitness, or examine her teeth for age.

Hill farmers, known for their steady gait on the fells, were not men for unnecessary movement so stood like a still life, enveloped in their own fug of acrid blue smoke, hands on sticks or crooks, weather-beaten faces unsmiling, eyes alert for any sign of a sick or lame animal, the chanting rhythm and miming gestures of the auctioneer like some sort of comic opera carried out for their entertainment.

'How's thisself?' Joe remarked.

'Ah was better afore I met thee,' replied Lanky, equally laconic.

They had commented upon the weather, the state of market prices, and then a silence had fallen between them as business began. Joe would not dream of asking Lanky what he was bidding for, or even how much stock he was hoping to sell himself. Nor would he give the small man any indication of his own bids. Only the auctioneer, from long experience of his clients, knew each farmer's sign. It might be a rub upon a bristly chin or the stem of a pipe, a twitch of a bushy eyebrow or tug of

75

a cap. The slightest gesture could signify a sale, so each would conduct their private business with the wily auctioneer out of eyeshot of each other.

The tension, at times, was palpable. The great heads of Europe might agonise over world peace but nothing was more serious to these men than the price they got for their stock, for upon that depended their very survival.

The room was damp and cold and Lanky succumbed to a fit of coughing.

Joe, his expression inscrutable, leaned on his stick and waited. 'You want to get that cough seen to,' he said, when the bout ended.

Lanky made no reply.

The auctioneer started a fresh lot of bidding and when it was done the conversation moved back to the price of stock, the favourite topic.

'If thee were ever to think of selling, I might be willing to take a piece of land off your hands,' Joe said, putting no particular emphasis upon the words.

'Now why would I want to do that?'

Joe was not put off by the difficulty in obtaining information. He expected it, it being all part of the game. 'Thee has too much, happen, for you and Jack to manage on your own.'

'We get by.'

Joe decided he had gone far enough down this track. Unusually, Lanky owned his own land, and though he no longer put it to full use himself, would not contemplate letting it out to anyone else. Joe envied him since he still only rented Ashlea, despite his best efforts to buy. It was common knowledge that Lanky's son and daughter weren't interested in the farm, yet he persisted in saving it for them. A criminal waste in Joe's opinion, and here he was with money set aside just waiting for a bargain, if there was one going. If Dan was growing restless, Joe could do with a bit more amenable land on which to increase the flock.

This wasn't by any means the first time the subject had been broached between the two men and both knew it would not be the last. Joe's only hope of success was entirely dependent upon Lanky's stubborn pride.

What he didn't know was that Lanky meant him to remain disappointed. Joe Turner wasn't a bad farmer, not by a long chalk, but in Lanky's opinion he was a mean-hearted man with no imagination or human feeling in him. He'd never give what the land was worth and Lanky would never take less.

The two men gave their full attention to the auction for a while, both feigning indifference.

When it was the turn of Broombank sheep to rush and jostle into the ring, seeking escape and companionship of their neighbours all at the same time, Lanky went in the ring with them. There was no question but that he needed a good price, this year more than ever if he was to keep his head above water. The ewes he didn't need and some he did but couldn't afford to keep were being sold off to lowland farms where they would have an easier time of it in their later years.

He knew each one of them individually. Their faces, voices, the shape of their horns, were as well known to him as his own family, better perhaps since he saw little enough of them these days.

'That didn't take long,' said Joe, as a sale was quickly made, far short of Lanky's expectations. And he still had the 'luck money' to find by way of discount to the new owner. But if he wanted the farmer's custom again he had no choice but to pay it. Besides, it was bad luck not to.

'Thee's not thinking of retiring then?' Joe laughed, making a joke of it.

'I'll retire when you do.'

Ashlea stock came next and it was Joe's turn to give his full attention to business. Good stock, all of them, fetching a good price. The bidding went briskly and, satisfied with the result, Joe went so far as to offer to stand Lanky a brew of tea and an Eccles cake. Installed in a corner at a nearby cafe, he moved in for the kill.

'You'll be seeing your way clear to settling that other little matter between us quite soon, I hope?'

The 'little matter' in question was a sum of nearly one hundred and fifty pounds, loaned to Lanky over the last year or two to buy stock and attend to running repairs to the barn, in danger of collapse at one time.

'I've not forgotten.' Lanky replied with careful patience, as was his wont, but for the first time that day some of his confidence evaporated.

Joe noticed and he smiled to himself. 'No hurry, mind. Some time this backend will do, and I'll not raise the interest yet awhile.' Knowing that if the money couldn't be found now, after the sales, there wasn't a hope of it later.

Lanky only grunted.

'Don't see much of your Jack these days, not like when he was a nipper. What's he doing with hissel these days? Is he still set on leaving the farm or has he sown all his wild oats?'

Lanky had no intention of telling Joe what he ought to be able to discover himself, so he made no reply to this either.

'Time he was wed, don't you reckon?'

The swift change of subject unnerved Lanky who was busily trying to work out where Joe was leading, while at the same time worrying over the huge sum of money that was no doubt mounting up in interest on top of the borrowed one hundred and fifty. He wished now that he'd let the barn fall down and not tried to keep his cows. 'He's only three and twenty. Plenty of time.'

Lanky's voice, Joe noted, sounded positively tetchy – and fetched him another pint pot of tea, strong enough to stand a spoon in it. 'Problem, aren't they? Family.'

'Aye,' said Lanky, looking doleful.

'I once thought summat might come of your Jack and our Meg, but they don't seem to be shaping to it, do they?'

'If you say not,' came the careful reply. 'You'd have to ask them about that. He tells me nowt.' So that's it, thought Lanky. If he can't get my land one way, he'll have it by another.

'Pity. They'd make a good breeding pair. Happen they need a bit of a push like.'

In answer to this Lanky only smiled and said what a grand lass Meg was. 'She's got a good head on her shoulders, that one, for all she's a bit quiet and shy. Come into her own proper one of these days, you see if she doesn't.'

'She's nobbut a female. I have to keep a close watch over her.'

'She's bright. Runs rings round most chaps. You too, I shouldn't wonder.'

At this attack on his authority, which was a mite too close to the truth for Joe's comfort, he got up to go. 'Right then, I'd best be on me way. Let me know if you change your mind about the land and find you can't keep it on.' When you finally admit you can't find the money to pay me, he meant.

Joe pulled on his cap and tugged at the neb to his colleagues as he walked out of the cafe, well pleased with the day's business. He'd made a good start. The idea was planted, now let it grow.

–

Dan Turner was likewise feeling pleased with himself as he strode out with his dogs. Sal Gilpin called regularly to pay the money her family owed, missing only twice in the last three months. Six shillings was a large sum to find each week, but then it wasn't his problem, was it? If women weren't capable of organising their lives better, was it his fault?

He'd just laid a trail of aniseed and paraffin over a short six-mile training run. Now he slipped the lead on Silver Lady and a new young bitch he'd bought at the last hound trailing day he'd attended. Both dogs, excited at not having run for a day or two, shot off across the field, their graceful bodies making light work of the distance, easily scaling walls, hills, ditches or whatever came in their path as they followed the scent.

'Aren't they lovely?' Sally Ann said and Dan puffed his chest out, pleased by the compliment, then set off after them at an easy pace. 'Come on, Sal, shape to. If we cut through Brock-barrow Wood we'll be at the finishing post about the same time as them.'

'Don't go so fast then, I can't keep up.' She began to run alongside, puffing slightly from the effort but soon falling behind as Dan strode off on his long legs.

'Aye, she'll make a good 'un,' he announced as he watched the tawny animal's loose-limbed rhythm. 'Bit of training up and she'll do well.'

He was pleased with her. Not that he would ever hold her in any great affection. Dogs were dogs, kept for work and naught else. He'd feed her with good protein, best shin beef and egg, no yolks mind, and other secret ingredients he kept to himself. Warm bedding and regular exercise, and like a good woman, all she had to do then was exactly as he told her. And breed of course. Which brought him back to Sally Ann Gilpin.

He stood and waited for her to catch up. Fine looking woman she was. He liked a bit more flesh on his women than on his dogs, and game enough or she wouldn't be here, helping him like this.

It had been a considerable stretching of the truth to say that Joe had handed all his financial affairs over to his son. Joe kept things very much under his own control, too much so in Dan's opinion. But Dan was glad he'd been allowed to take on this customer, despite his father's initial objections and Meg's protests. Far too good an opinion of herself that one. Always too ready to criticise him, ever since she was a nipper.

One day he'd get his own back on her for treating him like he was a fool, just see if he didn't.

Sally Ann reached him, and, pleased with this unexpected success with a woman, Dan grinned at her. 'You're all right, Sal,' he said, and she was. Friendly and comfortable, with a good sense of humour. Always cheerful and ready for a bit of fun and a laugh. 'You're not always wanting to pick holes in what a chap says. Not like our Meg.'

'Where is she?' Sally Ann wanted to know. 'Haven't seen her in ages.'

'Off on one of her walks. Quite a fetish she's got for walking these days.' Not one to waste energy himself, not unless there was profit in it, like his dogs, he couldn't understand this need in others. 'There's better ways to spend time and energy, eh, Sal?'

He clambered over a stone stile and strode off on his ambling gait along the stony track that led up to Brockbarrow and on to Whinstone Gill, Sally Ann tagging along behind.

The weather was good for the time of year and there were no mists on the tops today. Dan could see for miles.

'Come on, lass, let's sit here for a bit, shall we?' He winked at her. 'While we wait for them animals to come.' He laid his coat on the ground and Sally Ann raised a questioning eyebrow before hiding a smile and making herself comfortable beside him.

When he first spotted the fleck of colour on the distant hillside, Dan didn't think anything of it. Besides, he had other matters on his mind.

But it took no time at all for him to pound out his frustration into Sally Ann Gilpin. The wind was too sharp up here to dally so he pulled up her frock and got on with it. And she, gasping for breath, didn't seem to object.

Afterwards he had time to look about him and Dan's long-sighted shepherd's eyes found no difficulty in picking out the figure. It was Meg, no doubt about it. Across the other side of the dale on the lower slopes of Dundale Knott. And what's more she wasn't alone. She had a dog with her. He could see it darting about and running wide in the way of all sheep dogs, rounding up a pair of ewes. He saw her stop and whistle to it and the dog change direction to obey the call.

'Now fancy that.' As he'd said earlier, you never knew when a piece of information would come in handy.

Chapter Six

When Sally Ann called one day that autumn there was no sign of the scared, uncertain girl who had come begging for help months earlier. Meg was glad of the visit from a friend since she had seen little of Kath since the day they'd had words over Jack. It was silly really, but Meg had walked away from her friend, refusing to listen to any more, and Kath had stood and shouted after her, calling her a fool.

She poured out a cup of tea for Sal and herself, ready to enjoy a bit of a gossip as usual, then Sally Ann surprised her by wanting to talk about Dan.

'Has he always been this way, a bit touchy like?'

'Touchy, our Dan? Testy more like. Not even his own mother could manage him, bless her heart. Said he was the most stubborn of her brood.'

'He seems to blame you for that.'

Meg frowned. 'It's true he's always been jealous of me. I don't know why but there it is. Even when we were small he was constantly pushing me out of the way, grabbing my things, doing his utmost to stop me having or doing anything. He got so destructive he made it impossible for anyone to love him. Wild, he was.'

'Mebbe that's just what he needs.'

'What?'

'Loving.'

'You're not volunteering for the job, are you?'

'I might.'

Sal flushed scarlet. 'Well, what would be so terrible about that? It's all right for you, Meg Turner, food in your belly every day, wood for your fire, all your menfolk in work. My dad's been given the push again for not being fit enough to work hard and we're all living on the parish now.'

Meg was shocked by this news. Being hungry was far more dreadful than being dissatisfied with boring kitchen work. Meg noticed then that her old friend did not look half so plump as she once had. Her carrot hair was clean enough but the pale, freckled skin seemed somehow tired and grey. 'I'm sorry, I didn't realise things had got even worse.'

'He's thick, your Dan, I know that. He's rough and lazy and quick to anger. And he has an inferiority complex on his shoulders as big as the boulders in that quarry. It's because you're always so good at everything you do, and Charlie being so clever with his fingers, well, it makes Dan feel the odd one out. A proper fool.'

Meg was gazing open-mouthed, surprised by this unexpected view of her lout of a brother. 'Are we talking about the same man?'

'Aye, we are. I've known him nearly as long as you, don't forget. And he's been a proper gent these last months over our bit of trouble. I don't know how we'd have managed without him.' The cheeks grew pink and she smiled shyly. 'Well, almost proper.'

'Sal Gilpin, I do believe...'

Sally Ann got up and went to stand at the window which overlooked the farmyard. 'Look at him, great soft lump, feeding those hounds of his. They eat better than we do.'

'I shouldn't wonder at it,' Meg agreed, unable to resist a smile, astonished to hear her hard-bitten brother described as soft. Perhaps she should try to see him in a better light.

Sally Ann turned quickly to Meg, eyes suddenly merry and alight with laughter. 'Don't be surprised if you find yourself with a new sister one of these days. Would you mind?'

Meg stared at her for a moment, then opened her arms and wrapped them around the girl's shoulders. 'Oh, I should welcome it. Sometimes I'm bored witless out here on me own. Another woman around would be marvellous. You do realise how isolated it is, don't you? Farm life is hard and not all that comfortable. And Dan isn't the most talkative person in the world.'

Sally Ann smiled, a lovely open smile that plumped out her cheeks. 'It'd be grand. We'll find some way to fill the lonely nights.' And the two girls burst into a fit of giggles.

Dan came in at that moment and Meg turned away, not wishing to watch as the two of them went straight into the parlour without a word. If she hadn't been so full of her own delight these last months, she might have noticed what was going on before her eyes.

But how would all of this affect her?

The thought kept popping into Meg's mind all the next afternoon as she put Rust through his paces. She would enjoy having Sally Ann at Ashlea. Besides Sal's friendship, she'd have more help with the chores which would be bound to result in more free time. It was a good feeling. She'd be able to see more of Jack, and go more often up to Broombank.

But then she became absorbed, as always, with the dog and forgot about everything else, even Jack, as she worked.

She was having great difficulty in making him stay. Getting Rust to lie down when she was by him was one thing; at a distance quite another. But it was essential in a good sheep dog out on the hills.

'Take him up to the threshing loft,' Lanky had suggested, and gave her a few tips. So here she was, with Rust on the upper hay floor that came halfway across the open building and she on the cobbled floor below, urging him to lie down.

Rust, not understanding at all what was required of him, stood and gazed down at her with as close to a puzzled expression on his face as a dog could get. Every now and then he would bark at her, half in annoyance, half to remind her to come back and fetch him.

Meg climbed up the wooden ladder to reassure him. 'Lie down, boy. Lie down.'

Rust obeyed instantly, panting up at her, and remained still. She knew if she said 'good boy' now, he would bounce up and lick her to death, so she held a hand out flat telling him firmly to stay as she backed carefully down the ladder. By the time she was down again he was up on his feet, worried that he had lost sight of her.

'Lie down, boy,' she told him. 'Lie down.'

Up on the threshing floor of the barn he couldn't creep round her legs and roll over as he so loved to do. But he wasn't getting the message. It was all in the inflection of the voice with dogs, so the fault could be hers. Meg tried again.

She was still struggling when Jack called. She went to him at once and put her arms about his neck, lifting her face for a kiss.

He did not immediately oblige. 'Are you coming? I thought we were to go up Dundale Knott this afternoon.'

'Oh, goodness, I forgot,' she admitted.

'You'd forget anything once you start playing with that dog.'

'I'm not playing. Rust is working, learning his trade.'

'And when will you have chance to put him through his paces?'

'Jack, you're starting to sound like Father. Stop it. I've already tried him out if you want to know. And he's good.'

Jack glanced up at the dog, now lying obediently on the threshing floor, nose just over the edge, so he could have a better view of what was going on below. 'Looks dangerous to me. What if he were to fall off?'

Meg cuddled up against him and tweaked his nose. 'So you do care, you great bully. Of course he won't jump off. I've told him to stay. Besides, he's too intelligent.'

Jack ran his hands over her slender figure, warmly dressed in plain skirt and jumper. 'Why don't you put something pretty on for a change, and we'll go to the pictures? Then you could put me through my paces.' He kissed her then, making her head spin.

'Oh, I'd love to, Jack. Only I'm not sure Father would let me.'

He made an impatient sound in his throat. 'For goodness' sake. You're twenty years old. When will you stand up to him?'

'I do stand up to him,' Meg protested, feeling this to be unfair. 'It never seems to make any difference, that's all.'

'I'll ask Kath then and make you jealous. At least she doesn't spend all her time with dogs and sheep.'

Meg giggled. 'Stop teasing, Jack, and kiss me again. I like it. I'll be half an hour and then I could meet you by the gate, bottom of Coppergill Pass. How would that be?' And she kissed him, marvelling at the smoothness of his skin.

But she and Rust were having such a good time, it was more than an hour later when she reached the appointed spot. There was no sign of Jack, and the afternoon was fading to the dark of evening.

The mellow days of autumn were already drawing to a close and soon the bite of winter would be upon them. Out in the fields could be heard the crash of horns as tups battled for the right to mate. A strange way of courting but the necessary prelude to a good lambing season. She and Jack were always sparring. Perhaps that too was a necessary part of loving.

Mists lay thick on the valley floors and the bracken had long since turned brown and started to wither and die. It was a time of year that Meg loved. She hadn't seen Jack for a week since that day in the barn but meant to call today and put matters right between them. They would go for a walk and lie in the tickly bracken, kissing wantonly.

'Thee's got time to sit about, I see,' said Joe, coming in on a blast of cold air that sent a fall of soot all over the pegged rug.

'Didn't Dan sweep the chimney this year? Lazy item,' Meg groaned, reaching for a brush.

'You could have done it theeself. It'll happen do you good to have another woman in the house. Sharpen your ideas up a bit, stop your complaining.'

Meg sighed. She wasn't in the mood for a battle with her father today. 'You make out as if I complain all the time. That can't be true. I want a life of my own, is that too much to ask? A bit of independence.' Flinging open the warming oven door she pulled out a dish of stew, rich with mutton, potatoes, onions and gravy, and set it on the table.

'I want you to go up and see Lanky Lawson. He's still not well, or so I understand.'

Meg frowned. Unusual as it was for her father to show compassion, he was a man of the chapel and Lanky an old friend. 'I see him two or three times a week,' she said, trying to remember how he'd looked the last time she'd been up to Broombank but was ashamed to realise she'd been so taken up with Jack she hadn't paid much attention. 'I'll go up tomorrow, take him a hot pot.'

'Aye, do that. He'll be grateful I shouldn't wonder. He gets no interest taken in him by that family of his.'

Now was her opportunity. She'd never get a better. 'Jack's still there. He works hard on that farm.' She was trembling slightly as she doled out a portion of stew onto a hot plate. What exactly could she say? How to describe their relationship? She wished she could confront her father with a definite proposal from Jack. That would show him. That would be her escape, her revenge for his continued contempt of her. But it was too soon. Jack did love her, she was sure of it. He was only waiting until they had some money saved and she was twenty-one before he declared himself.

Less than a year but it seemed light years away to Meg. She was still trying to find the right words when Joe started speaking again. 'Has that lad of yours not popped the question yet? You'll be left an old maid if you don't watch out.' The look upon his grizzled face was triumphant. It said, quite clearly, I know it all.

Meg almost dropped the plate she was handing him, very nearly tipping it down his waistcoat.

As he chewed happily on his mutton stew, she put the question that burned in her brain. 'How did you know?' She asked it quietly but he only shrugged his shoulders and carried on eating. Meg turned away, not wanting to watch.

They'd been so careful. All those clandestine meetings, the careful planning, Kath coming along to give an excuse for Meg to be out of the house. And it had all been for nothing. Now, Meg guessed, he would take pleasure in putting a stop to the burgeoning relationship by making life as difficult for her as he possibly could. She felt sick at the thought. But she wouldn't let him win, she wouldn't.

At last he spoke again, his mouth full of hot potato. 'There's not much I don't know. You have to get up early to put one past me.'

'I wasn't trying to put one past you. We just wanted a bit of privacy, that's all.' The thought that her father might have been following them, even spying on them, made Meg feel quite suddenly ill. Her head spun giddily at the thought of Joe silently viewing those sweet, intensely intimate moments in their life together.

'Did someone tell you?' Surely not Kath, or Charlie? Dan perhaps? The prospect of her brother lurking behind trees and watching them made her feel even worse.

'I'm not daft. I can work things out for myself. He's not a bad lad. A bit of a rogue in his time, but he'll quieten. It wouldn't be so bad a match, I reckon. Like him, do you?'

Meg stared at her father, hope rising swiftly in her breast, blotting out the doubts in her anxiety to find what she sought in his expression. Could he really mean it? Perhaps he wouldn't disapprove at all, perhaps he really did care for her and want her to be happy. 'Oh, Pa,' she said, on a rush of affection. 'I do, I do. I like him very much.'

She wanted to run to him, to put her head upon his lap and have him stroke her hair and tell her that she was his own dear daughter and that anything she wanted she could have. She had seen Mr Ellis do that with Kath, but her own father had never shown affection, not when she was small, not ever. But that didn't stop her hoping for it. She held her place upon the chair and waited, her breath in check in her throat.

Joe spooned the last of the stew into his mouth, masticating noisily. 'Aye, well, it wouldn't be a bad match, as I see it. The Lawson land has its faults, parts of the valley bottom being a bit damp like, but it runs to a fair size and right alongside our own.'

It was as if he had hit her. It wasn't her feelings he cared about at all, nor Jack's. Meg managed, after a long moment, to get shakily to her feet and for the first time in her life did nothing to hide the contempt in her tone. 'You don't give a toss about me, do you? You don't care whether I love Jack or not, or whether he loves me. All you care about is the land, the damn land.'

'I thought you loved the land too? Thee has said so oft enough.'

'I do. I love the land, the farm, and the animals with a passion you will never understand. But never, as long as I live will I put them before those I love, or my own flesh and blood.'

'That's what you say now,' said Joe, chortling merrily as if she had made some joke. 'Things might change.'

There must be something wrong with me, Kath thought. She was sitting touching up the flawless beauty of her face in preparation for dinner, taking infinite care with the line of scarlet lipstick on her wide mouth. The dull November mists had turned to rain which battered against the window pane. Downstairs, in her view, was an equally dull crowd of people. Life, Kath decided, was boring and most confusing.

She stood up and swirled the skirts of her scarlet silk dress. They swished seductively against her bare legs. Delighted with the effect, she reached for her stockings and sat on the edge of the bed to pull them on, letting her thoughts turn back to her problem.

There was Sally Ann, a year younger than herself, and plump and homely to boot, walking out with stolid Dan. And Meg, whom she'd thought was on her side in seeking independence, eagerly hoping for wedded bliss with Jack on Broombank Farm. Though whether he was quite so eager for a starring part in this production was another matter. Kath had tried not to see Jack recently, in deference to her friend, but it was not easy. The prospect of enjoying the devilish rogue while she could was too tempting. There was a war coming. Everyone said so. Then they might all be dead.

In any case, nothing had been settled between him and Meg. It might fizzle out. But that wouldn't solve her own puzzle, would it? It was not simply a question of whether she wanted Jack Lawson, but whether she wanted any man, as a permanent fixture, that is. Why didn't she want the same sort of life that other girls craved? Marriage. Children. All of that stuff.

There had been several offers. From 'darling Richard' of course. He would repeat it tonight and Mummy would send silent messages across the room urging her to accept.

Richard was eligible. His father was in local politics, had acres of land and was considered comfortably well off. But Kath wasn't interested in land or politics though money held a certain fascination. It was a commodity she had never been short of and she could hardly envisage life without it. But marriage was a high price to pay.

Sex was much more fun than suburban fidelity, a crusty-faced nanny and endless coffee mornings with flat-chested, bored housewives.

The dinner gong sounded and Kath sighed. She really would have to make up her mind soon on what she meant to do with her life, she supposed. She fastened her last suspender and swished the skirt again, smiling at her image in the mirror. 'Far too good not to share,' she told the reflection.

Later in the evening when it was carefully contrived for the young couple to be alone together, Kath had to admit that she was no nearer a decision.

They sat on the sofa in the drawing room in the prescribed manner and Kath allowed Richard to kiss her. His kisses were polite, guarded even, as if he were afraid of startling her. They bore scant resemblance to the impatient demands of Jack's thrusting tongue. But she could never marry Jack. He had no money, and no prospects of getting any. He hated farming and had nothing else lined up. But he was delicious fun. His sunburned skin all smooth and rimed with sweat.

'Do you think you can have good sex and a good marriage all in one neat package?' she asked Richard, quite out of the blue. He looked startled.

'Is that important?'

Kath pouted. 'Surely you're not going to pretend that sex is only for men? Oh God, how old-fashioned.'

'I didn't say that.'

'Good.'

'I think you come out with these things just to shock me.'

'Perhaps I do.'

'Have you thought about what I asked you the other day?' Richard had placed one hand tentatively over the curve of her breast. Kath let it lie there.

'Of course I have, darling.' She wondered if he would jump a mile if she placed a hand upon him.

'And do you have an answer?'

If there was one thing she hated it was uncertainty in a man. Katherine Ellis always intended to be in charge of any relationship, but she liked the fiction of pretending it to be otherwise. 'I hate it when people try to pressure me into something.'

Richard at once demurred. 'No pressure, Katherine darling, but I would like to know where we stand.' He was such a very polite, well-meaning young man, medium brown hair, brown eyes, medium height. Everything about him, Kath thought, was medium. And profoundly sensible.

'Daddy once wanted me to go to university,' she said, making a tiny moue with her brilliant lips. 'His old one in Edinburgh for preference where I could learn the noble art of medicine. I might have done it too if he hadn't been so terribly pushy about it. Quite put me off.' She got up and went to refill her wine glass. She'd already had two and knew Richard wouldn't approve of her having a third so she filled the glass to the brim and offered him the small amount left in the bottle. He shook his head. So sensible.

'Just as well I didn't. Look what life as a boring doctor has done for him. He's a physical wreck, forced to take early retirement.'

'I was sorry to hear that,' Richard muttered.

'Yes, darling. I'm sure you were.' She sat on the chair opposite, and the silk of her stockings squeaked as she drew up her skirt and crossed her legs. Richard's eyes were riveted upon them. So he was human after all, she thought, smiling to herself. 'I told him, no thank you, Daddy dear.'

'If you married me,' Richard urged, almost on one knee as he leaned closer, 'you would never have to worry about working. I don't think it proper for a woman.'

Kath rewarded him with a delighted smile. 'How very tempting you make it sound. But don't you think I should discover something of myself first, and something of the world? Try for a career or job?'

He looked shocked. 'What sort of job?'

Kath gazed into space, quite lost for an answer. Unlike Meg, she had never given work any serious consideration. She changed tack. 'Wouldn't marrying too quickly make Daddy even more disappointed in me?'

'I don't see why. You could have lots of babies.'

The smile faded. 'So I could.' She stood up. 'Perhaps we'll think about it at Christmas, darling. If there's still no war, of course. Would that do?'

Richard reluctantly conceded that it would do very well.

By then, Kath thought, she'd have found some way out of the cage, some place she could spread her wings and fly.

Chapter Seven

As if deciding on self-protection, Kath invited Meg and Jack to spend Christmas Day at Larkrigg.

'I feel the need for moral support.'

Meg, thrilled and flattered by Kath's invitation, broke into gales of laughter at the very idea of her sophisticated friend needing support from anyone. 'Of course I'll come. After lunch, when the menfolk are snoring their meal off.'

There was every sign of a white Christmas. The clusters of larch groves on the lower slopes stood out darkly against the winter pale grass. A time of year that Meg loved and a merrier party than usual to celebrate the festive season at Ashlea. She had taken her father at his word and invited Lanky and Jack. Her regular visits to Broombank had been curtailed somewhat by the colder weather so it was important that Jack felt he could call on her at home, which so far he hadn't done. At least their relationship seemed more settled. Following their tussle in the wood there had been many sweet apologies and lingering kisses, and Jack hadn't asked her to go too far again.

Today being Christmas, Meg nursed a secret hope for more tangible evidence of his love. A ring perhaps?

'It's just like old times, when Mum was alive,' she said, on a rush of goodwill and emotion.

'Dinner was a bit late. Your mother was an expert cook. She'd never have been late,' complained Joe. 'You'll have to shape better if you want to catch theeself an husband.'

'Thanks for those few kind words.' Hot and flustered from her long stint in the kitchen, Meg nevertheless managed to laugh at her father's put down.

'Your Connie not come home for Christmas then, I see?' Joe addressed Lanky, seemingly determined to spoil the mellow atmosphere by bringing a frown to the old man's brow.

'She has to think of her husband's family now. Said she might pop over at New Year,' said Lanky, smothering a sudden tickle in his throat.

'Aye. Happen.'

Lanky rubbed his horn hard palms together, clearly agitated by the questioning.

'Anyone for more plum pudding?' offered Meg quickly, sending a glance of furious displeasure in her father's direction.

'What? What have I done?' Everyone laughed and the tension lifted again.

It was a lovely day, crisp and bright as Christmas should be, a rose pink sky against cool blue mountain tops. High above a peregrine falcon circled, perhaps seeking its own Christmas feast. The two families took a long walk together, to shake down the rich food, as Lanky said. And perhaps replete after his good meal, Joe was as good as gold and made no more ill-tempered remarks. Even Dan congratulated Meg on the excellent meal. 'You know Father only wants what's best for you,' he added.

'He has a funny way of showing it!'

Meg suspected that Sally Ann had deliberately engineered for them to be walking side by side and she could see that her brother looked suddenly nervous as he cleared his throat. 'Sal and me are thinking of getting wed in the spring.'

Meg turned to him in a burst of genuine pleasure that passed for affection between them. 'Oh, I'm so glad. I like Sally Ann a lot.'

Dan flushed like a pleased schoolboy. 'Aye, well, we thought we might as well. If war does come things might get more difficult.'

'It'll come,' said Charlie. 'Congrats, old boy.'

Meg usually turned her mind obstinately away from all thought of war. She knew the threat was there but far away, in Germany and Austria and Spain. How could it affect them here on the Westmorland fells? Even so it was hard to be completely oblivious as a general feeling of unease was beginning to spread.

Even the Ellises could talk of little else as Meg and Jack sat politely sipping tea and eating tiny slivers of Christmas cake later that afternoon. There were several friends and neighbours present. The Jepsons, Mr and Mrs Parker from Swillhead, Hetty and Will Davies in their best clothes looking faintly uncomfortable. And of course the vicar. Mrs Ellis was highly regarded at the church.

'They've given the schoolchildren gasmasks, can you believe that?' Rosemary Ellis was saying. 'Where in heaven's name would the gas come from up here?'

'It's only a precaution,' explained her husband, in his rather slow, kindly manner.

'Lanky says they were talking on the wireless the other day of evacuating children from the cities,' Meg put in.

Mr Ellis nodded sagely. 'Cities will be the worst places if war does start. We will be fortunate here. The war will not affect us at all.'

Kath, who had been feeding scraps of icing to the adoring Richard and taking little interest in the conversation, now turned abruptly to her father. 'That's the kind of talk that makes me wild. Of course the war will affect us. We could be bombed, even here. And there's talk of conscription soon. Some of us might be called up. Maybe even me.'

Rosemary Ellis laughed politely as if her daughter had made a lovely joke. 'Don't talk foolish, darling. Let's not spoil Christmas with all this morbid talk. More tea anyone?'

Meg was happy for the subject to change, for the thought of losing Jack in a war was too painful to contemplate. She slipped her hand into his when no one was looking and he squeezed it softly, as if to reassure her.

'Come on, everyone,' Kath cried, leaping up. 'Charades.' There was a general groan all round but she was adamant. 'You can't have Christmas without charades. I'll start. Come on, Jack. I've got a grand idea but I shall need you to play a part. Richard, you too.'

Grabbing both men's hands she pulled them into the kitchen and everyone was laughing again, the black mood gone.

Meg sat feeling suddenly left out. She'd been quite happy in her mustard and tan suit until she'd seen Kath, lovely as ever in a new turquoise dress with gold buttons. She didn't mean to be jealous, not really. It was an insecurity in her, a lack of confidence, that was all. One she usually accepted with equanimity. Not recognising her own fresh beauty, sometimes Meg longed for a touch of Kath's more exotic variety. Perhaps then Jack would declare his love more openly.

What she wanted most of all right now was for them to exchange their personal gifts in perfect privacy. She didn't want anyone to see her face when she opened Jack's. Meg was almost certain she would be engaged before the day was out. But privacy was denied them, although Jack did manage to sneak her a kiss when no one was looking as Kath handed out presents from the tree.

Sweetly sensual, his fingers slipped swiftly into the neck of her blouse to caress the swell of her breasts. Meg started, giving an embarrassed giggle, but a warm glow illuminated her face.

'I've knitted you some socks,' she said, and Jack took the carefully wrapped parcel in all seriousness, then they both laughed and hugged each other.

He held out his present to her, and her heart plummeted. Too big for a ring, and quite the wrong shape. Meg smiled up at him, swallowing her disappointment, not wanting him to see that it mattered.

She carefully unfolded the gold paper. 'A scarf. What a lovely blue. Just my colour. How did you guess?'

'Not good at shopping. I had some help.'

Some of the pleasure went out of the gift but Meg shook the feeling away. It was the thought that counted, wasn't it? He was saving the ring to give her later, when they were alone. This was the best Christmas ever. By next, who could tell? They might well be man and wife.

'Look, it's snowing,' Kath cried, and they all ran outside to find the garden already covered with a thick layer of snow, sparkling white in the soft moonlight. Laughing like silly children with not a care in the world, they started a mad game of snowballs, stuffing it down each other's necks. Jack kissed Meg, making her head spin, and out of the corner of her eye she could see Richard doing the same with Kath, although her friend didn't seem to be responding quite so enthusiastically.

Kat pushed Richard away. 'Go and fetch us some mince pies and sherry, darling, for a special toast to Christmas beneath the stars. Go on, there's a good boy.' And Richard obediently scurried off to do her bidding.

'The way you bully that young man is quite wicked,' Meg said, but Kath only shrugged.

'The choice is his. Anyway, I wanted him to go away so that we three can have a precious moment alone together to toast a very special friendship.' She linked arms, hugging them close, one on each side of her. 'I want us always to be friends.'

'Of course we will,' said Meg, leaning her head against Jack's shoulder. 'For ever and ever.' She shivered, drawing her coat closer.

'Are you cold?' asked Kath, concerned.

'No, I'm fine.' Forever was a long time, and she was far from sure of Jack's intentions.

'Things can go wrong sometimes, even between friends,' Jack warned, almost reading her mind. 'If there is a war we might be separated. I for one will have to join up.'

'We'll all join up!' cried Kath, reckless as ever.

'Don't joke about it. It's too terrible,' Meg said, grey eyes alight with all the love and happiness she felt on this special day. 'You are my best friends. Who else do I have but you two?'

There was a moment's silence as both acknowledged the truth of this bleak statement. It was the penalty of living in such a remote spot.

Then Kath wriggled free to stand before them, one hand held out. 'Let's make a vow. A promise that whatever happens, we'll always be friends.'

Meg, knowing she'd drunk far too much wine, started to giggle. 'You make it sound like the Three Musketeers.'

'It is in a way,' Kath agreed. 'Come on, promise. Friends for ever.'

Meg clasped Kath's hand and covered both with Jack's. 'All right. A solemn vow. Friends for ever.'

'Promise?'

'Promise.'

They both looked up at Jack and he grinned. 'Promise.'

–

It was after eleven when they walked down the lane, arms wrapped about each other in the starry darkness, and Meg was glowing with love. The lack of a ring didn't trouble her any more. She knew they loved each other, that was the important thing.

But then in the contented silence, as so often happened, her thoughts moved on to her secret dreams. Of being at Broombank with Jack, as man and wife. She traced the picture of the great inglenook in her head and she and Jack seated within it, talking about their flock, as generations of Lakelanders had done.

'Lanky isn't well, is he?'

'Doesn't seem to be.'

'He should see a doctor.'

'He won't even bring a vet to the animals. He's too set in his ways. If it can't be cured with treacle or embrocation, he doesn't want to know.'

'Is he going to let you take over the farm?'

99

Jack looked surprised. 'Why should he?'

'Because he's ill and it needs attention.'

'Stuff the farm.' Jack pulled her into his arms to kiss her and Meg melted against him, happily relinquishing all thought but that of desire. When it was over she curled against him, cheeks flushed, eyes star bright. Jack's hands tightened upon her buttocks, rubbing her against him.

'Sometimes I think you fancy my dad more than you do me.'

Meg smiled mischievously up at him. 'Maybe I do.'

Jack bit her ear, making her squeal. 'It's not often I get you to myself these days. You always seem to have dogs around, or sheep.'

His lips were finding the curve below her ear, his tongue tickling enticingly. 'I reckon it's starting to snow again. Or maybe rain.' He started to unbutton her coat. 'Better take shelter, wouldn't you say? How fortunate, here we are by our barn.' Jack was walking her backwards and with his arms still clamped tight about her she had no option but to go where he led her.

'Where are you taking me?' she asked in a breathless voice, not really caring. Violet-blue eyes, dark and teasing, ran over her face with a need that set a sharp and piercing ache somewhere deep in her belly. She knew what he wanted, what he had always wanted.

And Meg also knew that she wanted to go with him. Anywhere he asked.

It was warmer in the barn, amongst the hay. Rust welcomed her with thumping tail and wet tongue. But Meg had no time for dogs just now.

'Lie down, boy. Stay.'

Jack was leading her deep into the darkness, only a shaft of moonlight lighting the dust motes in the musty air.

Meg reached for him, taking his beloved face between her hands, smoothing the dark hair. How she loved the way it curled into a point at his nape.

There was an impatience in him, like a fever. She could feel him tremble as he laid her down, lengthening himself beside her so that he could smooth one hand over the curve of her breast and the flatness of her stomach. Very quickly it seemed to Meg, he had removed her blouse and camisole and her young, rosy-tipped breasts were exposed to his eager gaze. But she didn't mind, she welcomed it. She could feel the impatience rising in herself just as fiercely. When he caught her nipples between his sharp white teeth this time she did not protest, only arched her back and pushed herself into him, making him moan with agony.

This time she meant to show him how much she loved him. This time she would prove that she wasn't frigid. It would be her Christmas gift to him.

She wondered if it would hurt, the first time. As schoolgirls they had made wild guesses and there had been much talk of blood and piercing pain. Would it be like that? Meg hoped not. She wanted to feel only pleasure and the proof of his love. Would he tell her that he loved her afterwards, when they were one? Perhaps it was these confused thoughts that made the words she had so longed to say come out in a muddle.

Jack's fingers were fumbling with her skirt buttons and she was finding it hard to catch her breath. 'It's going to be all right. Father doesn't mind. About us. He thinks it's a good idea,' she said, meaning to encourage him, but at once felt him freeze.

'What did you say?'

Quietly, almost fearfully, she repeated the fateful words.

He pulled away from her to sit back on his heels and survey her. Meg drew her hands over her suddenly chilled breasts, feeling cheapened by the anger in his face. 'What is it? What have I done? I only said—'

'I know what you said. Did your father tell you to come here, with me, should you ever get the chance?'

'Don't be silly.' She reached for him again but he evaded her grasp. 'He tells me nothing, except to fetch home-made dishes for Lanky now and then, but…' It was the wrong thing to say, she could sense it the minute the words were out.

'To soften him up? And did he tell *you* to offer yourself to Lanky's son for afters. Did he?'

Meg couldn't believe what she was hearing. How had it all gone so badly wrong? What had she *done*?

'It's not like that,' she protested. 'I don't care about my father any more than you do. Anyway, it wasn't me who told him about us. He guessed, and didn't seem to mind. I thought it would make it easier for you to call and see me.' But she could tell Jack wasn't listening.

'Joe Turner has been wanting Broombank for years. And having failed by the usual methods, he's trying bribery and corruption now, is that it? Offering delicious home-made titbits, even his own daughter in exchange. Or is it wedding bells he's after, to get Broombank in the family, eh?'

Tears sprang to her eyes, filling her nose and mouth and seeming to run all over her face. This couldn't be happening. What Jack was saying was awful, terrible, *and surely not true.* But there was a doubt in her mind.

'I thought you loved me?' she said, trying to scramble free of him and hiccuping like a child on her tears. 'I love you.' For so long she'd tried not to be the first to say those words and now she had spoiled it all by letting them come. Jack would never love her now. He would blame her for everything, she could see it in the mutinous set of his handsome face. Her heart ached to see how it turned against her, to see the sensual lips curl with distaste.

'*Love?* Who are you to talk of love? For months you've hardly let me touch you. What do you think I'm made of? Stone.' He'd got her skirt unfastened and tugged it from her in a frenzy of frustration. Not listening to the voice of reason in the back of his head, he could feel only the pulsing heat of his loins.

'No, Jack.' Her voice sounded oddly cracked and surprisingly calm. 'Not like this. I don't want it to happen like this, in anger. You know you'll only regret it.'

'Damn you,' he said, flinging himself down upon her and starting to knead her breasts. She'd planned it all, he could see that now. Making him mad for her all these months, then when Joe Turner had yet another refusal on his latest offer for Broombank, it was suddenly all right. She was begging for it. 'All this time I've wanted you and all you've given me is the prissy miss act, but Daddy now says it's all right so here you are, the virginal sacrifice.'

'No. It's not like that.' Meg knew her words were lost on him. His legs straddled her and his mouth was grasping her nipple, suckling her, driving her mad with need. But this was all wrong. It wasn't meant to be this way. With shock she felt his fingers move deep inside her, thrusting and probing, and pain and pleasure swamped her. Dear God, how I love him, she thought. Let his anger go. Oh, please let him be kind. He must want us to be one, our love perfect, as she did.

'Kiss me,' she begged, but he ignored her as his fingers explored her with outrageous boldness, making the need worse not better, making her want him beyond anything she had ever imagined.

'Love me, Jack. I do love you so.'

She could hear her own voice begging for him as he'd said she would one day, feel her body arching against him, the wetness of herself a startling revelation. What was it he wanted of her? Not just to lie here, surely?

He was fumbling with something, talking of how much something or other cost and would she keep still or he'd tear it?

Then he was lifting her thighs, his fingers bruising her flesh as he pulled her against him. When he drove into her it took her by surprise and she cried out with the unexpected pain of it. Then he was pounding into her with such force her head was pushed uncomfortably against the wall of the barn. She lifted herself to him, wanting to be as close as she could get, to make the loving come right. Meg tried to match his energy and need with her own, but somehow all desire seemed to drain from her and she found herself wanting it all to be over as quickly as possible. When he finally withdrew, shuddering on the hay beside her, an aching disappointment left her spent and drained of emotion.

And feeling very faintly foolish.

Afterwards, they lay in the hay side by side, not speaking. Meg became aware of a strange soreness in parts of her body she had never considered before.

'Feel better now?' Jack asked, and she smiled shyly, not sure how to answer. It hadn't been exactly as she'd imagined. But perhaps that was because it was her first time, and she'd feel more involved when she'd had a bit more practice. Guilt washed over her. What was she saying? It'd been Christmas and the unaccustomed wine that had gone to her head. It mustn't happen again. Not till they were wed. 'We shouldn't have done that,' she said.

Jack was sitting up, lighting a cigarette. 'Why not? It's made me feel better anyway.'

'I wouldn't like to make a habit of it,' she said worriedly.

Jack chuckled, his eyes scanning her pale body in the shaft of moonlight. 'I wouldn't mind.'

She stroked one finger over the bow of his lips, giggling when his teeth nipped her fingertips. 'Why should I want Lanky's farm when I can have you? Land is easy to rent anywhere for a pound an acre. Love comes much more expensive.' And as his eyelids flickered slightly, eyes glinting, she kissed him softly.

'We'll marry in the spring,' she said. 'Then we can make love all the time. There. Will that make you happy?'

1939

Chapter Eight

Everyone in the farming community was glad that 1938 was over. What with the slump in prices and shortage of labour, things had been difficult and profits few. But with talk of a coming war it looked as if next year might be even worse.

Only Meg was happy. Meg positively glowed. Her life had changed beyond all expectation and she revelled in the joy of it.

She spent New Year's Day quietly at Broombank and it wasn't till a week after that the worrying started. Every morning when she got up, every night when she went to bed, she looked for the sign that would tell her all was as it should be.

But there was nothing.

Oh lordy, what if she fell pregnant? Meg felt sick with fear. She imagined facing her father with the terrible news, for that's how he would view it. He'd do more than slap her face then, much more. She must have been mad to allow her feelings to run away with her like that, just because it was Christmas.

As each day passed she could hardly eat with the worry of it. She couldn't concentrate on any topic of conversation above a minute, and her stomach churned with anxiety so much it almost felt as if there must be a baby in there already.

When at last one night she woke to the familiar stickiness between her legs she actually wept with relief. Never, never, she decided, would she put herself through such agony again.

'The wine went to my head,' she explained to Jack as they sat by Broombank fire taking supper together one evening. 'It must never happen again.'

'Why not, for God's sake? You don't seriously expect me to go back to sweet kisses and holding hands after that, do you?'

'It's only for a little while. Till we marry in the spring.'

'And what if your dad won't let us? You're not twenty-one until August.'

'Then it'll have to be August or September. He can't stop us then.'

The anxiety on Jack's face made her laugh. 'I've told you, he doesn't mind. But even if he does, this is just between you and me and nothing to do with anyone else.' She kissed him teasingly on the nose. 'Tell me you love me, go on, I want to hear you say it.'

'You know I do,' he said gruffly, and she laughed again at his embarrassment.

'Oh, Jack, I'm so happy. Isn't life lovely? Have you spoken to Lanky yet?'

'About what?' Jack's attention seemed to be far away. Tired, she didn't wonder, from his long hours working. He had probably been up at dawn to feed the animals and do the milking.

A great wave of love for him washed over her. When they were married she'd be able to help him by sharing the load. She'd get a girl in to do the rough work in the house so that she'd have the time to spend with Jack out on the farm. How she would love to make a warm home for him, sit with him here every evening, as his wife. Then he would turn out the lamp and take her upstairs to the big wide bed where they would make love. Meg went hot all over just to think of it. Best to keep to safer topics.

'I was talking to Lanky about him increasing the flock. Unless he wants to go in for more dairy? Has he decided yet?'

The violet eyes darkened and he kicked a log that had slipped a little back into the grate. A shower of sparks scattered like fireflies. 'You shouldn't bother him with such ideas. He's not up to it.'

'I thought you were dissatisfied with the farm and wanted to improve it. Perhaps he'll let you take over when we marry, let you do things your own way.' Meg knelt before him and leaned her cheek against his knee, eyes troubled. 'The farm needs proper attention from someone.'

'Don't blame me,' he said sharply. 'It's not my fault.'

She'd made him angry and dipped her head for a moment, blinking furiously as the colours in the rag rug blurred giddily before her eyes. Desperate to make it right, she plunged blindly on. 'It's only that this Christmas he's looked so gaunt, and that tweed jacket seems bigger than ever. The weight is dropping off him and he's coughing more. What is it? What's wrong? Can't you do anything?'

'You know I can't. I already told you.' There was bitterness in Jack's tone and he pulled her roughly into his arms. 'Now for God's sake stop going on about the farm. Give *me* some attention for a change.'

Spring came and the alder and hazel catkins clustered thick as clotted cream on the spindly branches. A blackbird sang his heart out, showing off to his intended, and Dan and Sally Ann married, as planned. Meg and Jack postponed their own plans to the autumn because she still hadn't plucked up courage to ask her father, and neither had Jack.

She was afraid Joe might put conditions on her, as if she were a cow at market and prove Jack right in his suspicions.

It wasn't long till she was twenty-one then she could please herself.

Sally Ann looked a picture in a dove grey dress and matching loose-fitting coat, despite the freckled paleness of her cheeks. Grey suede shoes with pretty leather bows and a tiny pink hat with a veil completed the ensemble.

She'd intended to be married in white and had spent hours with Meg poring over newspapers to see what 'This Year's Bride was wearing'. But somehow none of the designs had quite suited or been within her means and they'd always ended up reading depressing advertisements for black-out curtains or gramophones at six shillings a week that they couldn't afford.

'Look at this, sixpence to wash a bundle of clothes for an evacuated child. Well, I could always do that, couldn't I, as my war effort?' Sally Ann read, and Meg shivered, as if a goose had stalked over her grave. 'Don't talk about the war. I hate it.'

They told the postman, who delivered their morning paper, to stop bringing it if all it contained was bad news.

'I'll speak to the newspaper people about it,' he said laughing, and carried on bringing it, if only because he enjoyed the chat with Meg and Sal and the cups of tea they gave him.

They had gone into Kendal in the end to buy something pretty but serviceable. Meg too had bought a new dress, a deep cobalt blue that set off the burnished honey of her curls, now grown fairly long again as a concession to Jack. The dress hung in her wardrobe upstairs and she wondered when she would ever wear it again. On her honeymoon perhaps?

Sometimes, in the quiet of the night, Meg worried about the fact that she'd put a stop to their love making. She guessed it had something to do with her Methodist upbringing as much as her fear of her father, that she couldn't think it right to give yourself to a man before you were wed. Yet she had done so, hadn't she? Not that she'd been very good at it, mind. No bells had rung or fireworks exploded and she had felt, in the end, as if it was all a bit messy and embarrassing. That was probably the worry, she decided. It wasn't Jack's fault, or hers. Everything would be all right once they were married.

She didn't regret it though. At least now Jack knew how much she loved him.

The installing of Sal in the kitchen at Ashlea meant that Meg had more time for herself as well as more time to spend with Jack. She brought Rust home at last and was glad of his company for the dog had already proved to be a great friend.

'What are you going to do with the cur then?' asked Dan, watching her knock together a kennel for him out of some odd bits of wood.

'This is my dog. Leave him alone, right?'

Dan advanced a pace and Rust half rose from his lying position, giving a low growl deep in his throat. Dan stopped. 'You think I'd be interested in a puny creature like that?'

'He may be small but he's strong and a good sheep dog. He needs time to settle, so don't bother him.'

'You know nowt about sheep dogs, nor sheep for that matter.' He made no mention of having seen her once, working the dog. Never give away all your secrets, that was Dan's motto.

'Maybe I know more than you think.' Meg tied Rust to a post and rubbed his ear affectionately, much to Dan's amusement. But she took care to wait until her brother had left the yard before feeding the dog some titbits.

'There you are, boy. This is home now.' Rust gazed up at her with adoring brown eyes in which she could see her own image reflected. Every day she took him for long walks over the fells, or more often up to Brockbarrow Wood where they would sit in the shade for a while and Rust would drink from the small tarn. Then on sometimes as far as Whinstone Gill. The stream wasn't gushing with quite its usual force through the rock because May had been uncommonly dry but it was a peaceful, secret sort of place where you could be certain of being alone.

It was a pleasant surprise to find Kath there one warm afternoon in early June.

'What's this? Lady of leisure now Sally Ann is resident cook, eh?' Kath pulled a towel around her bare shoulders. Her hair wasn't wet but she was dressed for swimming in a pink cotton swimsuit. She started to pull on a swirling floral skirt.

'Taking a leaf out of your book.' Meg dropped on the grass beside her. A dipper was doing its clever underwater walk, forging its way against the current as it searched for tadpoles, worms and other treats. Meg watched it for a while, laughing, then rolled over on to her stomach. 'Have you been swimming? Why didn't you tell me? I would have brought my cossy and joined you.'

'I wasn't, I mean, this is hardly the place, is it? And the water's a bit too cold yet. It was just a walk, and a sunbathe. You're usually too busy working at this time of day.'

Meg wrinkled her nose. 'I feel lazy today. It's too hot to think, let alone work. I've been putting Rust through his paces and relaxing. Isn't that wicked? Oh, what's that?' She sat up quickly, staring into the bushes behind them. 'Did you hear something?'

'No. Didn't hear a thing.'

'Rust, what are you doing?' The dog was nosing about excitedly in the undergrowth that grew out of the cracks at the bottom of the crag, tail waving like a flag. 'What have you found?'

'Probably rabbits. There are loads about. Come on, let's go. I'm suddenly desperately hungry. You can take me home and feed me some of Sally Ann's wonderful scones.'

Meg laughed, enjoying the rare warmth of the sun too much to want to move. 'What about your diet?'

'Blow to that. Come on.' Kath tugged at her arm.

'I can take a hint. You should have brought a picnic if you were so ravenous.'

'We will have a picnic. Soon. A great big one.'

'No time. There'll be the clipping soon and Sally Ann and I will have to do the great bake-in for all the shearers who come to help.' Meg rolled her eyes. 'What a job. I think I'd much rather clip sheep than roll pastry any day.'

'You are a funny old thing. Personally, I'd rather do neither.' Kath linked her arm into Meg's and began to walk her along the path. 'Come on, let's go and be greedy piggies.'

'We're all very aware of your philosophy of life, Kath. Why do anything if you can get away with less? I don't know why I bother with such a wastrel.'

It was said in a good-natured fashion as it was an old joke between them but Kath appeared to be taking it more seriously for once. 'Maybe I'll change one day and surprise you all.'

'Now that I would love to see. I shall look forward to it.'

'One thing's for certain, it won't be here, in this Godforsaken place.'

Meg stopped. 'How can you say such a thing? This is the most beautiful country on God's earth.' She looked about her at the mountains she regarded almost as friends. She knew every fissure of rock, every footpath. She recognised the light and shade of their moods which changed as quickly as the weather, and could not imagine a life where she would not walk upon them, or simply feast her eyes upon their mystical beauty.

'For you, yes.' Kath met Meg's shocked expression with a wry smile. 'This is your special place. You have your plans, something to look forward to. Marriage, motherhood, Who'd have thought it? You with your constant cries for independence.'

'Things change. You could have the same if you married Richard Harper.'

Kath rolled her eyes. 'To make Mummy happy? No, it wouldn't be right. I don't love him. I don't love anyone, and I don't know what I want to do with my life. It's all very silly, don't you think?' There was an extra brightness to the hazel eyes and Meg felt a rush of affection for her friend.

'I used to feel the same way, as if I had no purpose to life.'

'And now you've found it, like a mission. Wife and mother, just as Sally Ann wants to be, as all normal women want to be, apparently. An essential part of life.' There was a tartness in the tone, unlike Kath's usual carefree self, that made Meg flinch.

'I don't see why a woman has to give up her independence just because she's married. I'll still be me inside. There are so many things I want to do. Life is so exciting.'

She wanted to be with Jack desperately. But the need to prove herself in other ways was growing almost as strong.

'So when's the happy day?'

'No date fixed yet.'

'Ah, yes, of course. Difficult to pin Jack down, I should imagine.' Kath half glanced back over her shoulder. 'Hadn't you best call that dog of yours? Not too obedient, is he?'

'What did you mean by that?'

'By what?'

'Being difficult to pin Jack down? It's not at all, as a matter of fact. We're waiting till I'm of age.'

Kath shrugged, still looking oddly strained as she smiled at Meg. 'You know my opinion of Jack Lawson. I haven't changed my mind. If you were to ask me, I'd advise you to stop seeing him for a while. Test him. See how long it takes for him to come running.'

Meg went very still. 'You're suggesting he wouldn't?'

'I'm not suggesting anything, except that you should tread warily, think carefully. Marriage is an awfully serious business. Try out a few more chaps first before you pick one.' The sensual scarlet lips pouted seductively. 'Spread a little happiness, that's what I say.'

Meg turned her head away to hide the quick flush of annoyance she felt at Kath's words and called to Rust. He was half inside the bramble bush by this time and she couldn't help but chuckle at the sight of his wriggling rump. Kath laughed too and it relieved the unexpected tension that had sprung up between them. 'Seems almost a shame to rob him of his quarry. Rust! Here, boy!'

The small dog, who was having the time of his life, was most reluctant to abandon this much loved, familiar scent but bellied backwards out of the bush and looked after Meg's retreating figure. He waited for a fraction of a second, tongue lolling, just to make sure that she meant what she said. But as she continued to walk away he put down his head and streaked after her. It was hard, sometimes, for a dog to learn to change his allegiance but he was getting the idea.

–

'Where's Rust?' Meg faced her father and brothers as they sat at the breakfast table, cold fury on her face. 'Someone has cut his rope and let him free.' Her eyes went straight to Dan but he did not look up from spooning his porridge.

'If the cur had any sense it would stay here without a rope round its neck,' said Joe.

'I was frightened of him wandering off.' She meant being driven away, by her jealous brother.

Charlie set down his spoon. 'I'll help you look for him.'

'No need for that. Anyway you've got work to do,' Joe complained. 'If it's gone anywhere it'll be back at Broombank where it belongs.'

Meg stormed up to the table and glared down at Dan. 'He was settling so well and you've ruined it. I expect you booted him out. He wouldn't go willingly, not now.' She felt helplessness overwhelm her. It was always the same. Anything that was hers, Dan would try to take from her and Joe wouldn't lift a finger to chastise him for his peevishness.

Meg blazed out the door and across the field on swinging, angry strides. She found the dog, as expected, comfortably ensconced in the old cruck barn at Broombank, looking pitifully guilty.

'No harm done,' said Lanky.

'Not this time, no, but what right has Dan to let Rust go? How dare he?' Meg's temper was firing on all cylinders so she didn't see Lanky put a hand to his brow and rub it with the heel of his palm.

'I shouldn't worry over it,' he said. 'One mistake won't spoil him. He's a quick learner.' He couldn't bring himself to get too excited about a dog that had come safely home even if it had been deliberately forced out. He had more pressing concerns.

–

1939 was proving to be the hottest summer that anyone could remember. The Herdwicks and Swaledales, in their newly clipped shorter coats, had climbed as high up the fells as they could get, to the benefit of the grass on the lower slopes, and lay gasping for breath in any shade they could find. Even the curlews were absent, spending their days seeking moisture in the swampy areas of Arnside and Leighton Moss. The air seemed uncannily still and languorous, the kind of day it was hard to contemplate work.

But Meg had been up since dawn, preparing the haytiming feast. 'Am I glad to have you to help me, Sally Ann!' she said with feeling, and her sister-in-law chuckled.

'I see, that's all you want me for, is it? A slave.'

'Sorry. I didn't mean it like it sounded.'

Sally Ann cast her a shrewd glance and jerked her head in the direction of the hayfield where the Turners and Lawsons were busy bringing in the crop.

'You'd rather be out there, wouldn't you, getting your hands mucky? Well, why don't you go? I can manage here.'

'No, no, it's all right. I'll finish slicing this ham.'

'You've been quiet lately. It's Jack, isn't it? Has he popped the question yet?'

'Oh, don't you start. I've enough with Father asking me day after day if young Lawson's intentions are honourable.' Both girls giggled.

'Well, are they?'

Meg flushed bright pink and followed Sally Ann's gaze to where Jack toiled along with the rest. He looked so handsome it made her heart ache just to look at him.

Every neighbour had come along to help, including the women and children. That was the best thing about the farming community in these parts, the way they helped one another. No family turned enough acreage over to growing crops to make the buying or hiring of a tractor pay, so the work had to be done mainly by hand. A lumbering fell pony pulled the Bamford mower over the smoother parts, with the men scything the corners and steeper areas in the old way.

They'd gathered the cut hay into small cocks, and then as it dried into bigger and bigger cocks to stand like a regiment of expanding soldiers' hats in the stubble for two weeks, or until the church bells had rung thrice, as the old adage said. And if the weather looked like breaking everyone would rush to load the hay on to the shelved carts and pack it into the high barns as quickly as possible, ready for winter.

It was a good feeling, Meg thought, to be part of a community.

'It looks very picturesque, doesn't it?' she remarked. 'But you'd think we could have worked out a quicker way of doing it by now.' Then glancing at Sally Ann's face, she smiled. 'All right. I'll answer your question. Nothing at all has been decided about marriage. But, yes, Jack is honourable. At least he doesn't push me to – you know. He respects the fact that I don't want to.'

'I suppose you've been brought up a bit more proper than me.' Sally Ann shrugged. 'Nobody would have cared if I'd got into trouble. Whereas with you…'

It wasn't necessary to finish the sentence.

'But now you're a respectable married woman. Oh, and, Sally Ann, I do so enjoy having you as a sister.'

Sally Ann reached for another loaf she had made only that morning, looking flushed and pleased. 'I confess I was a touch anxious about it at first. But we've got on all right, haven't we? And I'm getting used to this farming lark.'

Jack's muscled shoulders were burnt brown by the sun with scarcely any feeling left in them, having long since passed the pain barrier. He had been scything, mowing, raking and turning hay for weeks now, and he was bone weary. Long days working well into the night, able to snatch only a few hours' sleep before rising at dawn to start lifting and shaking the hay all over again. His legs felt hard as iron and his blistered hands burned as if they were on fire. All his hatred for the life he was leading was encapsulated in that pain.

The sun was starting to drop from the aching blue sky now, bringing a welcome relief, and he stopped to wipe the sweat from his brow.

As he stretched his aching back Jack wondered why he'd ever come back. Guilt and concern over Lanky, he supposed.

Connie had always been the clever one and he'd been glad to get away from the constant comparisons made between the two of them. What he'd discovered was a whole new world out there, a life in the cities and big towns that he hadn't even known existed. He'd been tempted to return home when his sister married, but his feet still itched to be off again.

This being the case, why was he committing himself to Meg? He could see her setting food on a long trestle table beneath the big old ash. She and Sal happily cooked and baked for the dozens of workers, now that the haytiming was almost over.

He had himself brought over an entire barrel of beer that waited to be supped. His mouth watered just to think of it.

'Is that food ready yet?' he called, and grinned as he saw Meg instantly turn her head towards him, her whole face lighting up as if from some inner glow.

'Ready when you are.'

'Right.' He flung aside the pitchfork with relief. 'Come on, Dan. I'm starving. Let's eat.'

'Aye, let Charlie finish on his own.' And when his young brother objected, a good-natured tussle broke out and the two men chased the luckless Charlie right up the hill to Brock-barrow Tarn. They were all breathless when they reached the top of the hill but Dan still found the energy to fling his brother into the deep pool, shouting with laughter as Charlie came up spluttering and gasping with cold.

'This is great,' he yelled, determined not to be bested. 'Just what the doctor ordered.' Then tugging off his boots and clothes he tossed them to the bank and lay back, paddling ecstatically in the fresh cool water.

Dan and Jack exchanged a glance then they too were stripping off boots and trousers thick with dust and hayseed and leaping in after him, slapping each other with sprays of ice water.

The worst part was putting the hot dusty clothes back on again, but, thoroughly refreshed, the men tucked happily into pork pie and home-cured ham, apple turnovers and great hunks of home produced cheese.

The food was delicious and Jack congratulated himself on his good fortune. A man liked to have his fling, right enough, but when it came to wife material there were other considerations. Marriage might not be such a bad thing after all, he decided.

He watched Meg as she sliced ham for Lanky and Joe, her rounded arms tanned by hours in the sun, breasts moving enticingly freely beneath the thin cotton of her dress, and felt warm life return to his nether regions. Yes, Meg had shaped up pretty good for all she still held some girlish inhibitions. Now if he could just persuade her to stop worrying about Lanky and Broombank, they'd be off over the blue horizon come the year end, no matter what.

His father could sell the farm to Joe Turner if he so wanted. What the hell did it matter so long as Jack could get away. He'd had enough of liver fluke, blowfly, sheep dung and daylong back-breaking labour to last him a lifetime. He had other plans for his life and Meg would have to accept that.

Then why hadn't he chosen Kath Ellis instead?

As restless as himself in some ways, she was the obvious choice. Yet Jack instinctively knew he could never hope to keep Katherine Ellis happy. Whatever good times they might have had, and they'd certainly had that, it was all in the past. To have Kath for a wife would be like trying to control a flock of sheep without a dog. She'd run rings round him, play every feminine trick in the book, spend all his money and more besides, then toss him to one side as easily as Dan tossed Charlie in the tarn.

Besides, she'd started getting a bit troublesome lately. Why, only last week they'd been in the barn, as usual, him lying on the dusty bales and Kath standing in a shaft of sunlight that came down through the rafters. Just like a spotlight in a theatre, it was. He hadn't been able to take his eyes off her.

Unlike Meg, Kath was always happy to take her clothes off. In one way he felt it a pity because it was always a pleasurable experience, part of the enjoyment as it were, to take them off himself. But he was not averse to a little strip show. And there was no doubt Kath looked gorgeous in her silk slip, those magnificent breasts of hers peaking wantonly. He'd felt an erection starting before she'd hardly got her blouse undone.

But when he'd reached out a hand to stroke their smooth beauty, Kath had slapped it away and not with her usual teasing touch either. 'What are you in such a temper about?'

'You, you great oaf. We can't go on like this. I've told you before, we have to stop.'

'Stop what?' he'd asked, surprised by her fervour. 'I can't think what you're talking about?'

'You've got to tell her.'

'Tell her? Tell who what?'

Kath had sighed but he'd been impatient to be done with talking and get on with the business in hand, or what he would like to have in hand. He'd reached for her again only to be disappointed. Kath kept herself enticingly out of reach.

'About us, you goon. Meg loves you, and she's my friend. We can't keep on hurting her in this way.'

Jack saw that he had a problem. Kath had totally misunderstood the situation. He'd never intended getting seriously entangled with her. She was big fish, out of his price range, fun to play with but never to land. He set about correcting her mistake.

'We haven't hurt Meg. She doesn't know anything about this and she's not going to. It was just a bit of fun.'

'I know.' Her face looked odd somehow, sort of stiff and fierce, and Jack suddenly saw how she would look when she was old. It was the weirdest sensation.

She'd come to sit beside him then, her long tapering fingers starting to unbutton his shirt. Damn the woman! How could he argue with her when parts of him were standing to attention? 'The thing is,' she was saying, 'I know it started off that way, but what if I decided to apply for exclusive rights? We might make a good team, don't you think? We could go places, you and I. Let's face it, we're neither of us country bumpkin types. If it weren't for you, and Bonnie, of course, I'd be bored sick here.'

'I'm glad you at least put me before the damn horse.'

She was starting on the buckle at his waist and Jack could scarcely contain his excitement.

'You're wasted on that farm.' She kissed his bare chest. 'Daddy could always find you a good job. He has friends, you know, contacts in Lancaster or Manchester, or even London if you prefer.'

If there was one thing Jack hated it was being organised, particularly by a woman, and he'd never expected it from the effervescent, fun-loving Katherine Ellis. It didn't appeal one bit. The pity of it was that she had a marvellous body but Jack's taste for it had quite gone. His ardour had evaporated as quickly as it had come. Some sixth sense told him it was time to end this bit of fun. If Katherine Ellis was starting to make demands then there must be a reason and he wanted no part of it. No, it was time to make changes. He didn't like a pushy woman.

Jack made love to her, as required, but more out of obligation than desire. It left a taste in his mouth as dry as ash.

But since he liked the idea of having a woman to look after him and needed to escape Kath, it had to be Meg. She was a worker, no doubt about that, and a damn good cook. And Meg adored him, didn't she? It was important to a man, to be adored.

She had other delightful attributes of which she was only just becoming aware. He slid a hand up her skirt now and over her bare leg as she moved close by him. His fingers had very nearly found her crotch when she gave a smothered squeal and cast him a fierce look, making him choke on his pie as he laughed. Oh, yes, Meg got better and better. Kath would see how it had to be.

—

It was August, and Meg's twenty-first birthday, so a holiday had been awarded. They were to climb to the top of Kidsty Pike for a picnic. Jack and Meg, Sally Ann and Dan, and Charlie. And Kath and Richard, of course.

'Where's Kath? She promised she'd be here.'

'Don't let's waste time waiting for her,' grumbled Dan, but Meg insisted and they all sat about in the August heat, kicking their heels and getting far too hot.

Three-quarters of an hour later, even Meg had very nearly run out of patience when Kath's little Ford came bumping up the farm track. 'Where have you been?'

She shrugged and apologised. 'Richard isn't coming. He's busy.' He'd refused her invitation. It was the first time he'd ever gone against Kath's wishes and she'd been puzzled, so had gone to his house to find out why. Then a young girl had called to her from the French windows and all had been made clear.

Kath shivered, feeling oddly cold inside despite the heat. It wasn't as if she loved him. It didn't really matter. Except that it left this problem, still unsolved. Oh, to hell with it.

Linking hands with both Meg and Jack, she tossed back a sleek swathe of hair and laughed. 'Come on, what are we waiting for? I'm starving.'

They walked for miles through lanes fringed with thick clusters of lady's bedstraw, speedwell, pink campion and great yellow patches of celandines. Then on over the tough, sheep-cropped grass where the only touch of colour was the pale mauve of sweet-scented heather, thick with bees. For the last part they had to scramble over craggy rocks and rough scree to make the ascent but it was worth it, Meg thought, just for the exhilaration alone, let alone the view.

Here in the mountains she felt in tune with her world, a part of the green and blue beauty of it, laid out like a map before her. Far below, further away than it actually looked as distances were deceptive at this height, was the strung out blue-grey of Ullswater with the majesty of Helvellyn, Fairfield and Scafell beyond. And in the other direction lay the humble simplicity of Broombank and Ashlea. They lay along the edge of a long dale with Broombank at the apex of the ridge and Ashlea below, as if a giant thumb had scoured out a place for them.

'How can anyone bear to leave this?' Meg sighed, resting her chin on her knees as she gazed, contented, upon her beloved land.

'I could,' said Charlie, with quiet firmness. 'If I could do what I most wanted.'

'Which is?' asked Kath, clearing stones and brushing the heather with her hands to make a comfy spot for herself so that everyone laughed at her. But she only pulled a face at her audience, spread a clean white handkerchief and laid her head upon it, fluffing her pageboy bob into place. 'Go on, Charlie. I'm listening. What is it you want to do?'

'Fly.'

'Oh, me too,' murmured Sally Ann softly. 'Like a great heron, soaring high in the sky.'

'More like a big fat buzzard if you keep on eating at that rate,' Dan said, and got a swipe for his pains. Sally Ann was heard to mutter something about greedy husbands. But they seemed to be grinning at each other so that was all right.

'You might well get your chance,' put in Jack quietly, when the laughter had died down. 'To fly, I mean. I listened to the news the other day. It wasn't good. People are putting out sand bags and building Anderson shelters in their back yards in the towns and cities. Maybe we should get one?'

'Where'd we put it and who would fly over here? Unless they'd taken a wrong turning and missed Barrow or Liverpool,' said Dan, carelessly. 'Can I have another cheese and pickle sandwich?'

Charlie stood up, his youthful idealism incensed by his brother's offhand attitude. 'Don't you care? There's plenty as say our bombers can win this war in a matter of months. It's not a joking matter. If we don't do something Hitler could walk all over us. And all you can think of is food in your belly. There could be people dying out there, in Europe.' He waved a hand vaguely over the idyllic view and then brought it down to slap the hunk of bread and cheese from Dan's hand and send it rolling downhill, bouncing over the crags and scree into Riggingdale below.

There was a short, shocked silence. Charlie was the quiet one, not easily roused to anger.

'I've already registered as doing work of "national import-ance", if you want to know,' Dan told him, getting slowly to his feet. 'I'm a farmer, not a fighter, and I'll not be bossed about by a young whippersnapper like you.'

'All right, folks, that's enough,' Kath said, not moving an inch from her supine position on the heather but bringing all eyes upon her nonetheless by the authority in her tone. 'Today has been declared a holiday so the rules are, no squabbling and no talk of war. Have we any cider left, Sal?'

'Plenty.' Sally Ann reached for a flagon, relieved to see Dan and Charlie sit down again, some distance from each other, but looking faintly ashamed of themselves.

'I think Meg and I will take a short walk,' said Jack. 'If no one has any objection?'

It seemed nobody had, so hand in hand they strolled away, and kept walking until they'd put several hundred yards between themselves and the others.

Only Kath watched them go.

–

The roebucks were the only active creatures on this hot August day. As the rutting season progressed their sleek red bodies were constantly on the move, often breaking into wild love chases as they protected their territory and searched for a mate. Trees and bushes were often damaged by the thrusting antlers as an animal deposited its scent around the boundaries of its kingdom. But let a huntsman kill the guilty stag and a host of young predatory bucks would flow into the territory, worsening the problem. Landowning bucks respected boundaries. If only men would, Meg thought, recalling her father's constant greed for more land.

She and Jack lay on the crisp, parched grass, staring up into a sky ribbed by soft cloud as white as snowy paw prints across the blue heavens. It was so hot even the birds were silent.

'We must have taken in our best crop ever this year,' she said. 'I hope the kale and potatoes are as good.' She let her eyes close so that the sun shone hotly through the lids.

Jack rolled over and tweaked her nose. 'Why do we always have to talk about the farm? I'm sure there are better things we could be doing.' He started to lift her skirt.

'Be careful, someone will see.' Meg artfully removed herself from his probing hands.

'No, they're miles away, I made sure of that.' He started to kiss her and for a long while talk was unnecessary and unwanted.

She always felt so alive in Jack's arms, so needed. She felt as if their love had made her grow as a woman in some mysterious way and he was now so much a part of her she would have trusted him with her life. The harshness of Joe's taunts couldn't touch her. Even Dan treated her with more respect.

'What you were saying earlier, about not wanting to leave here. Did you mean it?'

Meg looked at him sharply but he kept his face turned away and a small kernel of fear ripened inside her. 'Why do you ask?'

'I know you've taken it into your head to help me farm at Broombank. But what if I didn't want to? Would it matter to you, if you had to give up the idea of living there?'

Meg stared at him for a long moment as a small pain started somewhere deep within and began, quite slowly, to grow and spread right across her chest. 'Are you serious?' She was amazed her voice could sound so steady.

'You know I've never been as keen as you on farming. Would you mind if we didn't?'

Meg had known well enough but had always hoped he would come round to it, so had pushed any reservations to the back of her mind. But if she had to give up her dream of being a sheep farmer, would it really matter, so long as she had Jack? There were other things in life besides sheep. He would surely be worth the sacrifice. But it was less easy to say so, out loud, than she could possibly have imagined. 'I-I don't know. To do what?'

Jack slipped his hands under his head and a faraway look came into his violet eyes as he stared up into the bright sky. 'I've always had a fancy to travel. America, Australia, somewhere far away and exciting.'

'Just because it's far away from Westmorland, doesn't make it exciting,' Meg retorted, so abruptly he turned to look at her in surprise.

'There's nothing so very wonderful happening here.'

Meg was silent again as she considered the matter, then a thought occurred to her. 'Australia might be all right. They have a lot of sheep there too.'

'Sheep again.' He pulled her close against him, making her squeal with delight, and when he kissed her he robbed her body of every vestige of breath, making her head fizz with emotion. 'Say you'll come with me to the ends of the earth, if I ask it. Go on, say it.'

The mellow atmosphere of the late afternoon, with the sun slipping slowly down the sky, the soft breeze upon her flushed skin and the warmth of Jack's body beside hers, made her feel romantic and generous.

After the slightest pause she obeyed. 'I'll come with you to the ends of the earth, if you ask it.'

Jack was anxious to have the matter settled between them. The way Kath had been looking at him lately had made him increasingly nervous. He spoke next with a show of idle inno-cence. 'We could talk about your birthday instead, which is why we're here, if I'm not mistaken?'

Meg peeped at him from beneath her lids and her heart warmed to see his lazy smile. So he hadn't forgotten.

'Close your eyes again,' he ordered, and when she mildly protested, he got up and started to walk away from her in long loping strides down the hill. 'Okay, if you don't want it.'

She was forced to scramble to her feet and run after him. 'I'm sorry, I'm sorry. Please don't go. You can give it to me now.' She lunged for him, laughing, missed the first time then caught at his shirt with her hand and they were both falling and rolling over and over through a tangle of tall bracken, locked together. His mouth clamped tight to hers and desire flooded through her as it always did at his touch.

Then with her eyes tightly closed he was putting something into her hands and her fingers moved wonderingly, almost reverently, over the small square shape she held. Her heart leaped into her throat and for a moment she dare not open her eyes, dare not open the tiny leather box just in case it was not what she wanted it to be. For she knew she could never bear the disappointment if it was no more than an ordinary ring. He would see it in her face. She couldn't hide it this time, as she had at Christmas.

But she need not have worried. The tiny sapphire winked brightly in the summer sun and even as she hesitated, Jack lifted it out and slipped it on to the third finger of her left hand.

'It was my mother's.'

All she could do was look at him, aware of the tears rolling down her cheeks.

'Hey. I thought you'd be happy.'

'Oh, I am, I am.' Meg threw her arms about his neck, crying with delight, and then he was kissing away each tear.

It was the hardest thing she had ever done not to let him make love to her there and then but as she explained so carefully to him, it would be a pity to get carried away by the romance of the moment and make a mistake, when they'd come this far.

'Best to wait,' she insisted.

'Isn't the ring proof enough I mean to wed you?' Jack asked, frustration warring with his pride in catching such a lovely bride. 'If you loved me, you wouldn't wait.' He slipped a hand over her dress to caress her breast. Meg pushed it gently away and kissed him lingeringly.

'Bribery won't work, Jack Lawson. You know I love you. But I can't relax, I can't just – let it happen – not until we're married. Then it will seem right. Try to understand.'

'I don't understand at all. It didn't worry you in the barn that time. You're mine already, really, so what's the problem?' His arms came around her again and she wriggled out of them.

'You know why it happened then. It was a mistake. It being Christmas and me not being used to sherry. Be patient, sweet-heart, and kiss me. We don't have to talk to Father now. We can just tell him, make the announcement that we are to be man and wife.'

'You're a cruel, hard woman, Meg Turner.' But Jack knew when he was beaten and had to content himself with kisses. Meg kept her dress buttons very firmly fastened.

Later, with the sun staining the edges of clouds magenta and rose, they ran hand in hand down the hillside. She couldn't wait to show her ring to Kath and tell her the joyous news, tell her how Jack had made her the happiest woman alive.

Kath's lovely face went very pale when Meg proudly showed her the ring. She seemed quite lost for words.

'You never thought he'd do it, did you?'

'No,' Kath agreed. 'I never thought he would. Congratula-tions.'

'It was a surprise, for my birthday,' Meg repeated proudly, holding up her hand to admire her precious ring.

'It's certainly that.'

'Isn't it lovely?'

'Oh, love,' said Sally Ann, hugging her. 'I'm so pleased for you. We could have had a double wedding if he hadn't been such a slow clod.'

'Steady but sure, that's me,' said Jack.

'As steady as a rogue fox,' retorted Kath dryly and flushed as she caught Meg's raised eyebrows, awash suddenly with unaccustomed guilt. Then she put her arms around her friend and hugged her, as Sally Ann had done. 'Make sure he treats you well, love. You deserve to be happy.'

'You're crying,' murmured Meg softly. 'Oh, Kath. It won't make any difference, to us I mean. We'll still be friends,' she said, misconstruing. 'For ever and ever, remember?'

-

Later that afternoon when they got back to Ashlea and Meg and Sal went inside to brew fresh tea, Kath turned eyes more stormy than tearful upon Jack.

'Why didn't you tell her, you lout?'

Never had he looked more handsome, more desirable, and she hated him for it. One corner of his wide mouth was lifting in that beguiling way he had. She saw a glint of sharp white teeth and the pit of her stomach swelled and ached with a need so strong it unnerved her. Deep blue eyes looked frankly into hers, understanding her absolutely.

'Don't be a poor loser, Katherine Ellis. You know it's only my body you covet.'

'*Damn you!* I'd like to...'

'That's better. I prefer the mad Ellis to the guilty one.'

'You've played us both for fools. She'll discover that one day, then what?'

'Are you going to tell her?' He was careful not to show his unease. He didn't want his plans spoiled by a spurned female who was feeling a bit piqued.

'Do you think I would?'

'Who's played with whom, anyroad? I didn't see you protesting.'

'I didn't think you were interested in marriage with anyone. Why Meg? She's sweet. She's good. Too good for you.'

'Meg's okay, and she's got guts.'

'More than you deserve. Why marry her? You'll only make her miserable.'

'Perhaps I love her.'

Kath gave a scornful laugh. 'You love her tits.'

'Yours are pretty good too,' he said calmly, letting his eyes rove frankly over her body.

It was the last straw. Eyes blazing, Kath grasped the fabric of her lemon silk print frock that had cost her an arm and a leg at Kendal Milne's in Manchester, and ripped it apart. Her breasts gleamed with a pale beauty in the sparkling sun, dark nipples peaking with the hard fury of her need. 'Go on, check them out, just in case you've got them mixed up and chosen the wrong ones. I'd hate you to make a mistake at this late stage.'

For a long, terrible moment they glared at each other then Meg's voice called from the kitchen door, asking if they wanted the tea out there. Kath gave a little sob, pulled the wrecked fabric about herself and, turning swiftly, ran blindly away.

Chapter Nine

Poland had been invaded, Hitler had signed an agreement with the Soviet Union thus securing his eastern defences, and Britain was to fight for liberty and justice. King George VI told everyone as much on that fateful Sunday evening, 3 September. He said that by speaking to them on the wireless it was as if 'I were able to cross your threshold and speak to you myself'. Words of comfort and resolution, helping to ease the fear. Meg and Sally Ann, sitting listening alone at Ashlea, burst into tears and sang a patriotic song, all at the same time.

The tension that had been determinedly kept back all summer now expressed itself in action. Black-out curtains were made, windows taped, sandbags packed the walls of the local hospitals, beloved motor cars were offered to help move any wounded and people queued to volunteer for service or waited half fearful, half excited, for their call-up.

And everyone fearfully scanned the skies for sight of the first German bombers.

Having no cellar, nor access to a shelter of any kind, all Meg and Sally Ann could do was check that the window shutters worked and cut out black paper to stick round the edge of the glass to cover any possible chinks of light.

'What will it be like, war?'

Sally Ann shook her head, carrot hair sticking out at odd angles from being raked by anguished fingers. 'Heaven knows, but I'm glad I have you, Meg, and I'm not here all alone. Will Dan have to go?'

'Shouldn't think so. Farming is an important occupation in wartime. People still have to have food. But what about us? What do we women do? I feel we should have some purpose beyond making black-out curtains.'

'I suppose we look after the men. As we always do.'

Meg looked suddenly fierce. 'There's got to be more to it than that. Maybe I'll ride my bike into Kendal and ask around.'

'Joe won't like that.'

'Blow him.'

'Well, don't forget your gas mask.'

Meg put it on and they both burst into a fit of giggles. 'I think the stink of the rubber would knock me out if I had to wear it for more than a minute.'

But Joe wouldn't hear of her going into Kendal. 'We still have work to do, girl. War or no war.'

Life at Ashlea continued as normal, and, in a way, Meg hoped that would long remain so. She couldn't bear to think of the alternative.

But only days later, everything changed.

Charlie was the first. He came and told her he'd volunteered. Meg's heart dropped like a stone as she stared into her young brother's face, alive with idealistic fervour and suppressed excitement.

'How could you? You're only just turned eighteen. And you don't have to enlist, not as a farmer.'

He came and sat opposite her, took her hands between his. 'I'm not a farmer, Meg. Never was. Dad's the farmer, and our Dan. They wouldn't necessarily let me stay here, anyway. But you know, you've always known, that I want to fly. The RAF recruitment officer says I'm just the sort of chap they're looking for.'

'Yes, of course he does.' She snatched her hands away, too upset to keep the bitterness from her voice. She knew only that Charlie was going off into unknown danger and she was filled with a terrible fear. 'Silly young fools who haven't the first idea what they're letting themselves in for, that's what they're looking for.'

A bright stain of scarlet ran beneath his pale skin. 'Don't call me a fool, Meg, I'm not that. I'm doing my bit, in the only way I know.'

'But a flyer. Do you know how dangerous that would be?'

He stood up quickly and turned away, impatient with her inability to understand. Picking up his jacket, he made one last attempt. 'Goering says he will blacken our skies with his bombers. And I say, just you try, mate, and see what you get. We'll shoot every one of your damned planes down.'

'Oh, Charlie.' She knew they were naïve words, bravely offered, and folded her arms about him as she had so often done when he was small and had fallen and hurt himself. She hugged him as tightly as she could, wanting to keep him safe, keep him with her as if he were still a child and she could protect him for always.

Tears were streaming down her cheeks and he was hugging her now, assuring her everything would be all right, when they both knew he could offer no such assurance. Then Meg was packing sandwiches and clean underwear, issuing foolish instructions about keeping warm and taking care, and he was climbing into the old Ford van and Dan was driving him away into the unknown.

But there was worse in store.

It had started as a perfectly ordinary morning with the washing blowing on the line, Sal and she preparing vegetables for dinner and Joe taking a break with a mug of tea by the kitchen range. Then Jack stood in the kitchen doorway, the first time he had come voluntarily to her house. His dark hair brushed the door lintel where the lucky horse shoe was nailed to keep out evil spirits. He looked at Meg and she knew. He was leaving too.

'I'm going into the Navy.' His voice was quiet, unlike his usual confident self. And there, in the bag he dropped by the table, was the proof that she was about to lose him. Sally Ann put down the potato knife she was using and quietly left the kitchen, dragging a complaining Joe with her.

Meg lifted her chin and bravely faced the man she loved. She wouldn't cry, she wouldn't.

'Must you go right away? It's all happening too quickly. It's only yesterday that Charlie left.' She thought of the new blue dress upstairs in her closet waiting for her honeymoon, her mother's wedding dress waiting to be worn again, but he was nodding, not quite meeting her eyes.

'I don't want to be put into some Army unit. It's the sea for me. Always has been a fancy of mine.'

'This isn't a cruise you're going on,' she said, her voice breaking.

'I know that. We start our training in Liverpool, first thing in the morning.' There was an excitement about him, an intensity of expectation, and Meg fell silent as a sudden awkwardness hung between them. 'I'll be home again before you've even missed me,' he consoled her.

'Yes, of course you will.' They both knew this might not be true.

There was so much she wanted to say to him but no words would come. They seemed insignificant in comparison with what they now faced. But there was one thing she must ask.

'What about the wedding? Can't we marry before you go?'

Jack shook his head, very purposeful and decisive all of a sudden. 'No time. Have to wait till I get leave.' He thrust his hands in his pockets and walked to the window, looking out over the fells. 'Anyway, this is no time to think of marriage, with the war and everything.'

'I hear lots of people are rushing to get married before it's...' she stopped and hastily readjusted her words as she realised what she'd been about to say. 'Before their fiancé leaves.'

He turned to look at her, his eyes dark and unreadable, gone from her to some other place. 'I don't think that's a good idea, do you? Being rushed. Let's leave it, for the moment, till we see how things settle down.'

Meg lowered her head, blinked hard and managed to give a little nod. She thought her heart was breaking. 'You'll write?'

He came to her then, took her in his arms and held her close, his chin against her hair, drinking in the sweet fragrance of her. And for the first time in his life Jack Lawson wondered if perhaps he did love this sweet girl more than he realised. At least, as much as he was capable of loving anybody. 'Of course I'll write. I shall expect loads of letters from you too, every week at least, and a photo to make the other chaps jealous.'

She laughed, a small hiccupping sound, but dared say nothing, not just then. The pain in her breast was too much to bear.

'You'll look after yourself. Don't work too hard,' he teased. Then lifting her hands kissed each fingertip gently, sensually, with the warmth of his lips. 'Keep yourself pretty for me. No calluses on these lovely hands, eh?'

'You sound like Father. Women will have to work too, you know, if the men are all called up. I'll have to do my bit, Jack.'

'We're not going to quarrel, are we? Not when I'm leaving.'

She laid her head on his shoulder. He was so strong, so handsome, so brave. She felt ashamed of her outburst, wishing she could take back the words, spoken too fiercely because of her distress. 'No, course not.'

'There'll be plenty of time, when it's all over, for marriage and all that. Don't offer to come to the station with me. No goodbyes, eh? Just promise me one thing.'

'Anything.' Meg was proud and astonished how normal her voice sounded.

'Take care of Lanky for me. He's a funny old soul but he is my dad.'

'As if you need to ask.'

There was nothing left to say. His kiss was deep and long and broke her heart, then he was gone and she was alone looking out on to a beautiful sunny September day and wondering how it was the larks could still be singing.

Meg had never felt so alone in her life before. Charlie gone, and Jack, even Kath absent, gone off on holiday. What a time to choose. Perhaps she'd come back now that war had been declared. Oh, she did hope so.

More than anything, she needed a friend right now.

—

Ruby Nelson's boarding house took pride of place on the corner of a row of tall Victorian villas. The wide, tree-lined avenue, its pavements broad enough for the crinolines of a more genteel age, had one end open to the sea, a determined walk away. The wind funnelled up its length and swirled through the rarely open front door of number six, to rustle the newspapers piled tidily upon the hall table for guests to share.

Kath gazed up at the house with sinking heart. This was not at all the escape she had once planned or dreamed of. Why hadn't she gone to London? It wasn't as if she was afraid of being bombed.

It all came down to money. For the first time in her life Katherine Ellis was short of funds. She had her allowance of course, but had never troubled about sticking to it so was not good at budgeting. Daddy was always ready to stump up more whenever she needed it. Or had been, until recently. Lately he'd been complaining that his investments wouldn't last for ever and his pension wasn't going near as far as he'd hoped. He'd even cautioned her to acquire the art of thrift, which was perfectly ridiculous.

'We're surely not on Queer Street?' she had protested.

'No more are we on Easy Street,' he'd told her kindly, but with unusual firmness. 'This house costs a small fortune to maintain, not to mention Bonnie, whom you rarely ride nowadays anyway. All I'm asking for is a little more restraint. Times are hard.'

So the idea of her father financing a small flat in London, as she had hoped, was out of the question.

Kath had stormed and sulked, refused to speak to him for a whole five days while she sat in her room and picked at the food brought to her on trays by a devoted maid, wondering where she could turn for help.

Rosemary had been the one to come up with the compromise of Aunt Ruby. Bitter at Richard's defection, she fondly hoped a spell in Southport would put her rebellious daughter into the company of more prepossessing company than the farming folk she spent far too much time with.

'Spend a few weeks by the sea,' she had suggested. 'You're looking decidedly peaky. And I'm sure Ruby will be glad of your company. You won't be troubled by her guests. She keeps a strictly genteel establishment.'

So Kath had abandoned her hopes for the moment of a more exciting getaway and here she was, learning to make the best of things for the first time in her life.

She walked up the path and lifted the polished brass knocker. It sounded loud echoing along an empty passage beyond. She wondered if her mother had written. Not for a moment did she consider that Aunt Ruby might refuse to take her in, or have no vacancies. She was family. That surely counted for something.

The door was opened by the skinniest, shortest maid Kath had ever set eyes on. She wore a sacking apron that reached from a pert chin right down to her polished black boots. Her small face was almost obscured by a white hat pulled down low over her forehead. Not a trace of hair showed.

Kath adjusted her face into a pleasant smile and indicated the crocodile bags which the taxi driver had deposited upon the path. 'Would you have those brought inside and tell my aunt that Katherine, her niece, has arrived.'

'Miss?' The little maid looked terrified. 'Are you expected?'

'I'm sure she'll receive me.' And with grand assurance, Kath stepped over the shining clean doorstep and strolled elegantly into the house, drawing off her kid gloves and looking about her with practised ease.

'You'd best wait in the parlour,' the maid said, looking flustered. 'Madam doesn't like to be disturbed when she's taking her afternoon nap. I'll fetch you a cup of tea directly.'

'Thank you. Lemon, no sugar.'

'Very good, miss.' The maid bobbed a curtsey and closed the door softly behind her.

Kath walked over to the most comfortable chair and disported herself upon it. 'Well,' she said, addressing a tall aspidistra plant that guarded the front bay window, 'perhaps things won't be so bad here after all.'

—

Thank goodness for Sally Ann. Left alone with her father and Dan, Meg might well have gone mad. The thought of the days, weeks, months stretching ahead without Jack or Charlie made her feel ill.

The hens' complaining racket told her she had woken late. It was a wonder Joe hadn't come to drag her from her bed, as he had done so often in the past. Pulling on her skirt and jumper she ran to let them out, then quickly milked Betsy and Daisy. She fed the calves with skimmed milk and linseed and went into breakfast just as if life were normal, though with less than her usual appetite.

But this was war and nothing would ever be normal again. 'It's as if they've disappeared off the face of the earth.'

'I know. All we can do is wait, the thing women are supposed to be good at.'

Sally Ann was hurting too as three of her brothers had been called up.

'I'm not good at waiting. I prefer action.' Depression swamped Meg as she viewed the emptiness of life ahead.

'How will Lanky manage?' Sally Ann asked as they took their morning cup of coffee together.

Meg shook her head, fighting back tears. 'I shall go and see him this afternoon, try to help him work something out. He'll need extra labour now that Jack's gone.'

'Perhaps he'll decide to sell.'

'You think my father will start on him again?'

The two exchanged a long glance. 'Dan says he's set his heart on having that place. Says we need the extra land so's he can make more money now we're wed. But I thought there was free grazing land in plenty on the high fells.'

'Yes, but it's poor. Broombank owns good intake land as well as woods and water. And has easier access to the fells than Ashlea. It's a neglected farm but with good potential.'

'Well, I don't understand all the ins and outs of it, but I wouldn't put anything past your father, war or no war.'

'Perhaps Lanky will sell. Right now I don't even care, Sal. I feel as if someone has gone over me with a steamroller. How can I live without Jack?' Tears flooded the grey eyes despite her best efforts and Meg shook her head, angry with herself. 'If I don't pull meself together, I'll blubber right into me coffee cup.'

'Blubber away. I'll join you.'

The sound of a car drawing up in the yard surprised them both. Meg's first thought was that one of the men had returned and she flew eagerly to the door. Could Jack have changed his mind and decided to register for farm work after all? She flung it excitedly open. A tall, thin man stood upon the step. He wore a grey overcoat and a trilby hat which he lifted politely at sight of Meg. In his hand he carried a sheaf of papers and a pencil. He looked disturbingly official. 'Mrs Turner?'

'Miss.' Meg half turned to reveal her sister-in-law, her heart in her mouth. Surely not bad news already? 'This is Mrs Turner.'

The man gave a tired smile. He had been working flat out driving about the countryside for so many long days he was growing short on politeness. Nevertheless he drew in a deep breath and prepared for the worst. 'I'm from the evacuation board. I have an evacuee for you.'

For a short, stunned moment, Meg didn't understand. She put a hand to her head, trying to think. Of course. She remembered hearing it on the wireless. They were moving children out of the urban and inner city areas into the country for safety. Everyone was expected to find space for them. 'You mean from the city?'

The man licked his pencil and ticked something on his board. 'Manchester actually. Would you mind signing here, please?' Meg looked all around him. 'Where? Who is this evacuee?'

'She's in the car.'

'Oh dear,' said Sally Ann. 'Joe won't want a girl.'

'You have no choice what you get. If you'd been at Oxenholme Station when they arrived you might have been able to choose. It's too late now.' He didn't go on to explain that this child had been rejected by everyone who had visited the station. It wasn't his place to say, nor theirs to complain. This was war after all.

'That's all right,' put in Meg, anxious not to seem unwelcoming. 'It'll be nice to have some female company. It's only that my father thinks men are more useful on farms.'

But the man wasn't interested in the Turner family's problems. 'If you'd just sign here, I'll fetch her. It explains your rights and everything.' Meg did so, thinking that perhaps a young child would help to fill the lonely days ahead. She felt ridiculously buoyed up by the prospect.

'Can we see her now? How old is she?'

The man looked dubious. 'I couldn't say. But I should warn you that she's not too keen.'

Meg felt a rush of compassion. 'She must be missing her mother. How dreadful to be swept away from home to live with perfect strangers. Poor child.' She put a hand upon the man's arm. 'Don't worry. We'll take good care of her.'

Edward Lipstock looked up into clear grey eyes and fell instantly in love. He wished, with all the fervour of his forty-two years, that he could change places with the waif in his car and live day by day with this entrancing girl. 'I shall have to call from time to time,' he said, heart lifting a fraction at the thought.

'Of course you will. Sal, get Mr, er – Sorry, what did you say your name was?'

Mr Lipstock told her, the smile warming as Meg shook his hand. 'Make Mr Lipstock a cup of tea. You don't know how you've cheered me today. I just needed to think of someone beside myself.' Then she was off across the yard before he could warn her, wishing now that he'd done so right at the start.

The child sat on the back seat, hunched up like some wizened little gnome. It was difficult in this position to guess her age and when Meg opened the car door she reeled back as if she expected to be attacked.

'It's all right. You can get out. We won't hurt you.'

She was filthy. The stench of urine and stale dirt almost choked Meg as she leaned into the car but she gave no sign of it. It wasn't the girl's fault if no one had taught her how to wash. The only clean part of her face were the whites of her eyes. A dewdrop hung from each nostril and she was dressed in an odd assortment of indescribable clothing with a large luggage label pinned to her flat chest, rather like a discarded parcel. Someone had obviously tried to clean up the skinny legs, as two white circles of flesh showed upon the bony knees. Clearly the effort had been too overwhelming for the rest of the legs were ingrained with a lifetime's dirt. The child did not move.

'I bet you're hungry.'

Dark brown eyes stared silently up at Meg. Beside her on the seat was a square box, obviously a gas mask, and a small brown paper carrier bag which the child clutched tightly to her side. Meg tried again.

'Mr Lipstock says you come from Manchester. I've never been to Manchester. Why don't you come inside and tell us all about it? We're having dinner in a minute. Beef stew and dumplings. Perhaps you'd like some?'

She was getting no response. If it were possible, the silence appeared to compound itself with increasing resolution the more persuasive she tried to be. Meg decided to try a different tack.

Turning away from the car, she carelessly shrugged her shoulders and started to walk away.

'All right, it's up to you. We'll see you later, after we've eaten.'

'I'm not bloody well stoppin' here!'

Meg stopped dead. She saw the shocked expression on Sal's face but her own, she felt, was very near to laughter. Without turning round, she said, 'Why not?'

'Them.'

Meg had to turn now to see what it was the child referred to. As she saw the direction of her terrified gaze she very nearly laughed out loud but managed to stop herself just in time. 'You mean the cows? Oh, you don't have to worry about Daisy and Betsy. They're soft as butter.' She chuckled at her own joke. 'Well, they would be, wouldn't they? Since they make it so well.'

But still the child did not move and Meg felt a twinge of disappointment. A few steps behind her she could hear Mr Lipstock whispering something to Sally Ann, saying how difficult the child had been. No doubt that was why he had brought her to this remote farmstead. None of the good ladies who had taken the trouble to visit the station to offer their clean homes to a poor evacuee would have been interested in this one.

Meg felt a cold nose touch her leg and instinctively put down her hand to fondle Rust's ears. Rust. Of course. Well, it was worth a try. 'I don't suppose you like dogs any better?' she said, with studied carelessness. 'This is Rust. He gets a bit bored up here on his own with no one to play with. I'm often too busy, you see. I don't suppose you'd consider...' Meg sighed and half turned away. 'No, as you said, you don't intend staying. I quite understand. Come on, Rust, let's go.'

'Aye, I do.'

Meg's heart leaped. 'Do what?'

The child was standing beside her now, having slipped silently from the car. Still clutching the brown paper bag and with her gas mask hanging on a string over a coat that very nearly reached her ankles now that she was standing, her scrawny figure looked an even more pathetic sight.

'Like dogs.'

'Oh.'

'I used to 'ave a dog once. Of me own.'

'Really.'

'It got died.'

'Ah, that's sad.'

'Me mam said it was rat poison what did it.'

Meg nodded wisely. 'You do have to be very careful with rat poison. We have to use it here sometimes, on the farm. Would Rust do instead, do you think? Just while you are here. I'm sure this silly war won't last long. You'll be back home again by Christmas, I shouldn't wonder.'

Dark eyes regarded Meg with uncanny intelligence and she tried again to guess the child's age. Nine? Ten? Yet the eyes looked older. 'I'll stop an' have dinner with yer. Then I'll see.'

'It's a deal.' Meg started to walk towards the kitchen door, Rust at her heel as usual. The child followed them right into the house. Mr Lipstock bade them goodbye and made a hasty departure, while the going was good.

'Would you like to wash your hands before you eat?'

'No.'

Meg decided this was not the moment to advocate the virtues of hygiene. Nor did she make any comment as the child squatted on her haunches beside Rust and start to stroke the dog's back with meticulous thoroughness. He lolled his tongue and turned gently patient eyes upon his new admirer. He was never one to object to attention and this was the first time he could remember ever being allowed inside this kitchen with all its good smells.

'You haven't told us your name.'

Never taking her eyes from the dog's face the child answered. 'Euphemia.'

Meg and Sally Ann exchanged rapid, amused glances. It seemed a very grand sort of name for such a small, scrawny child. 'How lovely.'

'Mam says it's Greek, an' it was all Greek to her how she come to have me.'

Sally Ann spluttered and choked and had to give her attention to the pan of stew bubbling on the range to bring herself back under control.

'We won't wait for the menfolk today, since this is your first meal with us,' said Meg, and saw a pair of troubled eyes turn up to hers. ''Oo do yer mean? What menfolk?'

'Well,' said Meg, trying to sound encouraging as she set a chair at the table for Euphemia which the child ignored, 'there's my father, Joe, but you must call him Mr Turner. Then my brother Dan, who is married to Sal here. I have another brother, Charlie.' Meg swallowed. 'But he has gone to join the RAF.'

'Do they live here an' all?'

'Yes. But they're out in the fields most of the time,' Meg felt it necessary to add. 'You won't see much of them.'

Sally Ann placed a dish of succulent stew upon the table before Euphemia's empty chair. The steam from it rose enticingly and the girl's nostrils twitched.

She glanced at the stew, then quickly up at the two women before snatching the plate and running to a far corner of the room where she started to push fistfuls of the food into her mouth.

Meg was horrified. 'Be careful, you'll burn yourself.'

Sally Ann put a hand on Meg's shoulder, staying her as she would have gone to protest. 'Let her be. She's probably had to fight for every scrap, poor lamb, to survive.'

'Everyone calls me Effie,' the child mumbled at last through a mouthful of food, and held out the licked plate. 'Is there any more?'

Chapter Ten

Kath regarded her aunt with some trepidation. She sat like a matriarch in a wing-backed chair in her private sitting room, certain of her authority in the insular world she had created. Shrewd eyes lurked beneath a straight black fringe while fat ringed fingers were folded upon some knitting in her lap.

'You'll be looking for work, I take it?' The voice was well modulated, in a tone used to being obeyed.

Kath looked slightly startled, not having considered doing any such thing. A few restful weeks was more what she'd had in mind, while she sorted matters out.

'My stay would only be temporary. I intend going to London in due course. But until I've made my plans I'd like to stay here.'

'At my expense?'

'Indeed, no. I am perfectly able to pay my way.' Kath had rather assumed there would be no charge of any kind, since she was family.

'How old are you now?'

'Twenty, nearly twenty-one.'

'Hm. And Rosemary has kept you idle all your life, I shouldn't wonder. Always was an expert in idleness. Landed herself a rich husband and retired to cosseted domesticity. No doubt that is what you have in mind.'

'Not at the moment.'

Ruby Nelson sniffed. 'It wasn't the way my sister was brought up, I'll have you know, nor is it the way I have lived my life. You might as well understand that if you choose to stay here, you'll either pay your way or work. That's my creed in life, as you might say.'

'I understand perfectly.'

'I hope you do. There'll be plenty of war work about, I shouldn't wonder.'

Heart sinking, Kath readjusted her plans yet again. Perhaps she could find quiet employment somewhere, driving the wounded to hospital, for instance. That sounded useful and not particularly onerous. On a sunny September day in Southport with only the sound of gulls in the air, it was difficult to imagine where the wounded would come from.

'Breakfast at eight precisely, luncheon at one and dinner at seven. Latecomers do not get fed. I prefer all rooms to be vacated each morning by ten. It only makes for more work if people stay in them. And the front door is locked at nine-thirty. My rules are strict but fair.' Ruby lifted the steel knitting needles and began to click away at some navy-blue wool. The sound was almost as loud as the grandfather clock that stood in the corner and whose hands evidently governed the household routine to the second.

Kath said that she would make note of the times.

'No gentlemen callers, of course. I take only honourable single women or widows, and gentlemen with impeccable credentials. My charges are reasonable. You will find the tariff on your dressing table. Less, of course, if you intend to cook your own meals.'

'I would prefer full service, if you please.'

'I am correct in assuming you are unattached?'

A slight pause then Kath risked a smile. 'Yes, quite unattached.'

A nod of approval. 'Then I am sure we will get along splendidly.'

This was not quite the warm welcome Kath had hoped for. But what choice did she have? She couldn't go home and tell her parents the truth. If she had the courage, she'd go to some back street establishment and get the matter dealt with. But the idea of abortion revolted her. It wasn't the poor little mite's fault after all. She hadn't worked out all the details yet. How she would keep her pregnancy hidden for a start. But she hoped that here, in Southport, there would be good adoption agencies, or else in Liverpool not far away. Then she'd head south.

Her aunt's reaction to the news was another thing, best not thought about at this stage. Time enough to face that later.

—

The washing of Effie proved to be the greatest test of Meg's patience to date. The girl refused absolutely to remove a single garment. But she'd reckoned without Meg's own stubbornness.

'You are not sleeping in one of my beds dressed in those rags. Like it or not, you are taking a bath. Hold her down, Sal, while I unfasten her boots.'

'They ain't rags. Mam put me in me best to come 'ere.'

'Then God knows what your worst is like.'

'You can have hot cocoa if you take a bath like a good girl,' Sally Ann promised, using bribery in her desperation, but the offer resulted in only a momentary pause in the struggle.

It took the strength of both women to peel the coat and dress, both stiff with dirt, from the child's emaciated body. When they had her naked on the rag hearthrug they both stared in awed horror. Great purple bruises covered her body.

'I fell down,' said Effie.

'Several times it would seem.'

The lower lip was starting to tremble but the brown eyes blazed with hatred and fear. No wonder the child had clung so tenaciously to her rags. 'Come on,' Meg gently urged. 'The water will warm you and we'll be very careful, I promise.'

Effie had never taken a bath in her life, but testing the water with a tentative finger decided it might be worth the risk. She was curious to know what it might feel like to be clean. Mebbe the warm water would stop the continual itching that she suffered from. Very carefully, she lowered herself into the water and her small pixie face lit up at once with the pleasure of it.

Very gently Meg soaped the tender body while Sally Ann poured water from a large jug over the tangled hair. It took the best part of an hour and a half to bathe her and to clean and comb the walking masses from the hair, using copious amounts of lye soap and paraffin.

It was a shining little stranger who emerged. As the child sat wrapped in a towel by the fire, sipping the promised cocoa, Sally Ann and Meg smiled at each other.

'She's pretty,' Meg said.

'And smaller than ever. Have you realised, she's not got a stitch to wear?'

'I've still got me own bloody clothes!'

'I've put those in the outhouse to be burnt,' Sally Ann told her, so firmly that even Effie knew when she was beaten.

'You can have something of mine,' Meg offered. 'I'm sure there must be some of Charlie's old shoes in the attic. Though if you are to stay, you'd do best to curb that sort of language here.'

'Joe would have a fit,' Sally Ann agreed, stifling a giggle.

'He will anyway when he sees her.'

'I don't care what any old man thinks.'

'You will if he throws you out the door.'

'I'll go 'ome then.' But it was a chastened Effie who spoke, her voice already blurring with sleep from the depths of the warm towels. She took no persuading at all to go to bed. Eyelids drooping as Meg led her upstairs, Effie opened them in wonder at sight of the small attic room.

'Is this where I 'ave to sleep?'

'You're to share it with me. Do you mind? I've made a bed up on cushions in the corner.'

Since Effie had never shared a room with anything less than her entire family before, and sometimes with perfect strangers, she merely shook her head.

'We can buy you a proper bed when you've decided if you're staying.'

'You mean of me own?'

Meg laughed. 'Of course. Come on, little Effie, you look all in.'

Now that the face was clean, purple bruises could be seen quite clearly beneath each dark eye. The child didn't look as if she'd slept for weeks, nor eaten. Meg felt a warm, protective glow inside that here, at least, she could do something to help another human being in this terrible time of war. Effie would eat well from now on, if Meg had to starve herself.

'You're not going?' Meg, halfway to the door, stopped at the sound of fear in the high-pitched child's voice.

'I could sit with you for a while, if you like?'

'Don't matter.' The thin shoulders shrugged. But of course it mattered a great deal. Quite clearly the child had never been alone in her life before, Meg realised. In the tangle of bodies and human misery of the slums, privacy didn't exist. She tucked the covers up to the child's chin and sat with her until the sound of even breathing heralded a deep sleep. Only then did she go back downstairs. And found herself thrust into the fury of a typical Turner row.

'Who said this young thug could come here?'

'She's a child, not a thug,' Sally Ann was saying, patient resignation on her flushed face while her father-in-law stood before the fire, blocking all heat from the room, waving a fist in the air.

'I'll not have strangers in my house without my permission.'

'The government doesn't need anyone's permission,' Meg quietly told him. 'Evacuees are being billeted on everyone.'

'If we have to have one, then it should be a lad. At least he'd be some use.'

'Effie is here for protection, not to work.'

'This is *my* house. I'll be the one to decide such things. If she's not going to work, she can leave first thing in t'morning.'

'There's a war on, if you haven't noticed.' Meg reached for her coat.

'And where do you think you're going?'

'To see Lanky. I meant to go this afternoon but couldn't because we had Effie to see to.'

'It's too late.'

'It's no more than half-past seven. I won't be long.'

'I've not done talking to you yet.'

'Well, I've done talking to you.' Meg closed the door on his fury. Halfway across the yard she thought she heard a scream and stopped. She decided it must have been a fox or some other wild creature and, pulling her bicycle from the shed, rode off up the lane.

—

Over the following week Meg did her best to keep Effie out of Joe's way. It wasn't easy. Sally Ann was nursing a black eye as a warning to them all of the risks they ran if they failed.

'Why didn't that lump of a brother of mine protect you?'

'You know Dan can't bring himself to contradict his father. They have a mutual adoration society going for them. Anyroad, nothing can stop Joe's temper.'

Naturally inquisitive, the child poked and pried in every corner, often wandering off and reacting strongly if Meg tried to curb her freedom.

'I goes where I wants to go. I'll happen go 'ome tomorrer.'

'I hope you won't. Don't you like it here?'

'Not much. It stinks.'

Meg had trouble hiding her smile since this was an odd sort of accusation coming from a child who herself had been unapproachable until a few days ago. She meant the animals, naturally, and nothing would induce her to go anywhere near them, coming almost to the point of hysterics at one point when Meg offered to introduce her to Daisy at close quarters.

'Not bloody likely,' she said, and set off down the hill at such a pace that Meg had to run to catch her, and it took some persuading to bring her back.

'You mustn't run off on your own like that,' she warned. 'You might fall and hurt yourself, and how would we know where to look for you?'

It was only when Effie was fast asleep in her makeshift bed that Meg felt it was safe to leave her. She'd been so busy settling Effie in to life at Ashlea this last week that she'd quite neglected Lanky and decided one evening that it was time to put that right. Sally Ann agreed to look after the child when Meg said she would walk up to Broombank for a change, since it was such a pleasant evening.

She was glad she had made the effort but regretted not bringing her bike when she found Lanky in bed, coughing blood and in obvious pain. There was no fire or heat of any kind in the cold house and no sign of his having eaten. The air was acrid with the tang of the old ash that lay untended in the grate, and a thin layer of yellow dust powdered everything.

'I'm fetching a doctor. Just as soon as I've got some hot soup down you.'

'No, you're not. There's nowt he can do.'

'We'll see about that. And I shall light a fire in your bedroom, so don't argue.' With no telephone at Broombank and it being black dark outside by the time these essential tasks were done, Meg decided the doctor would have to wait until morning. There was no question of leaving Lanky alone, so she made up a bed for herself by the fire downstairs, and could only hope that little Effie would not wake and be frightened, all alone in a strange bedroom.

At first light Lanky seemed no better, though he took a little scrambled egg and a sip of tea. Meg quickly dealt with the milking, surprised and saddened to find Lanky had only four cows left out of what had once been a sizeable herd, then ran as fast as her legs would go to the doctor's house, more than two miles away. Her sides were near splitting when she got there but she leaned on the bell while she gasped for breath.

A large, well-set man, still with a marked north-east accent to his quiet voice even after more than thirty years in Westmorland, came in answer to the desperate ringing. But Dr MacClaren only gave a sad shake of his head when she told him the facts.

'I'll call in later this morning. Lanky has never been properly right since he got gassed in the First World War.'

'I didn't know. Why didn't he say?'

The doctor gave a wry smile. 'He's got his pride. Doesn't like to be a burden to anyone.'

'Oh, for goodness' sake.'

'That's the way he is, Meg. Your ma used to call on him quite a bit. It's good to see you taking over. He needs a bit of care.'

'I do what I can, I'm very fond of him.' She might have said he was the nearest thing to a real father she had known, her own being very far from ideal, but it wouldn't have been proper, not to the doctor who'd delivered her.

'Keep him warm, well fed, and above all quiet. Rest is essential. The farm is too much for him but he'll never sell it. You look more and more like your mother, you know.' The doctor grinned. 'No wonder he thinks you're special.'

Meg flushed with embarrassment, wanting to ask what he meant by that remark, but the doctor was on his way back indoors, anxious for his breakfast before starting on the day's calls and surgeries.

She was back at Broombank before eight but Meg knew she had a problem. How could she return home to look after Effie when she didn't dare leave Lanky? He needed care too. Fortunately this was a quiet time in the farming year but there were the hens to be fed and a hundred and one other jobs at both houses.

'You get off home,' he said, reading her thoughts. 'I'll be all right.'

'Like heck you will.' Sal would have to look after Effie for once. She'd stop on, for a little while, and see to the old man.

It was early afternoon by the time Meg felt she could safely leave him. Loyalties to her old friend and to Effie still warred within. First there had been the doctor to wait for and then she'd had to see that Lanky got a bit of dinner inside him. She'd spent a couple of hours hosing down the cow byre which really did stink, and had made some effort to clean up the house.

Then she'd written a short letter to Jack, explaining that his father was ill. Would the Navy give him leave to come home and sort it all out? she wondered. Somehow she doubted it, but oh, what she wouldn't give for Jack to walk in the door this minute, smile that wonderful smile of his and place a sweet kiss on her lips.

Perhaps she could bring Effie back with her, then she could look after both at once. Meg brewed a pot of tea and took the tray upstairs to discuss the matter with Lanky.

'Aye, bring the lass here by all means. I'll be up and about in an hour.'

'Indeed you won't. I shan't move an inch from this chair unless you promise me you'll stay right where you are.'

Lanky's old eyes twinkled with pleasure. 'Just as stubborn as your mother.'

Meg kissed the wrinkled cheek. 'And as determined to get my own way.'

'Eeh, your mam rarely got that.'

'No, I don't suppose she did, not with my father about.' Meg sat down on the edge of the bed. 'Tell me about her. You loved her, didn't you?'

His eyebrows lifted in astonishment. 'How did you guess?'

Meg gave a soft chuckle. 'I should have guessed long since if I'd had any sense, but it was something the doctor said. Go on, tell me.'

For the first time Meg could remember, Lanky flushed like a boy. 'It'll have to be our secret. It's not something to broadcast.'

'All right. I won't tell.'

'Aye, I did love her. I'd always loved her if you want to know, even when she was young Annie Follett. I rather thought that she had a fancy for me. We'd certainly talked about getting wed one day. Nothing definite, you understand. Just youngsters we were, dreaming.' Silence fell and Meg thought the old man had fallen asleep but then he suddenly opened his eyes and continued. 'Then the war came and I went away. Joe didn't go. Flat feet or summat, I don't remember. Mebbe he just had to stay and look after the farm. When the war was over and I came back, she'd already wed him.'

'Why?' Meg was shocked by this apparent disloyalty on the part of her lovely mam.

'By rights you should ask her that, only she isn't here any more so I don't suppose it'll matter. The truth is she thought I were a goner. It shook her when I come back. Not quite the man I was, admittedly, but with all me limbs in place which was more than some had. Anyway I met my Mary and wed her. We were right happy, but I never forgot sweet Annie.' He started to cough again and Meg was all concern.

'I've made you talk too much. Rest for a while. Don't say any more. I've seen to the animals. Now I must pop home, check on Effie and fetch you some food.' She leaned close and laid her soft, warm cheek against the old man's rough one. 'I'm glad you loved Mam. It makes us seem more like family.'

Lanky gave a quiet chuckle and, lifting a shaky hand, stroked Meg's hair.

'You're a grand lass. You remind me of her in a lot of ways. I shall always be grateful for the joy you've brought to a foolish old man in his last years.'

'Oh, don't talk so soft.' She kissed him, trying not to let her tears fall upon his cheek as his horny hand held hers, still with its startlingly strong grip.

'Don't hurry back. Do what you have to do. I'll be all right now.' Unable to find her voice through the choking tears, Meg could only nod and stumble to the door. How different her life would have been if only her mother had waited and married Lanky.

Ten minutes later Joe walked into Broombank yard with a determined stride. He would have driven up in the old van but petrol was getting expensive and he didn't like to waste money. He'd taken a short cut across the fields, so didn't see Meg running down the lane. And told no one where he was going.

It was more than twelve months since he'd last asked for his loan to be settled, the interest had accrued very nicely since then and he wasn't prepared to wait any longer. Now that war was a reality a man needed all his assets to hand. Particularly with a married son to keep.

He found Lanky by his fireside looking as if he'd just got up. No wonder the place was going to rack and ruin. 'Never would have thought to find you indoors at this time of day.'

Lanky, having politely offered Joe refreshment and been refused, took a quick sip of his honey and lemon mixture, hoping to quieten the cough that he felt stirring. He wanted none of Joe Turner's pity. 'I suppose a chap can stop for a bite if he wants to.'

Joe sniffed his disbelief, as well he might for it was a time Lanky would normally have been out on the fells, working. But that had been in the days when he'd been fit. It was plain he was far from that now. 'Getting a bit slack, eh? You'll be missing your Jack.' Joe, as always, had the knack of pouring salt on a wound.

'He has to do his bit for King and Country.'

'I don't hold with wars.'

Lanky was feeling too ill for the roundabout question and answer game he and Joe usually indulged in. 'I've only stopped for a minute,' he lied. 'So if you've owt to say I'd be glad if you got on with it.'

Nothing could have suited Joe more. 'Aye, you can be blunt with me, lad. We've known each other long enough.'

'Then you understand that I'm a patient man but even I have me limits.' The cough almost choked him as it burst forth and he quickly sipped the warmed honey mixture again. He preferred his own tinctures to the doctor's newfangled stuff.

'Thee wants to get that cough seen to.'

When the spasm had passed, Lanky faced his rival with as placid an expression as he could muster. He felt so ill he wondered how he was managing to keep upright. 'I suppose you've come for your money?'

'Well, I'm not made of brass, tha knows.'

'I haven't got it.' There it was. The truth. Out in the open at last. Plain and simple. 'I can't pay you. Not now, nor in the foreseeable future. I don't know if I ever can.'

Joe clicked his false teeth for a bit, deep in thought. 'Well now, that's a shame. I was hoping we could have this matter settled today. Have you made up your mind what thee is going to do about it?'

'No.'

The silence that now fell between the two men was filled with unspoken vengeance. A lifetime of resentments, one against the other. It was as if the veneer of friendship had finally been stripped away and the relationship shown for what it truly was: a jealous, bitter rivalry with its seeds sown long ago in the distant past.

'I'll have to take summat else then, in lieu.'

'You're not having my land, not now, not ever. Annie was right about you, Joe Turner. You're a cold-hearted son of the devil and no mistake.'

'And you're a stubborn old fool, that's what you are. And Annie a greater. one for wasting so much time on you.'

The last vestige of colour drained from the parchment cheeks. 'Don't you besmirch Annie's name! There were nowt between her and me after you and she wed and you know it.'

'So you say.'

'It's true.'

'You could have had her, and gladly, in return for a hundred acres or so.'

Lanky half rose in his chair. Incensed by Joe's taunting he had a longing to smash the self-satisfied face to pulp but the exertion even of moving was too much and he fell back, the burning rasping cough starting up again, the phlegm in his throat near choking him. He knew he shouldn't let Joe's taunts provoke him. Joe was not a man to let his women wander. He always liked to be in control, bragging that Annie belonged to him and would do only as he directed.

When the honey and lemon had soothed the cough sufficiently for Lanky to speak again, his voice was low and resolute in its calm. 'So you'd take away a sick man's animals? You're a hard man, Joe Turner. With few morals.'

'Morals have nowt to do with business.'

'Do your worst then and see if I care. Only leave my land alone.'

The cough threatened again and Lanky calmed himself before continuing. 'You didn't deserve Annie. I can't think why she chose you. She should have known I would come back. I told her I would, even if I was a poor study with writing.'

A heat was closing over his head. It was like a fire that blotted everything out but the sight of Annie's pretty face. A face that had kept him sane when he was in the army hospital. So lovely she had been with her cloud of shining hair, just like Meg's. He could scarce think straight now but he was almost sure that she'd stood here, less than six months before she died, and told him that she had never stopped loving him through all those long years. Words he'd stored in his heart with joy. So nothing Joe Turner could say would spoil that truth.

Joe, however, was determined to try. 'You should have written to her more, told her where you were. She got fed up of worrying.'

Lanky, an intensely private man, best with his own company, and, like Joe himself unable to read or write, still cringed at the embarrassment of having someone else write his feelings on paper. At first it hadn't mattered because he'd been given regular leave and their time together had been sweet. But then, without warning, he'd been sent to France and that was it. There'd been a third letter but that had never been posted as he'd been struck down by the gas and spent the rest of the war being moved from hospital to hospital.

He was glad she never saw him like that, so sick, spewing up blood and bile, half a man. He'd wanted to be well before he contacted her again.

But by then it had been too late. She'd married Joe and his dreams had crumbled to dust. That was the one time in his life when he, a grown man, had cried.

'You're right though,' Joe said. 'She might have waited. Only when I told her you were probably dead, she agreed to marry me.'

'You told her what?' The faded eyes went blank with disbelief. 'You hadn't heard that I was dead, had you?'

'No, I hadn't.'

'You told Annie a deliberate lie?'

'She had to see sense.'

'Why?'

'I wanted her. Annie was a good woman, hard-working, salt of the earth as you might say. Same as our Meg is, only Annie weren't nearly so rebellious.'

Lanky saw it all now. He saw that Joe had been prepared to lie to get his way, fooling himself that it might be the truth. He'd ruined Lanky's entire life, stolen the girl he had loved.

Oh, he'd come to love his own dear wife, Mary, and they'd been happy together. But it was true that Annie had remained special. Mary had understood and seen no threat in the sweet memory, for that's all it was in the end.

Whereas Joe had let the hatred and jealousy grow inside him like a canker. He had never forgiven Lanky for the fact that Annie still loved him, even to her dying day. He had won her in body, but never captured her heart. Getting Broombank land would have been revenge, as well as economically useful.

Lanky pulled himself upright in the chair and faced his old adversary with pride. 'Meg may be Annie's daughter, but she's also yours so not so easily squashed. She has a strength and a spirit that even you can't break, Joe Turner, try as you might. She'll follow her own plan in life, will Meg, not yours. Mark my words, she's a match for you any day.'

Chapter Eleven

The moment Meg walked in her own front door she knew she'd delayed too long. Sally Ann met her in the kitchen with the news that Effie had run off again.

'You'd best start looking for her. I've searched every corner of the house and barns and can find no sign. I tried to keep an eye on her but she's as smart as a ferret.'

'It's my fault, Sal. Don't blame yourself.'

Meg called for Rust and with dog at heel set off down the cart track, calling Effie's name. Oh, why hadn't she come back for her sooner, taken her to Broombank last night? Yet she'd had no reason to know then that Lanky would be ill and need her to stay.

Effie should have waited. Why hadn't she?

Because Meg had promised not to leave her and she had broken that promise. Probably no one had ever kept a promise to her in the past so why should she be surprised if a perfect stranger let her down?

Meg trekked on, longing to find some sign of the once noisome Effie. Used to solitary walking, she never felt lonely as a rule. Now, for the first time, she did. The fells and dales, so named by the early Norse settlers, looked more empty and bleak than they ever had before. The cracks and fissures forming steps in the rocks, punctuated periodically with patches of green, offered a deceptively easy climb to the top. Try it and your shaking legs would be the first to spot the mistake. But Effie was ignorant of which parts of this remote landscape could be traversed and which should be left well alone.

Responsibility for these two people, one an old friend, the other a new, weighed heavily upon her. Why couldn't she be more like Kath? Kath did not approve of responsibility. She said everyone thought only of themselves and that Meg should learn to do the same. It was not a belief Meg could ever subscribe to.

But supposing Effie were in trouble? One slip on those heights and you were done for. In her mind's eye, Meg saw the small child lying at the bottom of a crag like a broken doll.

'*Effie!*' she called out, her voice snatched and lost by the wind. Oh, Jack. If only you were here, you could help me look. A lump came into her throat. Where was he? Was he in danger? Would they send him to France? Perhaps she shouldn't even be thinking of taking on an evacuee when all she wanted to do was pack her bags and go to him, wherever he was, so they could be married.

If only that were possible.

The old oaks and yews, their trunks twisted into grotesque shapes by the wind, whined and creaked, making her shiver. Meg searched till the October light was fading from the sky but could find no sign of the tiny figure. Her foot skidded on a stone and she pitched forward on to her knees. Tears stung her eyes as she picked the shale from her bloodied flesh. She was tired. Time to call it a day and go home. She'd go and see Mr Lipstock in the morning. 'Come on, Rust. Supper time.'

Sally Ann met her at the door. 'She's back.'

Pleasure and relief flooded through Meg and she grasped Sally Ann's hands with delight. 'Oh, that's wonderful. Then she trusts us after all.'

Her sister-in-law looked doubtful. 'Joe found her. I think she was lost, and very frightened. It's a big world out there.' Sal nodded in the direction of the stairs. 'He's with her now. Says we are not to disturb him while he teaches her the meaning of gratitude.'

Meg needed no further warning. Very swiftly and quietly she flew up the stairs. Her hand was trembling as she lifted the sneck of the bedroom door. She had no wish to stir Joe's temper further but nor had he any right to chastise the little evacuee, if that was what he was about.

When she pushed open the door Meg did not immediately take in the scene before her. It fell upon her eyes bit by bit like a disjointed jig-saw puzzle.

Joe's arm raised. The silhouette of his lean body against the blue of the night sky framed in the window beyond. The flash of something long and leathery. The night light by the bed shining upon a shivering white body and over it all a terrible silence broken only by a rhythmic, repetitive thwack.

'No!' Meg flew across the tiny bedroom, reaching for the belt that Joe held high above his head, ready to stroke its telling cruelty upon the torn flesh below. 'No!'

She was thrust fiercely aside so that she fell, knocking her head against the window frame. But she was up again as the belt met its target a second time. Not a sound came from Effie, lying curled up in her clean vest and knickers on the makeshift bed, arms about her head. Had she mercifully lost her senses? Meg grabbed for the raised arm and this time grasped the belt firmly enough to twist it hard and wrench it from her father's grasp.

Joe Turner swung round upon his daughter and knocked her flying with the flat of one hand. It sent her into a crumpled heap in the corner of the small room, bringing the sharp sting of tears to her eyes as her head banged on the floor. Pain shot through her and the world tilted and turned black, fired by a kaleidoscope of colour in her head. But Meg did not care. She held tenaciously to the lethal belt beneath her.

'Stop that.' The force of the quiet voice from the door was electrifying. Joe, one hand on Meg's hair ready to drag her to her feet, stilled and half turned to face his daughter-in-law.

Sally Ann was standing in the doorway with a rifle in her hand. It was no more than an air gun used to pop rabbits but it could do considerable damage at this distance. Joe, one eye on the gun, attempted to brazen it out.

'There's no ammunition in that thing.'

'Try it and see.'

For a long moment everyone remained frozen. Joe felt a touch of admiration for Sally Ann. She was a fine figure of a woman standing there like some warrior queen with her red hair all about her head. It took guts to take up a gun against him. He gave no such consideration to his daughter whom he dismissed as a trouble-maker, beyond his control, but he released Meg's hair and she fell back upon the floorboards with a quiet sob. Before anyone could move, Joe had picked up Effie from the bed and shaken her like a limp white rabbit before tossing her back upon the thin mattress. 'Learn to do as you're told, brat. If I say you do summat, you jump to and do it. Have you got that?' He did not wait for any answer, which was just as well since the child could not have given one.

When he had gone Meg struggled to her feet and hurried to Effie's side. She found the child curled into a ball tighter than ever, eyes wide open, unblinking. Beads of blood showed on the white underclothing but she made no sound. No tears fell and not a muscle twitched. It was as if she did not feel any pain.

'Dear God, he's killed her!' Meg cried.

'No,' Sally Ann said. 'She's in deep shock. I'll fetch some salt water to clean her up. You stay with her. When she comes out of it she'll need a friend.'

It was perhaps to the child's advantage that she did not come out of it until the next morning. Even then she did not cry and Meg found her acceptance of the chastisement almost more terrible to bear than the act itself.

Effie was sitting up in bed when Meg woke. Gently, she held a cup of water to the child's parched lips. 'Are you all right? Did he hurt you?' Inane remarks, but what else was there to say?

Effie gave a little shake of her head, denying the obvious truth. 'But I still won't milk his soddin' cows.'

Meg gasped, then reluctantly laughed. 'Are you saying you took a beating rather than milk cows?'

She would have to speak to Effie again about her language. It wasn't proper for so young a child to have so filthy a mouth. Oh, but it was wonderful to see that even in these terrible circumstances the girl's spirit was not broken. She was glad about that.

'I've had a beating afore, and I don't like them monsters.'

Something hardened deep inside Meg and a resolution was born. 'Well, you'll not be beaten again. You and I, Effie, are moving out of here.' Eager to put thought into action, she reached for her brown suitcase in the closet.

'Where we going?'

'You'll see. A place where there is only kindness and love, not anger and beatings.'

'Are there any cows?'

Meg looked at the resolute, pointed face and started to laugh. 'You might find, in time, that cows can be more appealing than your fellow men. Come on, can you get up, do you think? I'd like to be out of here before it gets light if possible. Can you walk?'

'Oh, aye.' The child winced. 'I could dance a jig.'

They managed a steady pace up the path to Broombank, carrying the suitcase, Effie's brown paper bag and gasmask which she would not part with, pushing Meg's bicycle between them. It was all they owned in the world. Padding along between them came Rust, where he meant always to stay.

Meg had left a note on the kitchen mantelshelf for Sally Ann, explaining where she'd gone. But she did not expect Joe to come after her. She knew that once she had left home, he would never allow her to return.

She was entirely dependent now upon Lanky's goodwill, but felt certain of a warm welcome.

-

Breakfast at number six, Southview Villas, was the most informal meal of the day. Alice, the little maid, would set out tureens on the long sideboard, rather as if for a grand country house-party, and everyone was permitted to help themselves. It was folly though to arrive more than a moment after the gong sounded for the number of sausages, kidneys or slivers of bacon was strictly limited and a latecomer ran the risk of going without. There was no question of the dishes being refilled.

Kath, however, found she could not face even the smell of food first thing in the morning so she made a point of waiting until her fellow guests had departed to their various shops and offices before slipping into the breakfast room to nibble on a slice of dry toast.

She was thus engaged, wondering if the nausea would ever pass and if she could face coffee this morning, when her aunt strode into the room.

Ruby Nelson never walked. She marched, strode or flounced, head thrust forward as if in a hurry to get where she was going. She was dressed this morning in a dark green spotted dress with a square neck and rows of beads reminiscent of the roaring twenties, in which period, apparently, she had bloomed.

'You'll be off out job hunting again today, my dear?'

Kath agreed that she would, though she had as yet, made not a single enquiry. She felt far too ill. Whoever had said pregnant women bloomed must have been mad. Or a man.

'I heard they might be wanting some kitchen help at the Kardomah.'

'I'll go and ask.' Kath finished her toast and decided against the coffee. Perhaps later.

She'd reached the dining-room door when Ruby asked her more pertinent question, very sweetly, as always. 'Was that you in the bathroom this morning, dear?'

'I always go to the bathroom in the morning.'

'You sounded dreadfully ill. Not sickening for anything, I trust?'

'Not that I know of.'

Ruby adopted her sympathetic expression. 'That's all right then. I do hope you cleaned the basin down when you'd finished.'

Kath's hand found the polished doorknob and got the door open somehow. She grabbed her coat from the hallstand and left the house as quickly as she could without turning to say goodbye. That way she could avoid the suspicion in her aunt's eyes.

The expression in Ruby Nelson's eyes was more that of shrewd speculation and frowning disapproval. She didn't trust that little hussy, not one bit, she thought. What Rosemary was thinking of to send her here in that condition she could not imagine. Did she imagine that her beloved sister had been born yesterday? Old maid she might be, but she could recognise a girl in trouble when she saw one. Something must be done about it, and quick. Scandal was bad for business and Ruby had no intention of risking it.

'I'll not have her on my plate,' she announced, wagging a finger at the closed door. 'Dear me, no.' And spinning on her heel she marched to the kitchen and flung open the door. 'Alice. Get this table cleared. I have some letters to write.'

–

Kath decided to walk all the way down to the water line this morning. It took a long time. The sea was far out on the wide flat sands, deserted at this time of year, but she needed to fill the day somehow, give herself time to think.

She checked off in her mind the tasks that lay ahead. She had to find a doctor who would tend her without asking too many questions. Not an easy task in itself. It had been a mistake to come to Southport, she realised now, for how could she pretend to be a widow or a married woman with her aunt to give the lie to the tale? She needed to enquire about adoption agencies. Perhaps Liverpool would be a better place for that. And she still hadn't decided whether she should write and tell Jack about her problem. What did she want him to do about it if she did? Then there was the vexing question of money. Dare she write home and ask for more?

So many decisions to be made when what she really wanted was a bit of fun to cheer herself up. To go dancing and find some delicious young man. She was too young for all these problems. It wasn't fair. Kath decided to put it out of her mind for a while. There was no rush after all, months and months before she need worry. Thinking too much was unsettling, and she didn't yet feel ready to confront the reality of a baby growing inside her. A child that would one day be born and require looking after.

After her bracing walk she went in to the Kardomah. 'Coffee and a custard slice, please.'

'You'll be lucky, love. There's been that much panic buying and threat of restrictions we can't get half what we need. I can do you a nice toasted teacake and a pot of tea.'

'That'll do fine.'

Kath didn't ask about the chance of a job. The place seemed to be teeming with waitresses in their smart little aprons and caps. And the thought of working with food all day made her stomach heave.

It was raining when she got outside again but near enough to tea time to justify going back to Southview Villas.

'All the positions were filled,' she explained as her aunt sliced bread with lightning strokes. Kath crossed her fingers against the lie.

'I've been thinking about that, sweetheart. Since you are family, after all, I'd be prepared to forgo the cost of your board.'

'Thank you, Aunt Ruby. That's very decent of you.'

'What's family for, that's what I say? And you look proper peaky. A bit of peace and quiet is what you want, not working in a noisy café.' The shrewd eyes turned upon Kath. 'Have to stick together in troubled times, eh?'

'Er, yes.'

'So you can forget the job hunting and give me a bit of a hand here. That would be lovely, wouldn't it? Us working together?'

Ruby scraped off half of the margarine and butter mixture she had already spread upon the bread. 'Waste not, want not. Alice is set on going to work in a munitions factory in Liverpool. Sweated labour I call it but the money's good, or so she thinks, silly girl. So how about it then? You can work for your keep and that'll solve both our problems, won't it?'

'Y-yes,' Kath said slowly. 'I suppose it would.'

'That's a good girl. Now put an apron on and finish buttering this bread. Not too generous, mind.'

Thereafter, breakfast time was taken up with Kath cooking sausages and laying tables, or deep in suds up to her elbows at the sink. Her mornings were spent turning mattresses, making beds, sweeping floors, beating rugs, brewing coffee and peeling potatoes. It was a new, not altogether pleasant, experience.

'I thought you just wanted me as a waitress,' she said to Ruby one afternoon when her aunt presented her with a dustpan and brush.

'So I do, my dear, but there are plenty of other jobs involved in running a boarding house like mine. I have my standards and one of them is clean tablecloths. Naughty girl, you forgot to dust off all the crumbs after lunch before laying for the evening meal. I found several when I checked just now.'

Kath, in her best brown coat ready for off, stared in dismay at the implements. Her aunt must have scoured the cloths with a fine toothcomb to find one crumb, she thought angrily. 'But I'd have to clear all the tables and lay them all over again.'

Ruby wagged a chiding finger and smiled sweetly. 'Well then, that will teach you not to forget in future. It won't take a minute. Oh, and did you put the fresh counterpanes on everyone's beds this morning?'

Kath shook her head, feeling dazed. 'You didn't tell me to.'

'But we always put on clean counterpanes on a Wednesday. Now you know.'

'Don't go, Alice,' Kath groaned. 'Don't leave me to all of this.'

But Alice resolutely packed her bags and walked out, kicking the dust of number six from her feet with such joy in her step you could almost think she was glad about the war.

Kath tried not to grumble. Now that war had been declared she too could easily be forced to work in a factory. Southview Villas was surely better than that. Though sometimes she longed to take a proper part in the action. To do something crazy, or exciting, or dangerous.

In one of Rosemary's regular letters, Kath had learned that Jack had joined the Navy. She thought of him sailing across the seas to adventure and envied him. But the knowledge that he was on training in Liverpool, so close by, made her worry over whether she should go and see him.

But there was to be no escape. Reality came home to her each morning as she stuck her head in the bathroom sink, wretching as silently as possible, aware of her aunt's flapping ears.

Kath's only free time was in the afternoons. For two hours after lunch, always cold, and before afternoon tea and the evening meal had to be prepared, she was free to do as she pleased. She made the most of it. Whatever the weather, she went out.

Sometimes she wandered down Lord Street, in and out of the fashionable shops, spending money she could ill afford just to cheer herself up. At other times she would visit the Winter Gardens or take a ride on a tram. On very wet days she went to the pictures and had been known to sit through a film twice, one showing fast asleep. Once she went to the bus station and very nearly caught a bus into Liverpool to find Jack. She stood there so long that the bus conductor called out to her.

'Are you getting on, love, or taking root?'

'N-no, thank you. I-I'm waiting for someone.' Pink-cheeked and embarrassed, she hurried away.

But her favourite place was the long beach that stretched right to the sand dunes at Ainsdale if she walked far enough.

This, she had discovered, was a favourite place for a local stables to train racehorses. She loved to watch them gallop on the hard-packed sands, or spraying up the water on the edge of the tide. They needed no shoes on this surface as it was kind to their legs while strengthening the muscles essential to a good horse. Kath could understand this and sat for hours watching the training sessions thinking of her own much missed Bonnie, of dear Meg, and home.

Oh, how I do miss you all. Why did I imagine I was bored at home? This is much, much worse. She ran her hand over her still flat stomach. When would she start to show? Something had to be done. Decisions could not be kept waiting for ever. Jack had to be told some time. Perhaps it would be better if he came here, to Southport. She'd ask him to meet her, far away from the house of course and Aunt Ruby's prying eyes. It would be good to see a friendly face. This decision made Kath more cheerful and she started to sing.

'Well, will you listen to that now? You've decided to smile at last, have you?'

Kath jumped and swivelled about. A figure rose from behind the dunes. Tall and dark, his face weathered and tanned from long hours in the open, he had a grin on him that would put a Cheshire cat to shame.

Kath was incensed. 'Have you been spying on me?'

'And would it be such a crime if I had? 'Tis one of the great pleasures in life for a man to peek at a girl. It's not an arrestable offence so far as I am aware.'

'It is in certain circumstances. Peeping Toms are not very pleasant.'

'Well now, and how did you guess that my name was Thomas?' He bowed low, with great exaggeration. 'Tam O'Cleary to be exact. At your service.'

A voice called from the direction of the race horses. 'Tam, get over here will you, and stop wasting time.'

'Sure and is there no peace for a poor working man?' The stranger rolled his eyes in such a self-pitying way that Kath burst out laughing.

He started to stroll away, hands in pockets, whistling airily. He wasn't a big man, she couldn't help but notice, lean with a rangy long-legged walk, but well formed. Good to look at. He stopped and swivelled on his heel to meet her enquiring gaze.

'Have you had a good shufti then?'

She blinked and coughed, tugging her wind-flapped skirt down over bare knees. 'I wasn't staring.'

'You were too. So we're even. Except that you haven't told me your name.'

'Katherine Ellis.'

'Katherine, is it? Like my mother.'

'I thought all Irish mothers were called Kathleen.'

'And all Irishmen, Paddy, I suppose? And there's me forgetting to bring my shillelagh.'

Kath flushed. 'I didn't mean it the way it sounded.'

'Well, Katherine Ellis, I'll see you tomorrow mebbe, if I'm spared a minute for me own pleasure, and you've nothing better to be doing.'

Without waiting for her to agree or not, he swung on his heel and strode away.

'Of all the cheek. I won't come,' she called after him. Shivering, she returned to Southview Villas, putting him firmly from her mind.

Kath helped to prepare the evening meal and listened to the news on the wireless with her aunt which sounded far too grim for words, the BBC trying to say as little as possible about 'our boys in France' which made everyone worry all the more. Then at the earliest opportunity she went up to her room to write a note to Jack. She'd decided there was no reason why he shouldn't share the responsibility of deciding what was best to be done about the baby. It was his problem too, after all. She'd write and ask him to meet her.

The fire had long since died by the time they reached Broom-bank and Meg sat Effie by the empty grate, making her promise to stay put. 'As soon as I've seen to Lanky I'll get a fire going and make us some tea.'

'It stinks in 'ere.'

'It's mainly coming from outside, the animals and byre, but it's true the house could do with a good clean. Lanky hasn't been well enough lately to see to things properly. But we're here now and just the ones to do it, I reckon.'

'I'm no good at cleanin'.'

'No,' smiled Meg. 'I don't suppose you are. But you can learn.' She felt almost cheerful as she clattered up the stairs to Lanky's bedroom. Though she had been unable to return herself last night, as she had hoped, she'd left him the medicine and food by his bed. She hoped he would be feeling more himself as a result. She'd go and fetch the eggs in a minute and boil them each two for breakfast. Then she'd find some flour and make soda bread. You could face anything on a full stomach. Her mind was already stirring with wild, crazy ideas. Ideas that featured Lanky's son in an important part.

The bed was empty, the covers neatly in place as if it had not been slept in, or Lanky had been up and about particularly early. That must be a good sign, she thought.

The medicine bottle was on the bedside table with a spoon beside it. Very little had been drunk but some of the food had gone. She'd give him a piece of her mind about that, gallivanting around this early without taking his proper medicine. Oh, but she'd watch him like a hawk in future. Make sure he didn't do too much. 'Stubborn old fool. I shall enjoy looking after you though.'

Back downstairs she found Effie shivering in the cold, huddled with Rust in Lanky's big chair. She'd taken the sheep-skin that usually hung over the back of it and pulled it over them both. Child's and dog's small pointed faces peeped out above. The delight in the dog's eyes showed that he thought he'd landed in heaven. He looked so comical that Meg started to laugh.

'What's so funny? I'm frozen stiff.'

'Sorry, love. I'll light a fire.' She found some larch twigs and dead holly by the dry-stone wall outside.

'Nature's firelight,' she told Effie as she broke them into small pieces. 'We'll soon have this fire going.' The last thing she wanted was for the poor child to take a chill after her shock. Meg laid an ash log across the back of the small pyramid of sticks and soon the room was filled with the fresh, clean scent of burning wood. She filled the smaller of the two kettles with enough water for tea for them all. Then she collected the eggs, surprised to find the hens still shut up, and put half a dozen in a small pan on the trivet over a small flame.

'We'll light the boiler after breakfast, then we can start getting this place clean. It'll be fun, you'll see. And you'll like Lanky.'

'We didn't bother with no cleanin' at home.'

Meg chuckled. 'I don't expect you did.'

When the old man hadn't appeared by the time the kettle was almost boiling, she decided to go and fetch him. 'You'd best stay here. I won't be a minute. He's probably doing the milking.'

The trouble was that now Jack had gone, Lanky needed more help about the place, more labour. Even Meg's help would not be enough and she knew that a solution to this problem would have to be found soon. But then she and Lanky had a lot to talk about.

The cow byre was empty and only two cows were in the field. There were four yesterday. Had two wandered off and got lost? Surely not. Perhaps Lanky had taken it into his head to move them to another field. She couldn't think where, or why, but she would see to the mystery first thing after breakfast.

Meg filled a jug with milk from the kit and cradled the heavy jug against her hip as she pushed open the barn door. If the dogs were gone then Lanky was already out on the fells.

They came to her at once, Tess and Ben, whimpering their pleasure at seeing her.

Lanky too was in the barn. He was hanging from a rope fastened very carefully to the rafters. His milking stool lay over-turned on the ground beneath him.

The jug of milk slipped from Meg's hand and flowed into a pool as white as Lanky's face, all over the cold slate floor.

Chapter Twelve

It was a perfect, crisp autumn day for the funeral. Overhead a buzzard circled in the clear air and in the hedgerow a pair of stoats played. Lanky would have loved it. In her mind's eye, Meg could see his slight figure striding out over the fells, his familiar rolling gait making short work of the steep gradients as he checked on his beloved sheep. But Lanky was gone and would never breathe the clear, autumn air ever again.

Why had he done it? Dr MacClaren said that the sickness would never have got better, only worse, and that it was getting the old man down. But Meg felt she had failed him in some way. Why hadn't she been able to make him feel better, make him want to live?

'He knew I was coming back to him. Why didn't he wait?'

'Folks make their own mind up when they've had enough,' Effie said, with surprising wisdom.

Meg hated the air of awful sadness about the place. The work on the farm had ground to a halt and she supposed this was now the end for Broombank. Someone else would put the tups to the ewes and see to next year's crop of lambs. She couldn't bear to think it might be her own father.

A gate hung, creaking forlornly on a broken hinge. Stones from a wall that had tumbled down lay among long tufts of grass with no Lanky to put them back.

Meg got out her black hat and dusted it off. The last time she had worn it, for her mother's funeral, she had hoped never to wear it again. Now she placed it correctly upon her head, tucking up the honey gold curls as if it would be too frivolous for them to fly free.

She buttoned up her coat. 'There'll be a chill wind out, Effie, put your scarf on, there's a good girl.'

The child looked a sorry picture in a skirt that was too long, one of Meg's jackets cut down for a coat and tied in the middle with an old belt. It still came nowhere near her fragile size.

At least she was clean and the wounds upon her back, though still tender, were starting to heal. The bruises on her pinched face were purpling now and the fair skin had lost its perpetual greyness. There was even a hint of colour upon the too-flat cheeks. The country food and air was doing her good already, Meg thought with pleasure. She was looking forward to the day when the cheeks and tiny pixie-like body rounded and filled out to the childlike chubbiness they ought to be.

Effie was gazing up at Meg out of adoring eyes. Beside her sat Rust, his small black and tan body leaning against the skinny legs, his chin resting on Effie's knee.

How she would have managed without these two in the days since the discovery of Lanky's body, she couldn't imagine. They had all clung together for support and a bond had been forged between them.

It had been Effie who had made the watery porridge that dreadful morning and tried to force it between Meg's chattering teeth. Effie who had washed her face and undressed her with tender care, making her lie down between cold sheets while the doctor and the police went about their gruesome business.

Meg hadn't wanted to do anything, not even to think. Her limbs had felt like jelly. And though she had been vaguely aware that people came and went, to and from the house, that voices spoke to her, they seemed to reach her from a long way off, as if through cotton wool.

She could only concentrate on the pain that swelled about her heart, yet do nothing about its numbing effect. Great fat tears had rolled from the corners of her eyes, and her teeth kept chattering. She had lost Lanky, a funny little old man it was true, but she'd loved him. He was the only real father she had known, and the only friend in the world since Jack and Kath had left. How would she manage without him?

'I suppose I'll have to go now,' Effie had said, jerking her back to reality.

'What? No, of course you won't. Whatever gave you that idea?'

'Seems you've no home neither now.'

The child would be sent back to Manchester and very likely bombed. Meg knew that whatever happened, she mustn't allow that.

But how were they going to manage? There was no food on the farm. She knew that for a fact. Except eggs, and they couldn't live on those indefinitely.

Joe would never allow them back in Ashlea. He would take his revenge for this latest show of spirit. Meg had flouted his authority once too often and he would gladly abandon her to her fate. 'Spare the rod and spoil the child.' How often she had heard that text. Had it not been for Annie's frequent intervention she too might have felt the lick of that strap. But Annie was gone now, and with the passing of her gentle protection had gone the last crumb of decency from her hard-hearted husband. Even if Joe had permitted it, Meg had no wish to return to Ashlea while he lived. She could never forgive him for beating a defenceless child.

She'd pushed herself up into a sitting position and stared out through the window, a healing anger burning deep inside her. It wasn't right that Lanky had gone in this way. Whatever had driven him over that final edge would never be known. But life went on and he would be the first to say so. She couldn't neglect her responsibilities, to Effie and to Jack. Someone would have to take care of Broombank for him. Why not herself?

The thought had simply dropped into her head. Crazy, impossible, and wildly intoxicating.

She and Jack were to be married. She wore his ring, didn't she? So why not? Jack wouldn't turn her out. Meg's heart swelled with love and thankfulness. She would be safe with Jack.

–

The rain started as the coffin was lowered into the dark ground, needles in the cold wind that made people hunch closer into their coat collars. They sang 'Abide with Me', accompanied by the wheezing tones of the harmonium in the small dale church and now stood, black-suited, feet shuffling around the yawning grave in the tiny churchyard.

Everyone was here, all the neighbouring farmers in the good suits they always kept for funerals and weddings alike, paying their last respects to an old colleague they had known all their lives.

Meg watched them in silence. Joe looked suitably sanctimonious, Dan and Sally Ann trying to curb the smiles on their faces – news of a coming baby had been whispered into Meg's ear just as the service began. She had wanted to push her friend away, to shout, 'No, I don't want to hear about your happiness.' Instead she had managed a smile and a squeeze of Sal's hand.

There was Dr MacClaren, and Mr Capstick, the family solicitor. And a plump, matronly woman whom Meg assumed to be Connie Bradshaw, Lanky's married daughter. She wondered, fleetingly, why Mrs Bradshaw had not called at the house before the service but mostly her mind kept returning to the fact that there was still no sign of Jack. He had promised faithfully that he would be here, she had the letter in her pocket to prove it. But though they had delayed the little ceremony as long as was seemly, he had not arrived.

The statutory ham had been served, washed down by jugs of hot tea. In Lakeland the worth of a man was often judged by the size of his wake and Meg and Effie had slaved for hours to make Lanky's a proud one. Most of the ingredients had been supplied by Sally Ann from Ashlea's pantries, unknown to Joe. But Hetty Davies had likewise contributed a meat pie or two.

'Just to help out,' she had said kindly, and Meg had offered heartfelt gratitude.

The dalesfolk, having done their duty, felt they could relax a little in the warmth of Lanky's house. There was a log the size of a small tree sitting in the wide hearth, cut by Dan for this day, filling the room with an acrid scent of pine and spitting larch. Everyone was enjoying exchanging gossip and indulging in a little quiet bargaining while remembering to show respect.

Joe showed none of that. 'He's nowt much left to show for a life, has he?'

'Two of his cows have gone since yesterday.'

'Aye, lucky it weren't all four.'

For a moment Meg stared at him, uncomprehending. 'You took them?' Her voice grated raw in her throat.

'Aye, well, you should have told your friend not to borrow money he couldn't repay.'

Red hot fury exploded in her head. 'You can't do that!'

'I've already done it. Too old to be of any real value but they rightly belong to me in lieu of debt.'

'You took the others too, didn't you? Lanky used to have eight or nine at least.'

Joe ignored her and turned to help himself to a second piece of pork pie.

'Answer me. You took them all, didn't you?'

'Aye, I did. And he still owes me so I'll happen take the rest. Blame theeself. You should have persuaded that lad of his to stay and do his duty by the farm and his father.'

'There's a war on,' Meg said weakly, knowing it was no real excuse. Farming was a valid occupation during wartime and Lanky clearly couldn't manage Broombank on his own. 'He has more pressing duties to see to.'

'Lanky should have sold to me when he had chance then. There's still a sizeable lump outstanding and dead or not, some-body has to pay it.' Joe started to walk away and then stopped and turned back to her as if on an afterthought. 'You can pack your bags and come home any time. But don't bring that brat with you. Send her back where she belongs.'

Meg could only stand speechless, impotent fury boiling inside her heart. How was it, she thought, that when good neighbours were treasured in this farming community, Lanky had to get saddled with Joe Turner?

Nothing would induce her to go back to live in her father's household. With or without Effie.

Though how they were going to manage without milk or cheese if he took the last two cows, Meg dare not think. But manage they would, somehow. She straightened her back, unconsciously lifting her chin a fraction. If this was their own private war, her father was on the winning side. But only for now. Things could change quickly in a war.

Meg went to the window and looked down the lane. The rain had stopped, thank goodness, and a thin sun was trying to break through. Jack would arrive soon and sort it all out.

Then she saw her father walk over to Connie Bradshaw and Meg's heart sank. What was he scheming now?

–

'Thee'll be wanting to clear the estate up quickly, I reckon,' Joe pointedly remarked.

Connie Bradshaw was a woman who bore a grudge against life. Unmarried until the age of thirty-five, she still nurtured a feeling that life had passed her by. She had met her husband, a travelling salesman in farm machinery, when he had unsuccessfully tried to sell her father a tractor. Against all the odds, Peter Bradshaw had taken a fancy to Connie's robust plainness and called at the farm again. Within a matter of weeks they were 'walking out' and in six months they had married. Connie had gladly moved to a smart house in Grange-Over-Sands with her new husband. She had never relished the state of chaos that had always clung to life at Broombank. She disliked dirty boots, feeding buckets in the kitchen and nights constantly disturbed by the inconvenience of tending messy animals. Her well-scrubbed semi-detached with its pretty garden was much more to her taste. Until she and Peter could change it for a new detached with a view of the estuary, that is.

While there would be no children from this late union, the two of them felt perfectly content, united by their ambition for a neat, ordered, comfortable life. The only problem lay in the paucity of Peter's salary. Hard as he worked, the monthly sum fell far short of their desires, if not their needs. It was unthinkable, naturally, for Connie to take employment. Now, with the inconvenience of war to make matters worse, the death of her father had opened up to them the very real possibility of a useful windfall.

'Mr Capstick, our family solicitor, will be attending to the will shortly.'

Joe touched his forelock respectfully. 'I've no wish to intrude upon your grief, Mrs Bradshaw,' he said, with suitable deference in his tone. 'But I should point out that Lanky owed me a deal of money. A sizeable sum in point of fact.' Joe handed her a sheet of paper which he had made Sally Ann write out for him the night before. It showed the sums Lanky had borrowed over the last several years during the slow decline of Broom-bank. The interest was also noted, and from the total he had deducted the value of eight cows, far below their true market value.

This was something of a shock to Connie and she stared at the paper, perplexed. 'I had no idea, Mr Turner, that my father was in debt.' The sum outstanding amounted to a few hundred pounds. Not a fortune, but even so, hard to find just now. She had no illusions about the poor value of much of her father's land, and the business had as good as died with him. But she still hoped that the farm as a whole, with the house, buildings, implements and stock, would surely sell for a few thousand pounds. She smiled brightly at Joe.

'Your debt will be settled, naturally, when the farm is sold, Mr Turner.'

Joe returned her smile, the words music to his ears. 'Then I hope, if it is a sale you are considering, Mrs Bradshaw, you will give me first refusal on the land. It has little value to anyone, excepting meself, being in close proximity to the high fell where I graze my sheep. Much of it is thin and don't grow grass well, and down in the dale, well…' Joe pulled a doleful face. 'Too damp, d'you see, for sheep.'

Connie Bradshaw's sparse powers of concentration were already wandering. She was anxious to see the back of these people and hear how much money her father had tucked away. Debt or no debt, he had always been thrifty so there must be something. She dismissed Joe Turner with a vague promise to talk again and moved across to Mr Capstick to instruct him to get a move on.

Jack arrived just as the family was sitting down with the solicitor around the kitchen table. Meg ran to him at once and hugged him. He looked so tanned and handsome in his sailor's uniform he quite took her breath away. She wanted to lean on him and drink in his warmth but he only kissed her briefly, his eyes going at once to Connie's disapproving glare.

'Sorry I'm late. The trains were all held up. Have I missed much?'

'Only your own father's funeral,' his sister said in frosty tones.

Mr Capstick cleared his throat. 'Perhaps we might get down to business.'

Meg sidled to the kitchen door, pushing Effie through it before her. 'We'll leave you to it then.'

'You'd better stay, Miss Turner,' said the solicitor. 'This concerns you too.'

If Connie's eyebrows had climbed any higher they would have taken off, thought Meg. Hiding her surprise, she instructed Effie to start clearing the cup and plates and not to make any noise about it. Then she closed the door and sat at one of the kitchen chairs, opposite Jack. He smiled reassuringly at her and she took a deep breath. He still loved her, she could tell. The only worry was how long they would now have to wait before it was fitting for them to marry and she could become a real part of his life.

The solicitor was reading a lot of legal jargon about appointed trustees and executors from a piece of paper he held in his hand. Meg could see Connie frowning and fidgeting with her gloves.

'Can we cut all these unnecessary preliminaries, Mr Capstick, and get to the point. We are well aware my father has left the farm in a dreadful state. What we want to know is its value and how quickly we can sell it.'

Sell? Meg looked across at Connie Bradshaw with shock in her eyes. How could such a thing even be considered? Broombank Farm had been in the Lawson family since the seventeenth century. To sell it was unthinkable. Lanky had loved this farm. It was his whole life. She wanted to shout against the sin of such an action, point out its great potential, the large amount of good intake land it owned, the tract of fell it owned outright, in addition to accessible free grazing on the higher fells not easily available to all farms. The woodlands and water. Then there was the house itself, a house Meg already loved, neglected as it might be. She wanted to live here with Jack, and make it into a home. She wanted to farm Broombank land and make it good. How dare Connie Bradshaw come along to Lanky's funeral after years of never bothering to call on him, and declare it must be sold?

Meg had been so busy with her rebellious thoughts that she had missed much of what was going on about her. But a loud squeak of anguished disbelief from Mrs Bradshaw brought her back to reality.

'*Option to purchase?* You cannot be serious. He must have gone mad. My father was senile, demented, that is quite clear. Or *she* has twisted him round her calculating little finger.'

Meg realised that everyone, including Jack, was glaring accusingly at her.

'It is true that Mr Lawson left no money to settle his debts but neither did he wish the farm to be sold.' Mr Capstick tapped the parchment in his hand. 'The will states quite clearly that he directs his trustees, that is, myself and my partner, to…'

'I'm well aware who you are, and a right pickle you've made of it an' all,' protested Connie forgetting her usual resolution to speak 'proper'.

'If you will permit me to continue?' Mr Capstick, unflustered by the pent-up emotion that vibrated about the table, attempted to explain more fully.

'The will states that the farm business, including all the stock, farm implements and machinery, harvested and growing crops, be left to Meg Turner. Mr Lawson seemed to think that his son was not particularly interested in the farm.'

All eyes turned to Jack, who flushed with embarrassment but said nothing.

'He goes on to say, "I direct that my trustees shall not exercise their power of sale until they have offered to the said Meg Turner an option to purchase the said Farm and Land within five years of my death at the price of one thousand five hundred pounds."'

'One thousand five hundred?' Connie's voice was little more than a squeak. 'You cannot be serious. It's worth two at least.'

Mr Capstick looked over his spectacles at her and understood perfectly, perhaps for the first time, why his client had arranged his affairs in just this way. 'The market is depressed at the present time, made worse by the war. Mr Lawson was most anxious that Miss Turner have a chance, as he put it, to try her hand at farming. He seemed to think it was what she wanted.'

'I'm sure it is.'

'Is it, Meg?' This from Jack, his voice full of hurt pride, curt and strangely bitter. 'Is this what you wanted all along? Broombank?'

Meg, who had sat in a daze through all of this, tried to focus her gaze upon him. She tried to see him as he had looked when he had first smiled at her and kissed her outside the village hall, when he had made love to her in the barn. But that all seemed so far away now that she could scarcely reconcile it with the deep, hardening planes of his beloved face. 'I – no, of course it wasn't. That is, I mean – I do want to farm but—'

'There, you see!' Connie stood up and slapped her hands down upon the table. The sound was so loud that Meg actually jumped. 'She has planned this from the start. Who knows what she persuaded my father to do, wheedling her way into his good graces, moving in to make herself at home by his fireside.'

Hot-cheeked, Meg faced her adversary with some spirit. 'He was ill. He needed looking after. Who else was there?'

The implication that Connie had neglected her duties to her own father stung, and she reacted badly. 'We're living in the twentieth century. You could have picked up a telephone, I suppose, and let me know how my father was.'

Subdued by this justifiable criticism, though it would have necessitated a walk of several miles to the Co-op where a phone was located, and knowing she'd been too busy looking for the lost Effie at the time to think of it, Meg mumbled an apology. 'It all happened so quickly. I ran to fetch the doctor to him, then thought he was on the mend. How was I to know that he – that he—'

Mr Capstick cut in quickly, seeing the welling of tears in her grey eyes, and anxious to keep trouble to a minimum. He attempted to dampen the heat of the atmosphere with a smile.

'Ladies, ladies, there is little point in going over old ground. I am sure Miss Turner did as she thought best in what must have been very difficult circumstances. For whatever reason, Mr Lawson felt he could not go on. Painful as it is, we must accept that fact and as his trustee it is my duty to see that his wishes are carried out to the letter.'

Silence fell, embarrassed and strained. Connie resumed her seat on persuasion, but with reluctance.

Meg, trying to come to grips with all the implications, was the first to break the silence. 'May I please ask a question?'

'Of course.'

'This option to purchase within five years. Does that mean that I can stay here in the meantime?'

'But of course.' Mr Capstick picked up the document again. 'I'm sorry, perhaps I haven't made it properly clear. Until the five years expire, or until you find the purchase price earlier than that date, you are permitted to lease the farm from the trustees. Mr Lawson has stated in his will that the rent must be two hundred pounds a year, payable on the usual quarter days. Your first payment, since this is October, will be on Christmas Day, which is the first quarter day following the date of his death.' He smiled at Meg. 'Do you think you can manage that?'

The rent was reasonable, no one could deny it, less than the going rate. But a quarter of two hundred – fifty pounds – in how long? Less than three months. Not a chance. 'Yes,' she said, nodding briskly. 'I can manage that.'

'He asked me to give you this.'

'What is it?'

The solicitor held out a coin. 'He said that you would understand.'

Meg took the coin and cradled it in her palm. 'It's a Luckpenny.' Her eyes filled with tears. 'He told me about the old Norse custom many times. It's to transfer one person's good will to another, and with it friendship. Always give something back, Lanky said.' She felt her heart swell with love and pride that he should have so much faith in her that he would leave her his beloved farm.

'Oh, I'll take good care of it, I will, I will,' she said.

'Good. Then everything is quite clear? You do understand the full responsibility facing you?'

Oh, yes, she understood perfectly. Taking in Jack's stunned expression and Connie's furious gaze, Meg understood that she had gained her long-held desire for a farm of her own, but very likely at the cost of something far more precious: Jack's trust.

'You shouldn't have done it. You didn't ought to have laid a finger on her.' Sally Ann spoke the words quietly as she walked with Joe and Dan back down the lane towards Ashlea.

'The little brat is bone idle. And wick with fleas.'

'No, she wasn't. We cleaned her up. Anyway, that was hardly her fault, was it?'

'Then I don't know whose fault it was.'

'Joe.' Sally Ann laid a hand upon his arm. 'You do realise that Meg will never forgive you for hurting Effie in that way? You'll be lucky if your daughter ever speaks to you again.'

'She just has. I told her she could come home but all she cares about is Lanky's Shorthorns.'

'And all you seem to care about is getting your hands on Broombank land. Why? What does it matter?'

'Happen I think there should be only one head to a family, and that's me. Besides which, our Dan reckons he's underpaid.'

Dan took interest at this point. 'Does that mean I'm to get a rise?'

'Oh, shut your face, you daft ha'porth.'

Sally Ann hooked a hand into Joe's arm and gave it a gentle squeeze. 'All you have to do is say you got a bit carried away and you're sorry for hurting the child.'

'Sorry?'

'Yes. Sorry.'

'You want me to apologise?'

Sally Ann turned to her husband who was doing his best not to become involved. 'Tell him, Dan. He only has you and me now, with Charlie gone off to war. He shouldn't alienate his only daughter.'

'Charlie shouldn't have gone. He knows Dad didn't want him to.'

'Aye, that's right. What good did fighting a war ever do, that's what I say.'

Sally Ann swallowed her vexation. 'I despair of you both, I do really. I know you care about Meg really, deep down. Why in heaven's name won't you ever show it?' And because Joe had not shrugged off the closeness of her arm and she sensed an uncertainty in him, well disguised by bravado, she dared to voice her concern a touch more precisely. 'Well, I'll tell you this, Joe Turner. You'll not touch a child of mine in that manner, when it comes. Not while there's breath in my body.'

Keen dark eyes turned upon her. 'Are you saying it's likely there'll be a child?'

'I might be.'

A moment's considering pause. 'Aye, well, thee will have a son. That's different.'

Meg could not deny that the news excited her. She nurtured the thrill of this news in her heart and couldn't wait for the time when Connie and her long-faced husband had departed and she could plead her case with Jack, persuade him to start planning properly.

But Mr and Mrs Bradshaw were relishing their little holiday, at someone else's expense, and in no hurry to depart. The family passed a difficult weekend together, Connie taking every opportunity to make snide remarks, openly scathing that Meg could ever hope to find fifty pounds for the first payment at Christmas.

'So that will put paid to your fanciful notions.' There was grim satisfaction in the tone and Peter nodded in agreement, as he usually did.

Meg was hard pressed at times to bite her tongue but compelled herself to manage it, for Jack's sake. She was too busy in any case for argument, since the days were filled with putting on kettles for the endless washing up following the gargantuan meals she was expected to produce.

'My father always kept a good table,' Connie had a fondness for remarking, though where she imagined the food was coming from she never seemed to wonder and certainly never enquired. Nor did Meg enlighten her. If it ever got back to Joe that he was temporarily supporting two households, Judgement Day would surely dawn early for them all.

The atmosphere was so chilled at times with Connie either finding fault with Meg or at loggerheads with her brother that Meg felt dizzy with the worry of it.

If only she could speak with Jack alone, and see that he was happy for her. It affected them both, didn't it? The war wouldn't last for ever. But all she could do was keep in the background as much as possible, even banishing little Effie to bed unreasonably early to avoid any danger of confrontation. And there was not a moment for Jack and Meg to have to themselves.

Chapter Thirteen

Monday morning at Broombank came in dank and cold. A mist clung to the upper reaches of Dundale Knott like wisps of hair round an old man's bald head. The mood in the farmhouse was equally grim. Though Connie and her husband were finally leaving, Jack too had announced he must be on his way and Meg volunteered to walk with him as far as the road, grabbing the first few precious moments for them to be together since the reading of the will.

'You don't believe I engineered all of this, do you?' she asked.

'I don't know what to think. One minute we're going to get married and start a new life together somewhere yet to be decided, the next you're setting yourself up as a farmer.'

He turned his face to hers and for a moment Meg looked into the eyes of a stranger. A cold shiver stroked the length of her spine but she shook it away, dismissing it as fancy. He was jealous, that was all, because there'd been nothing for his father to leave to him. She slipped her hand into his. It felt large and warm and strong, and she certainly had no intention of spoiling these last moments together in disagreement.

'Don't be cross, Jack. You know I always wanted to stay here. You like it too, deep down, or you would if you'd only give it a chance. You're just depressed, feeling left out of things because of the war. But can you blame Lanky for dealing with it in this way? You never said you wanted Broombank.'

'It doesn't greatly matter what I want at the moment, does it?' Jack said. 'There's talk of us going abroad soon.'

Meg stopped dead. 'Oh, Jack, why didn't you tell me? All this talk about me and Lanky and Broombank, and all the time you're going overseas, into the fighting. Oh, dear God.'

'Don't start. I'll be all right.'

Meg moved into his arms and Jack felt the warm pressure of her breasts against his chest. He slid his hands down over her small rump and pressed her closer. Drat Connie being there, they might have spent a much more pleasant night without his sister around with one ear cocked. He nuzzled into Meg's neck, relishing the sweet scent of her. He'd forgotten how tantalisingly feminine she was, not at all like the rough types who frequented the bars around the Pool at Liverpool.

'I'll get some leave before I go. Embarkation leave they call it. We can have a good time together then, eh?'

He moved his mouth to hers and teased open her lips, feeling her sigh against him. He didn't let the kiss go on too long though because he had a bus to catch.

Meg's eyes were shining up at him. 'Oh, that would be lovely. I wish we could get married before you go, but it wouldn't be proper, would it? So soon after the funeral.'

Panic came into his eyes but Meg was pressing her head against his chest so didn't notice. 'I don't know when we're going yet. It could be months. But anyway—'

'No, don't.' She pressed her fingertips to his lips when he might have said more. 'I understand you're going into danger. I know – that the worst might happen.' There was a catch in her throat. 'But I want to think that we at least had something, some time together, as man and wife. If they don't send you abroad for a few months, we could get married, couldn't we? Then we'd have known some happiness.' She stopped and swallowed carefully. 'I love you so much, Jack.'

He kissed her again and found himself sharing her rising excitement. It might not be such a bad idea. It might give him some hope for the future, to be married. Lots of his mates were doing it. Rushing in and marrying the first good-looking girl who crossed their path. Seemed to be all the rage. Meg would never let him have her again otherwise. He'd given up all hope, knowing that her Methodist upbringing and fear of her father were too strong in her. Sometimes he wondered what it was about her that made him want her so badly when there were any number of girls only too glad to have him.

'Let's think about it for a bit,' he said. 'You still wear my ring?'

'Oh, yes.' Meg held it out so they could both admire the sparkle. 'I wear it all the time.'

'Well, see that you do. Some of the lads have been let down by their girls back home already, playing about the minute they'd gone.'

Meg looked shocked. 'Oh, but that's dreadful. To cheat on somebody when they've gone off to fight a war. I would never do that to you, Jack.'

He hugged her close, enjoying the feel of her small body against his. 'See that you don't, or I'll make you sorry.' He bent his head and kissed her lips, nipping them with his teeth so that fire shot through to her belly, shaming her.

She pulled away a little, feeling flustered. 'Have you heard from Kath?' She linked her arm safely in his as they sauntered on.

'Not for ages.' Then as an afterthought, 'Well, I did get a postcard from Southport.'

'Southport?'

'Staying with an aunt, she said.'

'I do wish she'd write to me. What have I done? Why doesn't she write? Or do you think she sent me a postcard too and Father threw it away?'

'I wouldn't put it past him. Mean beggar.'

Meg considered. 'Southport isn't far from Liverpool, is it? I don't suppose you could call and see her? Find out what's wrong. Perhaps she's not well or something.' Meg held her breath as she waited for his reply. She missed Kath.

'What time do I get for going visiting?'

Meg sighed. 'I suppose not. Was there an address on this postcard?'

Jack shook his head. He didn't tell her what the message said, that Kath had asked him to call and see her. Made him feel a bit jumpy, though he couldn't rightly say why it should.

He pulled Meg into his arms. 'Stop worrying over Kath Ellis. She's probably married someone rich by now and forgotten all about us. Come here, let me show you what's really on my mind.'

Squealing with delight she let him chase her for a full hundred yards before she allowed him to catch her again. His kisses and his demanding hands upon her body more than quenched her worries over her old friend. How silly she was. Jack was right. Kath always came up smiling.

'Maybe I do like the idea of your waiting here for me, making a home. Maybe one day starting a family.'

Meg gasped. 'Oh, Jack. Really?'

The thought of going overseas thrilled and scared the hell out of him all at the same time. It might help to know Meg was here, a loving home to come back to. Who would buy the farm anyway, with a war on? It rankled a bit that his father had overlooked him in this way, yet it didn't surprise him.

But they didn't have to keep it for ever. Five years was a long time. The war would be over long before then and there was no possibility of Meg's finding the purchase price in any case. She'd be lucky to manage to pay the rent. After the war they could sell it at a good profit, give Connie her share and put all this nonsense of farming out of Meg's head. It would only take a baby or two to do the trick, and everything would be fine and dandy then. For now, he'd leave things just as they were.

It did not occur to him to ask if Meg was all right for money or if she needed anything. And Meg, being Meg, did not mention her need. He gave her one last lingering kiss.

'We'll give it twelve months, as we should in the circumstances, then see what we can do, eh?'

'Oh, Jack.' Meg squealed with delight and flung her arms about his neck while he spun her around, startling a flock of hedge sparrows into chaotic flight.

–

Meg was as near happy as she had been in a long while, not unaware that she had Lanky as much as Jack to thank for it. 'I'll make you proud of me, you'll see,' she said into the darkness that night as she snuggled down in bed, dazzled by her good fortune and terrified by it all at the same time.

She had no illusions about the amount of work involved but that didn't worry her. Meg had every faith that she could make a success of Broombank and restore it to its former glory. She certainly meant to try if only because it was something she could do on her own, to help Jack while he was away fighting. It would be her contribution to the war effort.

She tucked the Luckpenny beneath her pillow and with a smile still upon her soft lips, fell quickly asleep.

But there was little time for dreaming now. Dawn found her out in the farmyard, paper in hand, making an inventory. If she was to make a success of this business she must first work out its assets. What exactly did she own? She knew the acreage but had no idea how many sheep there were. Though she saw, with sinking heart, Joe had kept his threat and taken the two remaining cows.

She studied the barns. Only one was sound, the hay barn filled with this year's harvest, so she ignored that and examined the others. They were in a worse state of repair than she had feared. Some of them were cluttered with old rusting hand tools. She would need to check every item for its likely useful-ness, clean every fork, rake, pail and sickle. Mend what was broken, if she could. Fix the holes in the barn roofs, rebuild the miles of dry-stone walls that lined the land, count every bale of hay, and most important of all, check the well-being of every sheep.

She must talk to Effie. For a city child with a fear of animals this was hardly the best place to be. Life was going to be hard, no doubt about that. Effie had to be told what was involved and be allowed to make up her own mind about staying.

It was a subject Meg intended to raise over breakfast but the reality of their situation was brought sharply home to her before she got the chance.

'This is the last of the oats,' Effie announced. 'You'd best get some more.'

The last of the oats. Get more? How? She swallowed a sudden fear that constricted her throat, dipped her head so that Effie could not see the dawning horror in her face. 'Right,' she murmured, remembering her vow never to let the child go hungry again. But she had underestimated Effie.

'Mind you, there's plenty of cabbages round the back,' she said, pouring out a mug of black tea and passing it directly to Meg. 'The milk was sour.'

'Yes, I'll see about that,' said Meg vaguely, not quite sure how. 'Cabbages, you say?'

'Aye. A person can live on cabbages, if you have to. Surprising what you can do with a good cabbage if you set your mind to it, my mam says.'

'We don't have to live on cabbages,' Meg protested, quickly rejecting the very idea. 'We have eggs, the chickens if necessary, though admittedly we can't kill too many as we need them to lay and improve the flock. We have the sheep, but no lambs, of course, and we daren't slaughter any ewes right now as we need every one.'

Effie spooned porridge into her mouth and stared at her for a time in silence while she finished it, showing off her new table manners. 'So what do we eat fer our dinner?'

It was such a pertinent, commonsense question that it left Meg breathless. 'Is there nothing left from yesterday?' she asked, incredulous that so much food could disappear so quickly.

'With that lot going at it night and day? Not a crumb.'

Meg put down her spoon as her throat closed up, quite robbing her of appetite. Their situation was more dire than she'd bargained for. How very silly she'd been. Here she was starting on an inventory of farm implements and stock, excited at the prospect of running her own farm, and the reality was that she couldn't even feed the two of them for a day.

Most farms kept a pig. Lanky had been too sick to bother. Most kept ducks or turkeys to sell for Christmas. Lanky had sold his few ducks long since, and Meg had no money to buy fresh young birds. It was probably too late in any case. Most farms had at least one, and preferably two cows who kept them in milk, butter and cheese. Yet Joe had taken all of Lanky's.

As if on cue, she heard a voice calling her name in the yard. Meg and Effie exchanged a speaking glance.

'Keep my porridge warm. I shall need it later. I'll see what he wants.'

Before she could move from the table, the door was flung open and Dan's bulky presence filled the frame. 'I'm not stoppin', so no need to put the kettle on.'

Meg hadn't thought to do so. 'I'm always glad to see you, Dan,' she said quietly. 'But I'd appreciate it if you'd knock in future.'

'Knock?'

'On the door. This is an all female establishment. I'd appreciate it.' The sneer was back and his ears seemed to stick out further than usual as he grinned. 'Gettin' fussy, are you, now you 'ave a place of your own?'

'I just want our privacy respected, that's all.'

'Aye, well, that's as maybe. I only called to tell you that the debt's settled now, you'll be glad to hear. We've taken what's due to us.'

Meg was across the room in a second. 'What have you taken?'

'What's due to us. You can get on with trying to make a do out of this ramshackle hole.' Laughing as if he had made a joke, Dan turned to go.

Meg struggled against the rising heat behind her eyes which seemed to stop her seeing properly. 'What exactly have you taken?'

'It's all legal and above board. Don't look so shocked. You know very well that lawyer chap said as how we could. Well, like I said, it's all done with.'

'Tell me.' She leapt forward and grabbed his arm, feeling the broad muscles ripple beneath her hand as he instinctively flinched from her. Meg dropped her hand and again he grinned at her.

'All right, all right, if tha wants to know. We've taken a tup or two, and a portion of hay.' He looked beyond her to Effie who sat like stone at the great deal table. 'Is that your idea of a farm labourer? Well, I should say you'd be bound to make a fortune with that sort of brawn to help.' Throwing back his great head he laughed till he was forced to hold on to his aching sides.

The sound of his boots clomping across the farmyard cobbles echoed in Meg's ears long after he'd gone. Only when the silence rushed back at her did she run across to the hay barn and fling back the doors. It was completely empty. While she had been busy feeding Connie and her husband all weekend, her father and Dan had brought a horse and cart and robbed her of her winter feed.

Weeping never did anyone any good, Meg told herself crossly, rubbing her eyes red raw with her efforts to make the tears stop. The Herdwicks didn't do well on hay anyway and she no longer had any cows. But it was upsetting all the same for them just to come and take it. Every farmer likes to know he has a barn full of hay, just in case the weather turns bad and the grass is used up. But she'd manage. She wouldn't let this put her off. The farm could survive without a bit of hay.

The tups. Dan had said, *'We've taken a tup or two.'*

Meg ran till her sides were splitting, to the lower fell where she knew the rams had been enclosed. Her awful suspicions were correct. Lanky had kept at least half a dozen good strong rams. Now only two inexperienced young ones remained. Her shoulders slumped in despair. How could they survive now?

Though this was the quiet time of the year and the flock could largely tend to itself for a bit, within the next few weeks it would be time to gather the Herdwicks from the high fells and bring them down to be served by the tups. A portion of the lower fell was fenced off for this purpose since the good grass of the intake land must be protected for the weaker stock as winter progressed. Forty or fifty sheep would be put with each ram and Meg knew that it was a complicated task, necessitating careful markings of ram number and week served, so that it was clear which ewe would lamb in which week.

But without rams, there would be no tupping season. No seed would be sown for a crop of lambs next spring. She was finished before she had even started.

No rams, no money, no food, no cows, no small animals and no emergency feed for the sheep that she did have.

What had possessed her to think she could ever manage?

As she stood racked by the bitter wind and her own desolation on the bleak hillside, a small warm hand slipped quietly into hers. 'Yer not going to send me back, are yer?'

Meg looked down into the pinched features of little Effie. She had known this child for only a few short weeks and yet felt as if she had known her a lifetime. By Effie's side stood the devoted black and tan collie dog, loyally wanting always to be with them. If Rust ever left Meg's heels, which was rare, it was only because he felt it his duty to protect this small stranger he had taken to his big heart. Tongue lolling as usual, one brown ear erect while the black one lolled like his tongue, he gazed from one face to the other and waited patiently as if knowing a decision was about to be made.

'I don't eat much,' Effie continued earnestly. 'I know as how I med a fuss when I fust come – first come. But I like it now and I promise to be good and learn to speak proper and everything.'

She sought Rust's ear and nervously gave it a tug. The dog rubbed his face lovingly against her hand, eyes never leaving the child's face. 'I can work hard. I'm strong.' She flexed a skinny arm so fiercely that Meg would have laughed out loud had it not been unkind to do so. She knelt down beside the child and gathered her into her arms.

'Effie, I would love you to stay, really I would. But it won't work, do you see? We have no food and I have scarcely any stock. I know very little about sheep and nothing at all about managing a farm all by myself.'

'You could learn.'

Meg sighed and stared up at the dark specks as they moved over the tawny ridges, wondering how Lanky had managed all on his own. 'You see those ewes standing guard on their favourite crag?' Effie squinted in the direction she pointed. The size of these mountains made her feel smaller than ever, and she worried a bit that these same crags might drop down one of these days. But Meg said they'd been there since the ice age so why should they fall down now, onto her? And if Meg said they were safe, then they must be. 'You see they can easily become trapped on the narrow ledges in bad weather,' she was saying. 'Blown off in high winds or fall from simple panic. Lanky would climb down, agile as a monkey and rescue them with a rope and his own strength.'

'Can't you do that then?'

Meg gave an odd little laugh and shook her head. 'I thought I could but I don't have Lanky's agility, nor his strength. I don't have his knowledge or his expertise. I wish he was here now, Effie, to tell me what to do.'

A sense of awful inadequacy swamped her. Following the old man about on his daily tasks had taught her little about sheep farming, particularly since her mind had been too fully occupied with Jack at the time.

Her throat was growing tighter as she listed these very sensible reasons for giving up now, before she'd even started. 'I'm a woman, nowhere near strong enough to do all the jobs that need to be done.'

''Oo ses so?'

Meg smiled sadly. 'I do. Oh, I'm strong inside, and proud with it. But it takes more than inner strength to be a good farmer. You need long legs to walk the hills, and broad shoulders to lift the sheep and heavy stones and sacks. I don't know how to gather the tups so I can put rud on them, how to catch and mark the sheep, how to keep them safe all winter.' Her voice tailed away as her eyes moved over the smooth rounded foothills, the blue and white crags that hazed the horizon beyond. Tranquil as it appeared it was a hard land, unbending, a remorseless taskmaster. But she loved it all the same. Meg swallowed and blinked.

'We'd best go and see Mr Lipstock this afternoon. I'm sure there are plenty of other people who would love to have you stay.' Taking Effie's hand she started to walk down the hill but the child tugged her to a halt.

'Where will you go?' The dark brown eyes were burning into Meg's, beseeching, compelling her to find a better solution.

It was some moments before Meg could answer and the smile was more brave than convincing. 'Maybe I'll have to become an evacuee like you, and find someone to take me in too.'

'Can't we leave it till tomorrer? Goin' to Mr Lipstock, I mean.' And then as if anxious to clinch the matter, she continued, 'I've found some tatties an' all. We could have bubble and squeak fer us dinner.'

The small face, and the careful, rational appeal in the voice, so touched Meg that she burst into a peal of merry laughter. But only because if she hadn't laughed, she would have cried.

—

The next few days were the hardest Meg had ever spent in her life. She worked from first light to long past dark and still did not seem to get through half the amount of work needing to be done. She spent hours checking the sheep, mending walls, repairing the sheds, barns, fences and gates with odd bits of wood and rusty nails, pieces of netting or, when all else failed, bits of tatty string because when the sheep were brought down, she couldn't afford to lose any.

But she was only putting off the evil day. It was all a waste of time really.

As she worked, her mind gnawed away at her problems. If she had money she could hire tups. But she had no money. If she had no pride she could ask Joe for help. But she had far too much pride. There seemed to be no answer.

Effie proved herself surprisingly useful. If she had learned nothing of social graces and table manners in the slums of Manchester, she had certainly learned how to survive. Nor did she complain about the work. Her tiny, wiry body never stopped, the sound of her tuneless, high-pitched singing filling the dale.

She found and dug up quite a good store of potatoes and Meg taught her how to cover them with straw and soil in the darkness of an old shed, to keep them dark, dry and fresh.

'These'll last us all winter,' Effie said with pride and Meg tried to look happy about the prospect of living on cabbages and potatoes for months on end. Soon, too soon, the hens might stop laying. She would ask Sally Ann for some isinglass, then she could store some eggs in readiness for that dreaded day.

They picked blackberries from the hedgerows, filling their mouths till they were black, like young children out on a picnic. They even chopped down nettles and made soup. It tasted surprisingly good.

Each morning they would look at each other and Meg would say, 'We should go and see Mr Lipstock today.'

Effie would shake her head. 'Tomorrer.'

Meg had the feeling that by taking the little evacuee back she'd be somehow admitting failure. Something she would much rather not do.

But for all Effie's hard work and inventiveness it was a meagre diet, with too little protein and energy in it. How could a child grow strong on such fare? How could Meg do the work of a strong man on bubble and squeak?

And if she did not solve her problems soon, they would not be able to pay the rent at Christmas and then they would be homeless. The end of her dream, and Effie's peace.

But nothing got Effie down. To the child, this was paradise. One day she brought Meg's lunch up to Dundale Knott where she was working, and drew in great gulps of fresh air as if she could eat it. 'It's bonnie here, in't it? We're all right now, aren't we? We're managing.'

Meg paused in her labours of slashing back the bracken which, if left, would choke the much needed grass that fought for light beneath. Thankfully she sat down to drink the milkless tea and eat the cold potatoes. 'We still need to find rams, by November, to provide next year's crop of lambs, and the rent by Christmas. But apart from that, yes, I suppose we are managing so long as my family don't decide to try any further funny business.'

'Why should they?'

'Because my father likes to be top dog, always in control. He doesn't care to be bested by a mere woman.'

Effie snorted her disgust. 'Sounds like my mam's sort of fella.'

'He wants me to fail so that Connie can sell him this land. Then him and Dan can have it all to themselves and he can keep me in my place, by the kitchen sink.'

'Can't you talk to him, get him to leave you alone? He might lend you some money if you ask proper.'

'Over my dead body.'

'You'll have to talk to him some time or other. He's yer da,' said the too-practical child.

Meg gazed at her in astonishment. 'Don't you hate him for what he did to you?' The physical scars on the child's back were healing well but surely there would be mental ones too, harder to cure. To have suffered bruising abuse in her own home was one thing, to find the same treatment in the place offered as sanctuary was inhuman in Meg's opinion, and filled her with an odd kind of guilt, as if she were in some way responsible.

Effie shrugged. 'I've been belted afore. It dun't get to me, not the real me, d'yer see?' Fierce brown eyes looked up at Meg, dark as chocolate, like great melting pools in the white face. Meg did see. She understood perfectly. The child was showing more courage than herself, and was wise beyond her years. What you were inside could remain untouched, private and special. Not even Joe could quench her spirit, if she didn't let him.

Effie was right. She would have to make some sort of peace with her father, for Meg would need his help with the gather. The ewes needed to be brought down from the fells and given the autumn dip whether or not she found any tups for them, and she couldn't do that by herself. Nor could she risk not seeing Sally Ann or Charlie again.

But she still had to find solutions for all her other problems.

A voice shouted in the distance and they both looked up. Far below them, coming up the lane from Ashlea to Broombank, was a figure, waving an arm madly.

'Someone's coming,' said Effie.

Meg's heart leapt. Could it be Jack? Even as the hope came to her she rejected it. Hadn't he only just gone back? The figure had reached the farm door and was waving two arms and shouting up to them now.

Meg was on her feet, pulling Effie with her. 'Dear God, I think it's Charlie.' Then she was running down the hill with the wind behind her and joy in her heart.

Chapter Fourteen

Waiting in the farmyard was a young man dressed in RAF uniform, forage cap set at a killer angle just above his right ear, and a huge grin on his face.

Meg leapt at her brother to give him a big hug.

'I called at Ashlea first. They said you were up here. How? Why. Where's Lanky?'

'Weeks you've been gone and no more than a postcard,' Meg scolded.

Charlie had the grace to look sheepish. 'We've been drilling and square-bashing in Blackpool.'

'Landed on yer feet there then?' chipped in Effie.

'Effie, don't,' Meg protested but her eyes were merry with laughter. It was so good to have her favourite brother home.

While Meg told Charlie of Lanky's worsening illness which had driven the old man to take his own life, Effie went quietly into the house and put on the kettle. A sudden shaft of hot jealousy stabbed her young heart. It surprised her a bit how possessive she had come to feel about Meg and the farm, but she didn't want their private peace spoiled.

Privacy was a new phenomenon to Effie. She hadn't minded leaving the sewers of Salford, the squalor and overcrowding and the grunting of men and women doing unspeakable things to each other at all hours of day or night.

'There must be summat better in store for Euphemia Putman, that's what I allus thought,' she told Rust now as he stood patiently beside her while she watched the kettle, just as if he were going to enjoy a cup of tea himself. 'Me having such a grand name an' all.'

But she'd been sorry to leave her mam. Mam was special. A bit short tempered mind, but then who wouldn't be, as she said herself, with six brats and a man to feed? It wasn't always the same man, but a man there usually was. And another family too often sharing the same room so that between them they might manage to find the rent from time to time. Enough anyroad to stop them being evicted.

Now Effie could have a whole room to herself if she wanted it, not that she did. This great farmhouse had been a bit over-whelming at first with its lobbies and two staircases, any number of pantries and six great empty bedrooms. Effie still didn't want to sleep on her own but she liked being here, with Meg. She liked it in the evenings when they banked the fire up with holly and juniper and the rich tang of old oak, and the flames would rise, straight and true, up the dry stone circular chimney. Then they would snuggle up in the sheepskin on the big carver chair and Meg would tell her stories, just as if she was Effie's real mother. She missed her mam a lot but Meg had made it all right.

No, she didn't want nobody else here. Particularly if this one was anything like the rest of Meg's family.

Meg was bringing him into the house and they looked so happy together Effie's heart softened and she decided to be generous. This brother was in the war, so he wouldn't be stopping long. And he looked pleasant enough. Quite good-looking in fact.

'I'll peel some more potatoes for the soup,' she offered.

'Oh, yes, you must be hungry, Charlie. Worn out,' Meg said, all concern. 'Have you been travelling long?'

'Hours. If a train runs on time it can stop for no reason at all. Then you're stuck in the middle of nowhere with not the first idea where you are, even if you could see, which generally you can't because the journey has taken so long it's gone dark and there's only a daft blue light in the crowded carriage. I had to stand all the way. Don't know why I bothered making the effort.'

Meg pulled a face teasingly at him, filled with a surge of fresh optimism just seeing Charlie's cheery smile again. 'I'm glad you did.' It would be just like old times, she thought, as she hurried to liven up the fire. With them having fun and not caring a jot about the world outside.

Effie held out a steaming mug of tea, small dark eyes measuring, assessing. She was starting to like this tall man, so like her lovely Meg.

'We've no sugar nor milk so there's no point in asking for any.' She silently added there was precious little food either.

'Right,' said Charlie, and grinned, making Effie his slave for life. 'I've been having a great time, Meg.'

'I thought you were training?'

'We are. But we find time to go dancing.'

'Dancing?'

'In the Tower Ballroom.'

'Oh, you've time to dance then, if not send your sister postcards?'

He playfully punched her. 'All the dances were stopped at first, and the cinemas closed. But then they opened again and we all went along to celebrate. There's some pretty girls in Blackpool. I can tell you of one in particular.'

Meg hugged him. 'You're growing up too quickly, Charlie lad. Come on, sit down and drink your tea. You must be dropping on your feet. You'll stay, won't you? I'll take your things upstairs. We're not short of room here, that's one good thing. We've more bedrooms than we know what to do with. You don't know how glad I am to see you.'

—

The three of them were sitting down to a much-thinned potato and cabbage soup when there was a light tap on the door before it opened. 'Hallo. Anyone in?'

'Sally Ann!'

'Watch out. I'm carrying precious cargo. One of my best steak and game pies.'

Whoops of joy and it was hard to tell who was the most welcome, Sally Ann or the pie. The table was swiftly cleared of its odious soup and it took no time at all to demolish the delicious pie, succulent with meat and running with gravy.

'Oh God, that was good,' groaned Charlie, staggering from the table on exaggeratedly bent knees. 'I shall never move again.'

Effie brought the tea and they all stared at the milkless fluid in the cups and then at each other.

'We could go out to a pub,' Charlie declared. 'Father won't know.'

'How wicked,' Sally Ann said, but Meg was forced to remind them of Effie.

'We can't leave her here alone while we go off enjoying ourselves.'

'There's the potato and beetroot wine I made,' Effie suggested, eager to be a part of this delightful party. 'It's not that bad,' she protested as faces were pulled and lips sucked.

And after two or three glasses, it wasn't.

'Or else it's scoured all the taste buds off my tongue,' murmured Charlie, half asleep in the chair. 'God, it's good to be home. No, I'll correct that. It's good to be here with you Meg.'

Brother and sister exchanged knowing smiles. 'It's good to have you here.'

'Has Dad been causing any trouble?'

'Nothing I can't cope with. More wine?'

'I've tried to talk to him,' said Sally Ann. 'But he just says you should come home and bring your head down from the clouds. He thinks I need help, which is ridiculous. I can manage perfectly well.'

'He was saying something of the sort to me,' Charlie blithely added. 'I told him you couldn't be in two places at once, and that you had the right to pursue a dream if you'd a mind to,'

'Bless you.' But Meg's heart fluttered. Looking at Sally Ann, she did seem a bit washed out. 'You mustn't let him work you too hard.'

'Don't worry, I won't. You're the one with your work cut out.'

'Sal's right. How on earth are you going to manage here, on your own?'

Meg bounced to her feet, anxious not to go into it all right now. It was so lovely to have Charlie here, and Sally Ann too, she had no intention of bothering them with any of her problems.

'Mrs Lawson's old piano is in the other room. Let's have a singsong.'

'Can you play?' Sally Ann cried.

'Charlie can. Mum had one in the parlour for years at home. Come on, lad, give us a tune.'

'Right, you're on.'

That evening was the happiest that Meg could remember. Charlie thumped out song after song with more energy than accuracy but nobody minded. 'Kiss Me Goodnight', 'Little Brown Jug', 'Colonel Bogey', and a lively rendition of the 'Woodchopper's Ball', amongst others. They all sang their socks off, even young Effie who didn't know half the words. Later, Meg had them all in tears with a particularly moving rendition of 'Over the Rainbow'.

'Stand aside, Judy Garland,' murmured Charlie, grinning broadly. 'You've missed your vocation, Meg girl.'

Replete and happy, with Charlie tucked up in the best bedroom, Meg hugged him and gave him a kiss before turning out the lamp, just as she had always done when he was growing up. For all there was only two years between them, she was still his big sister, wasn't she? 'Go on, don't be so soft,' he laughed, pushing her away, but with the sort of expression on his face that told her he didn't mean it.

Meg knelt beside the bed, a patch of moonlight washing the bright colour from her face and hair. 'You will take care, won't you, Charlie? I couldn't bear—'

'Don't say it. It's bad luck to say it.' His face had gone white too with no help from the moon and she saw the extent of his bravery, covering up the raw fear beneath. She nodded, blinking away the tears.

'It's hard to think there's a war on out there. I forget sometimes.'

'You've got your own war to fight here. It'll take some doing.'

'I know. But I mean to try. Thanks for coming, anyway. You've been a real tonic for me, Charlie. Don't worry,' she quipped, 'only the good die young.' And ignoring his protests, planted another kiss on his cheek before going to her own bed.

–

Charlie left all too soon as he only had a forty-eight-hour pass. Meg consoled herself that it had been good to see he was well, though it was hard getting back to normality, and to potato and cabbage soup.

But a day or two later their luck seemed to have changed when Mrs Davies from Melgate called with a side of bacon.

'I hope you won't take offence by it, but your Charlie passed by our place the other day, on his way back, he said. Proper swank he looked in his new uniform, I must say. You'll be right proud of him, love.' She gave a soft smile. 'Anyroad, he happened to mention how you were a bit strapped for provisions like, Lanky not having kept any pigs this year. I should have thought of it myself. So I've fetched you a piece then you can take a shive off whenever you want.'

Meg gazed longingly at the huge, muslin-wrapped bacon that reposed behind the seat in Mrs Davies's old cart. 'It's very kind of you but I'm afraid we have no – I mean...' Meg swallowed her pride and met the older woman's kindly face with an embarrassed smile. 'I've no money to pay you for it.'

'Lord above, I don't want no money for it. I'm glad to be of use to you. We've more'n enough for our needs, Will and me. Even though we have a hired man and an evacuee to feed, we'll not go short.' She gazed sternly at Effie. 'You'll be sending her to school, I trust. How old is she? Nine? Ten?'

'About that,' said Meg, realising that until this moment she had never given a thought to school for Effie. But Mrs Davies was quite right. She should go.

'And church.'

It was not a question and Meg assured the good lady they would both be there, come Sunday. Well satisfied, Mrs Davies took tea, was shocked to find they had no milk and promised to look into the matter without delay.

Meg, worried that she meant to tackle Joe on the subject, urged her not to trouble. 'We can manage,' she assured her, but felt ashamed that she couldn't even offer the farmer's wife a scone or tea-cake by way of refreshment. As if divining the depth of the problem, Hetty Davies went on talking.

'You'd be doing me a service if you took some flour off me hands too. I don't know what William was thinking of to buy two sacks at once. Just because there's a war on there's no need to stock up for the duration already, I says to him.'

'Mrs Davies, you are an angel in sheep's clothing.' And they both laughed.

Meg's embarrassment washed away before the cheerfulness of her visitor. Mrs Davies had always been a kind neighbour and a stalwart of the local ladies' circle.

'Did Lanky keep a horse?' she wanted to know as she delicately sipped her tea.

'I'm afraid not.'

'Well, you're going to need one.'

'Why?'

'For the ploughing.' She looked into the blank face and sighed. 'Nay, don't tell me you haven't been taking in any news since you come up here?'

'I'm afraid we haven't seen a newspaper in weeks. Why, what's going on?'

'Only started a War Committee to tell us farmers what to do with our land, that's what. Got to plough up thousands of acres, and pretty quick too or you get in proper trouble.'

'Thousands of acres?'

Hetty Davies chuckled, making the flesh of her chin wobble alarmingly. 'Not you alone, Westmorland in general, I mean. I daresay someone will be calling to see you but in the meantime you'd best look out the likely land that'll take a plough. Not that there'll be much. We grow better stones up here than corn. I dare say Lanky has one rusting away somewhere. But if you don't want to have to do it by hand, you'd best find, beg or buy yourself a strong horse. And some labour to help you.'

'Labour?'

'Aye. You can't manage all this by yourself, now can you? Eeh, I remember the old hiring fair up at Ulverston. There'd be any number of farm girls and lads ready for taking on. Some of 'em had never been away from home before. Don't know whether it's still going on. I recall a grand fair in Staveley too when I were a girl. Only that was for sheep. Shepherds came from miles around. They'd pay us children a penny to block off the gateways so's they could channel the sheep into the right field. We'd do it gladly for there were stalls and sideshows, swings and roundabouts to enjoy, and hot pot suppers. Grand it were. Nothing like that these days. All gone now.' Swamped by nostalgia, the farmer's wife shook her head and sipped sadly at her tea.

Meg attempted to direct Mrs Davies back to this new information she was giving them.

'Do you think Mr Davies could give me a bit of instruction? With the ploughing, I mean. I can't afford labour. Nor a horse.' But the prospect of ploughing even an acre by hand was too daunting to contemplate.

'Eeh, course he would, lass. Be glad to.' A plump lady in her fifties who, as she said, had never been blessed with children of her own, Hetty Davies looked with compassion upon Meg. 'I'll see if Will can lend you our Arlott for a day or two. He's an old fell pony, bit of a clodhopper but reliable, not one for easy panicking.'

Meg's heart swelled with relief and thankfulness. 'I'd be most appreciative. There's just one more thing you could help me with.' The enquiring eyes were kind so she found the courage to continue. Clearing her throat, she began, 'I've found myself a bit short of rams this year. I wondered if...'

Mrs Davies stood up. 'Say no more. I'll send our Will round first thing. He'll see what you need and put you right.'

Satisfied with her good neighbourliness, Mrs Davies said her farewells and climbed stiffly back into her cart. Instructing a very plump pony to walk on, she clicked the reins at it for some moments before it finally deigned to lift its head from the sweet grass verge and obey.

'I'll see you at church then, come Sunday. Don't forget to put that child into school.'

Meg promised she would and waved goodbye, sighed with relief then danced a little jig of delight with Effie all around the kitchen.

'Bacon for tea. I'll find some eggs and we'll have a real feast. Oh, things are looking up.'

'Flour too, didn't she say? Oh joy! I never thought to be so grateful for such a basic substance. We can have dumplings and potato cakes, soda bread, all sorts of good things.'

Effie's small face was alight with the promise of satisfying the rumblings of her continuous hunger. 'Do that mean that I dun't have to go and see Mr Lipstock? Do that mean I can stay?'

Meg sobered at once and regarded the young girl before her, very seriously. 'If I say that you can, Effie, you have to realise that the work will be hard. It won't always be warm. Winter will come and we might get hungry again. We have a lot to learn with the sheep and we mustn't risk losing any. We'll have to go out in all weathers to look after them. This is a farm so we will get more and more animals, I hope, as time goes by. Perhaps even cows again one day. You will have to learn to like them or at least get used to them.'

Effie chewed on her bottom lip. 'Will I 'ave to milk 'em? Hold their tits and things?'

Meg smothered a giggle. 'Not if you don't want to. But if you don't milk, you'll at least have to help sweep out the muck and clean the byre. I know you're getting pretty good with the cooking but you will have to go to school, like Mrs Davies said. And church. If you live here, you have to become a proper part of the community.'

Effie would have agreed to stand on her head every morning if that was what it took to stay in this lovely place. 'I've never been to no school.'

Meg looked shocked. 'Then it's long past time you started. You'll also have to wash your face when I tell you to, instead of sneaking off and pretending that you've done it when really you haven't. You'll have to wear shoes instead of going barefoot. You'll need to learn to keep your clothes tidy and wash them regularly. And you'll have to get on with the village children, do your arithmetic and spelling and learn your scriptures, same as everyone else. Say please and thank you and no swearing. Do you think you can manage all of that?'

Effie gazed at Meg with her big dark eyes. She didn't quite know what half of these big words meant. But if Meg wanted her to do them, then she would find out how, and do it. Very solemnly, she nodded.

'I will, if you want me to.'

'That's settled then.'

They grinned at each other.

'It's going to be all right, Effie, you'll see. Hard work, painful, difficult, and no doubt loads of problems ahead, but we'll be all right. I know we will. Get slicing that bacon. I'm starving.'

The next day Effie came screaming into the kitchen as if the devil were on her tail. 'There's a man in the yard with two monsters.'

Meg glanced out the door then burst into laughter. 'You've a strange idea of what constitutes a monster.'

William Davies stood patiently waiting by the old yew chopping block. And two Shorthorn cows stood with equal patience by his side. 'Hetty said as how you were needing a couple,' he said by way of explanation. 'They're not me best by a long chalk but they still give good milk.'

When Meg asked about payment he shook his head with its white grizzled beard. 'See me right some time. When you get on your feet like.'

'That's very kind of you.' A shy man, unused to company, Will brushed her thanks aside, anxious to be off.

'I've put the flour and rice in the lean-to. Let me know when you want to borrow our Arlott for t'ploughing like, and I'll give you a quick lesson. We can sort out the tups you need to borrow when the time comes. Owt else you want, give me a shout.' And touching the neb of his cap he refused all refreshment and swiftly departed.

Buoyed up by the generous support of her neighbours, Meg rode into town on her bike that very afternoon to find out the details from the War Committee about ploughing and came back pink cheeked with the thrill of discovery.

'They'll pay a grant of two pounds an acre when the work's done. And there are more grants available for land draining.'

Effie looked blank. 'Is that good?'

'If we can do ten acres, that would be twenty pounds. Almost half the rent next quarter day.' Whether or not she had ten acres good enough to plough Meg had no idea, nor where the rest of the money was to come from. But her optimism was soaring.

Seth Barton from Cathra Crag stopped off a day or two later with five young goslings and half a dozen turkeys. 'I'm well stocked,' he said gruffly. 'They only need fattening up. Missus has sent a li'le bit of smoked macon.' This last proved to be a piece of mutton, smoked like bacon, delicious, and sufficient to feed them three months or more. Their winter was secure.

'You're very generous,' gasped Meg.

'Aye, well,' Seth explained. 'We were right fond of Lanky. It's good to see the old place working again, and, beggin' your pardon, we know help won't be forthcoming from Joe. He won't like the idea of you getting one over on him. You might do too well, and he won't like that, will he?' Seth went off chuckling, as if he'd cracked a joke.

They celebrated that night with a thick slice of fried macon and potatoes, followed by creamy rice pudding with a touch of homemade raspberry jam that Sally Ann had brought. Meg, who had never gone short of food in her entire life before, thought a king could not have eaten better. Effie knew it for a fact.

They fell into an easy routine. Meg found she could cope with the work so much better now that she wasn't troubled by the nagging pangs of hunger.

Effie worked hard in the garden, digging and weeding. 'Next spring we could grow onions and turnips and carrots,' she said, getting carried away with newfound enthusiasm.

Monday was to be her first day at school and she was not looking forward to it.

'You'll love it, just you see,' Meg assured her as they sat beside the fire together going over the day's events, as they so enjoyed doing. 'You'll make lots of new friends.'

'I dun't bloody want to go.'

'Effie! What have I told you about your language?'

She muttered a sulky apology. 'Who'll help you? Who'll make the dinner while I'm gone?' she protested.

'We'll make it together in the evening. It'll be all right, you'll see. You'll love school. I did. Miss Shaw taught me and you'll love her too, I promise.'

Effie looked astounded. 'Is she that old?'

'Go on, you cheeky tyke. For that, you can make the cocoa this evening.'

Without rancour, Effie happily obliged. Oh, yes, life was good. If only Jack were here, Meg thought, it would be perfect. A real family. Later, when she tucked Effie up, she sat on the edge of the bed and smoothed the sheets beneath the child's chin with a tender hand. She was growing at last, her cheeks were plumping out a little and glowing with the good food and fresh air she was enjoying. The purple bruises on her body were almost gone, showing as no more than yellow stains on the pale flesh. Meg felt she had achieved wonders in such a short time but there was still room for improvement.

'Do you need me to come with you on your first day? Only I'm pretty busy and—'

Effie made a scornful sound in her throat. 'I'm not daft.'

'Well, you can find the school yourself, can't you, now that I've shown you where it is? You won't get lost?' She meant, you won't run away, and they both knew it.

Effie shook her head very solemnly, then grinned her sudden, impish grin. 'You won't let my half of the bed to someone else, while I'm gone?'

'No, I won't do that.' They exchanged happy smiles.

Meg hoped that the discipline of school and regular contact with the other children would be good for Effie. She'd succumbed to regular washing, agreed to sit up to the table and hardly ever resorted to her more colourful words and phrases these days. But Meg had so little time to spend teaching her that she hoped some of the other children's finer points would rub off.

'I think it's all a waste of time,' said Effie, as if reading her thoughts. 'They'll never manage to teach me owt.' Secretly, the prospect excited her. Perhaps this was the start of her new life, her destiny. She might learn so much that one day she could get a job and earn real money of her own. Eeh, that would be grand. Then she could send some home to her mam.

Meg read her the *The Tales of Ivanhoe*, and Effie let her eyelids droop, enjoying the rhythm of Meg's voice while she played out her mother's joy and amazement in her mind.

Meg's mind too was elsewhere as she read. Oh, Jack, if only you could see how happy we are here at Broombank. She would write to him in a minute and tell him of all the improvements she'd made already, and about the generosity of her neighbours. She wondered when his embarkation leave would come. It seemed almost sinful to be so happy when he was waiting to be posted overseas.

The postman had brought her a postcard the other day. It showed a picture of the Liver building. It seemed so far away it might as well have been on the moon. The thought of Jack going even further away filled her with cold fear, when all she wanted him to do was write and say he was coming home so that they could be married.

When Effie was asleep Meg sat on by the fire, feeling very alone. Effie was good company but still a child. Sometimes Meg ached for another adult about the place. For Kath. What was she doing? Why hadn't she written? Too busy enjoying her new life no doubt. Oh, but it would be lovely to see her. Kath always helped put things into perspective.

I wonder what you're up to, lass? Some mischief I'll be bound.

Chapter Fifteen

Kath was having a hard time too, though in a different way, and Tam O'Cleary was her only friend. Had she not felt so very unwell and unlike herself she might have been tempted to take it beyond friendship for he was a good-looking man. But this was not the moment, nor Southport the place.

Already preparations for war were encroaching upon life, making it less comfortable. The horses rarely galloped along the sands now and men in uniform shouted at her sometimes when she walked along it, as if they expected Hitler to arrive in a boat at any minute and kill them all. Kath ignored them and took no notice of the sandbagging that was starting in earnest along the front, the barbed wire that was being unrolled. She didn't want to think about the war.

She had plans. As soon as the baby was born she would move on. When, how and where were still undecided for she knew it was not going to be easy. Aunt Ruby continued to watch her like a hawk. Kath told Tam as much one day as they sat in the sand dunes.

'You always think you're being watched.' His reply, as usual, was light hearted.

'You would too if you lived with that dragon. She sounds such a sweet dear, till you get to know her. Inside she's like a wire pan scrub just waiting to scratch you. Why my mother imagined it would be a rest cure staying with her sister, I can't imagine.'

'And what would you be doing here then, might a fellow ask? Why should a fine healthy girl such as yourself be in need of a rest cure?'

Kath met his shrewd, velvet gaze. 'Some people ask too many questions.'

Tam merely quirked his brow and looked out to sea, pretending to have lost interest. Kath let the silence hang till she could bear it no more.

'All right then, I'll tell you. I have to tell someone or I'll burst. I'm pregnant. There. What do you think of that?'

'The thought had crossed my mind.'

'*What?*'

'I hadn't noticed the glow about you that pregnant women are supposed to have. More a sense of tension. I take it you have no husband and no intention of getting one?'

'You take it correctly. I don't want to talk about it. All right?'

'All right by me.' Once more Tam O'Cleary addressed his full attention to the sea. It was miles out, no more than a thin line of silver on the horizon. They huddled deep in the sand dunes, trying to avoid the chill wind blowing through the marram grass. Kath shivered.

'Is that all you're going to say? Aren't you going to give me a lecture?'

'Nope.'

She fell into a thoughtful silence and after a while slanted a look at him. She hadn't known Thomas O'Cleary long but she had learned that he was an eminently unfussy person. Quiet, patient, usually keeping his opinions to himself. She liked that. Nor did he make any demands upon her. He hadn't even tried to hold her hand when they'd gone to the pictures the other night. She couldn't imagine that he didn't fancy her. He was simply a man a woman could trust. Not like Jack Lawson who had not bothered to turn up when she'd asked him to, nor written to say why.

'I can't stay at my aunt's for ever. I swear she's getting suspicious. I might move into a flat, if I could find a job.'

'Difficult to keep a job with a baby on the way, I would think. Unless you find someone sympathetic.' They both knew the impossibility of that.

Kath sighed. 'I suppose so.'

'What about your family? Can't they help?' Silence again.

'I take it you haven't yet informed them of this joyous news?' Kath was on her feet in a second. 'If you're just going to take the mickey…'

Tam grabbed her ankle to stop her running off. 'Don't fly off the handle. All right, it's got naught to do with me. But since you've told me the worst, I thought I might be allowed one or two questions.'

Kath sat down again but remained stubbornly mute.

'I'll start by telling you about myself, shall I? You know me name. I'm what you might call rootless. I came from Ireland originally and America more recently. I'll work for the British even if I won't fight for them. I'll turn me hand to anything but I prefer working on the land. In the summer I did vegetable picking in Ormskirk, and now I'm working at a local yard. Though heaven knows what the war will do to racing. I muck out mainly, but they're starting to trust me with the horses every once in a while, if not as often as I would like. There now, that wasn't so difficult. Now it's your turn.'

'Some things can't be talked of,' Kath said at last, in a very small voice. 'I just thought, there's a war coming, we could all be dead next year, so what the hell?'

'Did you love him?'

Kath paused a moment. 'I don't think so. Not sure I could love anybody. Mummy says I'm too selfish.' She smiled, rather ruefully.

He grinned at her. 'I cannot believe that to be true.'

'You don't know me. As for my family, let's just say that they would not approve. Bringing home an illegitimate baby would result in the "don't darken my door" routine. Mummy could never take the scandal. It would ruin her reputation at the Ladies' Circle.'

'And what about *your* reputation?'

Kath laughed. 'That's ruined already. I'll tell you about my best friend, Meg, instead.'

And so she did. About Meg and her young brother Charlie. About Ashlea and Broombank, Sally Ann and Dan. About swimming in Brockbarrow Tam and picnics on Kidsty Pike. She made no mention of Jack.

'Katherine Ellis, these sheets have not been ironed.'

Kath lifted her eyes to the ceiling at sound of the shocked tones and whispered a silent oath. Caught out, she turned to face her aunt's fury with her most winning smile. 'I've smoothed them well enough. No one will notice.'

'Don't try cutting corners with me, girl, I always notice.'

You would, you sharp-eyed old cow. 'I'm sure Mr Wilson won't. He very rarely sleeps in these days. He spends more time at his fiancée's house.' There was light hearted mischief in her tone but Aunt Ruby did not respond to it, putting on her shocked expression.

'I hope you are not judging my guests by your own standards?'

Kath became very still. 'What do you mean by that?'

Ruby sniffed and fingered the glass beads over her flat chest. 'You must know, my dear, that I have only your best interests at heart. Your mama would expect it of me. But I have to admit that I've seen you, walking along Lord Street with your young man.'

If Kath hadn't felt so annoyed at being very likely followed on her afternoon off, she might have laughed at her aunt's quaint way of speaking. She sounded very like a Victorian novel.

'He is not my young man.'

'Whatever he is, dear, you know nothing about him, now do you?' No man had ever looked twice at Ruby Nelson. Rosemary had been the pretty one with boys falling over themselves for her attention. It had rankled then and it still rankled now that some girls found it so easy to find a man. 'You have surely no wish to be accused of being...' Ruby coughed delicately. 'Loose is the word that springs to mind. That sort of behaviour does your reputation no good at all. Take my word for it.'

Kath's cheeks went pink. 'I'm not at all — loose, as you call it. And he isn't my young man. He's a friend. The only one I have here as a matter of fact.'

'You should find yourself a decent girl friend from a respectable family.' Ruby frowned. 'I'll speak to my neighbours. They may know of someone suitable.'

Kath stiffened. 'There's no need. I'm perfectly capable of choosing my own friends, thanks very much.'

'But are you?' Ruby wagged a finger at her niece, a chiding smile upon her face as if she were talking to a child with half a brain. 'Mark my words, such lewd behaviour will bring you to no good.'

Kath's cheeks burned with indignation. 'Lewd? Walking along a main shopping street?'

'People jump to conclusions.'

'Then they shouldn't.'

'All I am asking is that you behave with a little more discretion.'

What would the old cow say if she discovered Kath had already come to no good, or fallen, as she would no doubt call it? Having a child out of wedlock would be a sin beyond redemption in Ruby Nelson's eyes.

'I'll bear your advice in mind,' Kath said coldly, and wondered why she'd ever agreed to come to Southport.

'Splendid. Now strip those sheets off, like a good girl, and iron them properly before you put them back. Don't think I won't notice. Nothing slips past Madam Ruby, mark my words.'

If ironing sheets was a trial, washing them was worse. Kath had nightmares about the mangle. An old fashioned, turn-the-handle-if you-had-the-strength variety, Kath hated it with a venom.

Mummy had a new electric washing machine, a vacuum cleaner and a maid to operate these modern delights. Aunt Ruby, for all she had more sheets to wash, stuck to a dolly tub and posser. The mangle, with its vicious set of rollers, either stuck fast and chewed the sheets to ribbons or took your fingers with them. Every time Kath operated this equipment she felt exhausted for hours afterwards, and anxious over whether the effort would harm the baby. She might not want to keep the little mite herself but she wished it no harm.

Kath eased her aching back and suggested, quite politely, that Ruby might care to enter the twentieth century and buy a washing machine.

'It'd be much easier to manage than this old dolly tub.'

She saw at once that this small criticism of the way things were done at Southview Villas did not go down at all well.

'Electric washing machines are no substitute for good scrubbing, that's what I say.'

Since you don't have to do the scrubbing, but Kath wisely kept that thought to herself. 'Come to think of it, you could send all the linen to the laundry. That would save hours of work.' Particularly for me.

'It would cost a small fortune. Trouble with you young people today is you don't know when you're well off. I sometimes wonder why you stay, miss, since you seem to dislike it so much.'

There was a small silence, Kath for once at a loss for words. She couldn't tell the truth. Ruby would inform her mother without delay. She had recognised a malevolent streak in her aunt during the weeks she'd been here. She called it 'keeping up standards'. Kath recognised it as plain bloody mindedness.

'I like the sea air, and there are things going on here, at the Winter Gardens and the pictures. Then there's Liverpool quite close by. Westmorland is too boring for words.'

'Hm.' Ruby gravely considered her niece. 'Feeling better, are you then?'

'Better?'

'Your tummy upset passed?'

'Oh, y-yes. I'm fine.' Kath decided it would be politic to make no further complaints at present and started to fold the next sheet ready for the mangle. But Ruby was not one for letting things pass.

'You'd tell me if there was something wrong, wouldn't you, dear?'

'What could be wrong?' Hazel eyes opened wide with feigned innocence.

'I owe it my sister, your dear mother, to see that you are properly taken care of. You are young yet, Katherine, and could easily fall prey to all manner of unspeakable sins.'

Kath sucked in her cheeks. 'I'll do my best to manage not to.'

'I'm pleased to hear it. And should there be anything, anything at all on your mind, you must feel perfectly free to come and speak to me about it.'

Perhaps in view of this tricky conversation it was a touch reckless to allow herself to be lulled into saying what she did. But Kath had never been one to guard her tongue. She pushed back a damp lock of hair with a tired hand. 'If you want to know, I think it's time we had a bit more help around here. I don't see you doing much these days.'

'I *beg* your pardon? I am the proprietress.'

'I know, Aunt Ruby. But it's not fair to leave everything to me. The washing, the cleaning and the bed making. Even most of the cooking. I can't cope. Perhaps a young girl? Strong. Willing. I won't be able to manage this job much longer on my own.'

Glassy eyes surveyed her unblinkingly.

'I think we've had enough of willing girls around here.' And with this enigmatic statement, Aunt Ruby left the scullery.

The following Saturday Kath and Tam arrived back later than usual, having taken a bus into Liverpool to a dance. Tam had insisted on walking her home from the bus station.

'I don't want you accosted in the blackout, or falling down any holes. I heard tell of one man who rode his bike straight into a tree. He thought he was on the road, d'you see, but the pavements are so wide here in Southport, he was riding on the pavement instead. He bounced up so high he landed on a branch and it was morning before anyone found him and brought him down.'

Kath was holding her sides with laughter. 'What whoppers you do tell. It's true about Irishmen and the blarney stone.'

Since it was pleasant to be mildly cosseted by a man, even one who hadn't laid a finger on you, Kath was happy to let him walk her right to the door. They were still laughing, swinging along arm in arm as they rounded the corner, feeling young and happy, till Kath saw the lace curtain twitch in the front parlour window and the face of her aunt peering out.

Before she had time to lift the brass knocker the door was flung open. 'As I thought. This is what you get up to, is it, miss?'

Kath swallowed the first bitter retort that came to her lips and turned, smiling, to Tam. 'Thanks for seeing me safely back.' And just to prove that she was twenty years old, twenty-one on 3 December, and could do as she pleased, she rested her hands on Tam's wide shoulders and kissed him full upon the lips.

And with that little show of rebellion, sealed her fate.

The next morning Ruby was at her bedside a full twenty minutes before six-thirty, the usual time Kath was expected to rise and prepare breakfast.

'Get up and put on a decent frock. No lipstick or fancy combs in your hair. Plain and respectable, no more nor less.'

'Why? Is the king coming?'

'I'll take no lip, neither. I've had enough of your clever tongue, madam. Looking down your nose at me because I'm not so well placed as your darling mummy, and all the time walking the street with any Tom, Dick or Harry.' Gone was the smiling, social front her aunt usually adopted. Ruby reached down and stripped the covers from the bed while Kath still lay in it, still not properly awake.

'Here, what is this?'

'When you're dressed, finish stripping the bed and fold all the sheets. Then come straight to the kitchen. You can have a bit of breakfast before you go.'

'Go? Go where?'

'I've found you a job. You are to leave right away.'

Kath gasped. 'What kind of job?'

But Ruby, having reached the end of her tether so far as this little madam was concerned, had nothing more to say. She marched from the room, glass beads clinking with indignation, and Kath had no option but to do as she was bid, anticipation and the smallest degree of disquiet beating a dull pulse deep in her stomach.

Greenlawns showed not a speck of grass to mark its name before an austere, grey-stoned exterior. A tall, gabled house, much larger than Kath had expected, it stood on the outskirts of Liverpool. It had taken a long bus ride to reach it but Aunt Ruby had said the place was prepared to offer her work, so here she was, dressed in her best blue suit with tan shoes and bag to match.

Kath had read in a magazine that a girl should look bandbox smart if applying for work in a city establishment. She carried only one small attaché case, Ruby having promised to send on her luggage later, on the railway.

'If you like Liverpool so much, you can go and work in it,' her aunt had said, and Kath had quickly agreed.

'But how did you find out they wanted someone?'

'Her next door told me,' said Ruby vaguely. 'I've given them a ring and it's all fixed.'

It would certainly be an improvement on that dratted mangle and the constant changing of bed linen, Kath thought, not to mention all the vegetable peeling for the boarding house guests.

It was worth a try. A quiet clerical job would do fine. She saw herself sitting neatly at a typewriter. Not that she knew how to type, but she could soon learn. No need to mention her little 'difficulty', just wear a jacket all the time, or a loose blouse and a light corset. They wouldn't be too fussy anyway, not with a war on. She could buy a cheap ring from Woolworths in case it got to be a problem.

Then find herself good digs and enjoy city life. Just what the doctor ordered. She might even look up Jack. She should have come to Liverpool in the first place. Kath could see that now. There'd be loads of adoption societies around here. She felt quite optimistic.

Pulling the bell pull by the great iron gates Kath waited patiently for a woman to cross the tarmacadamed forecourt and open it. She was grey haired, about sixty, wearing a sour expression and a green wraparound overall. One of the workers, no doubt.

'Yes?'

'I have an appointment. To see Miss Blake.'

Green Paint not Greenlawns would be a more appropriate name, Kath decided as she was shown in to a small office which seemed to be thickly coated from stem to stern with the stuff. But she meant not to be put off by the appearance of the place, or the stern thinness of the woman who sat behind the wide desk. At four and a half months gone she couldn't afford to be too fussy. Work must be found. It was time to get herself sorted out.

The woman seemed to be all spectacles, long nose and thin lips. Owning herself to be the Miss Blake Kath had been detailed to find, she started to speak. Kath was so mesmerised by her lips which hardly seemed to move, that she missed most of what was said.

'...and such is the result of romance.'

'I beg your pardon?' It was that last word, romance, which had jolted Kath's wandering attention.

'It is our task to care for the feeble-minded.'

'Oh, is this a hospital?' Kath glanced about her. That explained the rather institutional, antiseptic feel to the place.

'No, not a hospital, more a kind of sanctuary.'

Kath smiled politely. 'I see.'

'It is our duty to protect people from themselves. Many are weak creatures, with little or no control. They fall by the wayside, overcome by their passions and used by merciless hands. It is our call in life to protect their physical and spiritual needs at all cost. We are not linked to any particular church but you will find that our aims are that of charity all the same.'

Kath was concentrating hard but still finding it difficult to follow where this long explanation was leading, being more anxious to learn about the job. 'I'm not sure that I...'

The woman had risen and was ringing a small tinkling handbell. 'You will be shown to your quarters and told of the daily routine and issued instructions on your work detail. You will find it in your own best interests to settle in as quickly as possible.'

'Of course, but – settle in? Am I expected to live here?' Kath too was on her feet, smoothing her gloves in her most ladylike manner. 'I'm not sure that I would wish to. I rather thought I'd find digs in town. Could you tell me a little about the work, so that I can judge whether it would suit? Is it clerical?'

The woman looked irritated, as if she were unused to being questioned. 'It might be. It might be anything. Whatever needs doing and you are instructed to do, you will do it. It is not your place to judge or make decisions.'

'I see.' Kath supposed that was the way of all employers, of whom she had no knowledge. 'And the pay?'

The woman's face went blank with shock. 'Pay?'

'My wages. What am I to be paid?'

'You are very lucky, child, that we do not charge you for the privilege of staying here. Though it is true that we depend upon goodwill for much of our income. However, Greenlawns was started by the Misses Harris, now sadly departed, in the early part of this century, for those girls less fortunate than themselves. They left a large trust fund to go with the property so we are largely independent.'

'Trust fund? Less fortunate? I'm afraid I don't understand. What is this place? Where am I for God's sake?' Kath was starting to feel a prickly heat all down her back.

Miss Blake looked slightly taken aback and then something very close to a smirk came over her glacial features. Ah, so that was the way of it. She had seen it many times before. A family no longer able to cope with a rebellious girl, not even able to discuss the delicate matter with her. So tragic, that weakness of character could split whole families apart. In the end they were forced to call upon Greenlawns, where people of note and respectability could safely rely upon complete discretion. Greenlawns had learned such delicate skills, along with many others needed in its work, over the years.

'You are, my dear, at Greenlawns Home for Wayward Girls.'

—

Effie sat huddled in the bushes. Rain was drizzling down but she paid no heed to it for her eyes were fixed upon the school. Square and squat, it was surrounded on three sides by a paved playground that seemed to teem with tiny bodies. All clean and well dressed.

Nobody had ever considered schooling necessary before. Certainly not Mam, nor any of her many 'lodgers'. There'd been no time for learning. It had been Effie's task to mind her younger brothers and sisters while Mam slept, so she was fit to go out at night, to work, she said. No wonder she was an expert at boiling spuds and cabbage, Effie thought.

Where her siblings went or what they got up to all day she couldn't rightly say. Nor, apart from Jessie, the youngest, whom she'd kept with her, did she rightly care. Effie only knew that if they stayed in the house and woke Mam and her boy friend there'd be one hell of a row. And Effie was always the one who got belted, not them.

Effie would spend hours standing on street corners begging, often getting enough to buy a stale barm cake and stave off the constant hunger. But as she'd grown older it'd got more complicated. Men seemed to think she should pay them in kind for their coin, which was not at all what she had in mind. Effie was no fool.

Then the evacuee ladies had come round. None of her brothers and sisters was keen, but Effie had scented escape and jumped at the chance.

So here she was, staying in this lovely place with Meg and eating regular meals now they had a full pantry to go at. If it meant putting up with queer monsters with things stuck under their bellies, and going to school, so be it. She was sure the sickness in her stomach would go in a minute.

Effie heard a bell clang but didn't emerge from behind the bush until all the children had lined up and started to march through the school door.

'And who is this?' Miss Shaw smiled down at her. 'It's Effie Putnam, isn't it?'

Effie nodded. 'Yes, miss,' she said, remembering what Meg had told her.

'Come along inside and I'll introduce you to everyone.'

Taking Effie's hand, she led her into a long room filled with wooden desks and laughing children. Above the teacher's high desk was a picture of Jesus. Effie guessed it was Him because he had a beard like in the Bible Meg had at Broombank. He had loads of children around his knee. The place seemed overrun with them too.

There were other pictures around the panelled walls, of children picnicking or playing with dolls. Things Effie had never done in her life. There was a big round clock with cardboard hands and a fire burning brightly in a corner grate, surrounded by a mesh fireguard on which hung an assortment of the children's hats and scarves, steaming in the heat.

'Take off your coat, Effie.'

She did so but didn't rightly know what to do with it so dropped it in a corner.

'There's a hook with your name on it in the cloakroom,' Miss Shaw told her.

Effie, heart pounding, went to look at the gummed squares stuck on the panelled walls. They might have been Greek for all the sense they made to her. A group of children, hanging up their own coats, started to giggle. Effie began to feel quite hot around her middle.

'Go on. Don't be shy,' said Miss Shaw kindly. And, never one to allow herself to look a fool, Effie thrust her coat on the first hook she could find.

A great guffaw of laughter erupted from behind. 'She's put it on John Buxton's hook, miss.'

'That's all right,' said Miss Shaw, looking suddenly concerned. 'We can sort it out later. Come along, Effie. You can sit next to Susan and Jeffrey. Quiet, children. This is Effie, our new evacuee.'

Silence fell and Effie was aware of all eyes drawn towards her, as if they'd never seen such a creature in their lives before. In a way they hadn't. Poor as these rural children were, they were scrupulously clean, secure in their little world, and knew what was what. Here, to their delight, was someone who didn't seem to know anything.

Effie began to feel hot and uncomfortable, sure that at any moment she would disgrace herself and pee down her legs. She glared back at them, scowling furiously.

All the girls were dressed in warm jerseys and neat wool skirts in blue, brown or check. They had socks and shoes, and ribbons in their hair. The boys had the same sort of jerseys which they wore over grey trousers that came to their knees. None of the clothes had holes in, as her own brothers and sisters had, though some sported patches on elbows, or neatly darned squares.

Embarrassment washed over her in a great scalding wave. Meg had done her best from a limited range of garments. She had shortened a navy blue skirt for her. Even so, Effie was aware that it swamped her skinny figure, and was so big at the waist that it had to be gathered in with a belt from an old mackintosh. Over the skirt she wore one of Sally Ann's old cardigans that had shrunk and felted in the wash. It hung unevenly over a thin cotton blouse that had several buttons missing which meant that if Effie pulled back her arms you could see bits of liberty bodice over her flat chest.

On her feet were a pair of clogs. Meg said they had once belonged to her brother, Charlie, when he was small. Effie had been proud of the clogs, for they made a grand clopping noise across the yard and she could make sparks with the iron bottoms on the stone cobs. Now she wriggled her bare toes within them and squirmed with agony.

Miss Shaw was staring at these items as if they offended her, and it was evident that her embarrassment was as deep as the child's. 'If we wear clogs to school, we usually leave them in the cloakroom.'

'I've got naught else to put on.'

'Haven't you brought any pumps, in a little bag, Effie? We'll be having country dance later and I'm sure you would like to join in.'

Effie shook her head. The only pumps she knew about stood in a back street, and you yanked the handle up and down to get water in your bucket.

She looked up into the teacher's kind, flushed face. Then at all the curious faces gathered about her. She could see the other girls in their smart jerseys, with their hands squeezed over their mouths to smother their laughter, the glee bright in their eyes. She hated them, instantly and intensely.

'I dun't like dancing. Anyroad, I'm not bloody stoppin' here.' Satisfied by the sensation she had caused, she turned and ran out of the room, sparking her clogs all across the school yard just to show how little she cared.

Chapter Sixteen

The dull days of November were upon Lakeland. The birches and wild cherries, sycamore and oak, stood naked with their feet in a mire of dead leaves. Only the red-barked yew and the tall spires of Norway Spruce stood green against the cloud dark sky. The deer had withdrawn to their winter quarters, the red squirrels were hibernating and most birds had followed the north-south axis of the dale and headed for warmer climes.

At Broombank, rain ran from the roof into the barrel and overflowed to swill over the slate paving stones and wash down the lane, soaking anyone who ventured out even for a moment. On this day Joe chose to call.

'Right then. Let's be having you. We've had enough of this nonsense.'

'What nonsense is that, Father?'

'Don't play games with me. Pack your bags and come home. Farming is a serious business, not for schoolgirls.'

Meg drew in a slow, deep breath. 'I'm not a schoolgirl. I'm twenty-one if you haven't noticed, and can please myself what I do.' Then, feeling a wash of compassion for him, standing on her doorstep stiff with pride, Meg reached out a hand. 'Why don't you let me show you round and tell you of my plans?'

'Plans!' Joe snorted. 'Selfish dreams more like. It's time you thought about someone else beside yourself for a change. Get your coat on. Sally Ann isn't well. We need you at home.'

'Oh no, what's wrong with her?' Meg was upset, filled with a sudden shaft of guilt to think Sally Ann might need her and she'd been too busy to notice.

'She's having a bairn and can't get through the work she normally does.'

Meg stiffened. 'That's all you want from your womenfolk isn't it? Work. Well, I'll call on Sal and see if there's anything I can do, but for her sake, not yours.'

He glared at her. 'Get along then.'

Meg didn't move. 'I'll call tomorrow.'

Joe looked as if he might drag her from her own doorstep there and then so furious was he at this show of stubbornness. 'You've gone soft in the head if you think you can manage this place on your own. And that lad o'yourn won't thank you. Why don't you do yourself, and him, a favour and let Mrs Bradshaw sell it like she wants to.'

'So you can have it for Dan?'

'He's a man. He needs his own place.'

'Then give him Ashlea.'

Unusually, Joe looked uncomfortable. 'Ashlea needs to be bigger if it's to keep us all.' On a sudden burst of anger he thrust a finger at her. 'And thee have it in your power to help us, your own family.'

'I'm sorry, I can't.' She stood in wretched misery, watching him storm away.

Every Saturday morning Meg and Effie stood the free farmer's market selling eggs, butter, milk, bundles of kindling and any number of cabbages.

Will Davies harnessed the reliable Arlott and went through twelve acres as if it were butter and Meg duly collected the grant of two pounds an acre. It was her job, assisted by Effie, to take off the stones and pull up the rushes and thistles first, a task that left them both speechless with exhaustion.

Will also brought down her sheep with his own autumn gather so that she didn't need to call upon her own family, which proved a relief in the circumstances. Not that she had many sheep to gather in, she discovered. Lanky's flock was in a very depleted state and building it up again would be her major concern.

She'd called on Sally Ann the day after Joe's visit, and regularly every Wednesday afternoon since. Her sister-in-law seemed a bit sickly, which she supposed was normal in this stage of the pregnancy. Meg could do little but offer moral support.

'I wish I could do more.'

'You have enough on your plate, Meg, I'm all right. I'll get Dan to help.'

'See that he does.'

Hetty Davies showed Meg how to pluck the geese and turkeys ready for market.

'Don't scald them,' she warned, 'or you'll have pink meat. Best to dry pluck for pure white meat. Takes a bit longer but it's worth it and you get a better price.'

And indeed they did. The remainder of the rent was raised by selling three of the fat geese and all the turkeys at one shilling and threepence a pound on Christmas Eve. A good price which pleased her. Meg paid her first quarter's rent with an immense sense of achievement.

One goose had been used as down payment to the Co-op shop on a new set of school clothes, boots, and the seemingly essential plimsolls or 'pumps' for Effie. The outfit had so delighted her that she had returned to school, head high, mouth grimly set. Meg had undertaken to give her extra reading lessons at home in the evenings.

The other goose was already in the bottom oven for their Christmas dinner which all her family were coming to share.

–

The fog on Christmas Day was so thick that visibility was down to thirty yards. Sally Ann was the first to arrive, feeling her way up the lane like a blind woman, bringing presents and the sad news that she had lost her baby.

'Broke Dan up it did. The baby would have been something of his own, you see, to love. But we'll try again, he says. We'll manage it next time.'

'Oh, Sally Ann, why didn't you let me know?' Meg hugged and kissed her sister-in-law and they wept together. 'Dan's right, for once. Sometimes it's nature's way if things aren't quite right. You're young and strong, there's no reason why you can't have a dozen babies if you've a mind to.'

'I know.' Sally Ann smiled bravely through her tears.

Then, because it was Christmas and they all needed cheering up, Meg insisted on bringing out some of Effie's potato and beetroot wine. 'It tastes awful but it's very potent, so who cares?'

She poured out three glasses and raised her own in a toast. 'Here's to the next time, and to an early peace.'

They all echoed the sentiment and drank.

'Lord, it gets worse,' gasped Meg, setting down her glass in a fit of coughing. 'What this girl will do to avoid milk.' And they all fell about laughing.

'What about Jack? Is he getting home for Christmas?'

Meg shook her head, eyes bright. 'I've had a lovely letter from him. But he says all leave has been cancelled while they take part in some special training exercise. He hopes to be home some time in the New Year. Oh, I can't wait to see him. It seems ages since he was home.'

'And Kath?'

A shadow crossed Meg's face. 'Haven't heard. I saw Mr Ellis in town and he gave me the address of her aunt's house in Southport. I've written a couple of times, but had no reply yet.'

'She might have moved on. Can't really see Kath staying too long in a place as quiet and genteel as Southport, can you?'

'No, probably moved to London and has all the fellas eating out of her hand. Jack says she's probably married someone rich by now, so hasn't time to think of writing letters.'

Sally Ann laughed. 'That sounds more like Kath.'

'Maybe I'll ask Mrs Ellis. She's bound to know, then I can write to her at her new place, wherever that might be. Meanwhile, come on, drink up, we've got work to do. You know how my dear father hates his dinner to be late. He will come, won't he?'

'He promised. I had a job persuading him, but he'll come, if only for the food.' Sally Ann glanced across at Effie who was whistling 'Jingle Bells' as she peeled potatoes, Rust by her side as usual. 'You've forgiven him, then, for what he did to Effie?'

A small thoughtful pause. How could anyone be forgiven for such a barbaric act? 'Let's say I've learned to live with it.'

Sally Ann nodded, understanding. 'She's looking well, little Effie, isn't she? But you'd best get that dog outside before the menfolk come or they'll think you've gone soft in the head.'

The jollity of Christmas was quickly quenched with the start of food rationing in the New Year and the announcement that the Ministry of Food was to become the sole buyer at fixed prices of all produce and fatstock, including pigs and lambs that went for slaughter. Meg wasn't sure whether this would be a good thing or not, but at least it offered a guaranteed market.

Although things seemed to be running fairly smoothly, her problems were far from over. In the spring she would have to plant corn and barley, potatoes and kale, as ordered by the War Committee. She would need to find the money some time next year to pay for the two cows that Will Davies had given her, buy tups in readiness for next year, or at least have the money to hire. She couldn't depend upon good neighbours indefinitely.

She'd been forced to borrow hay for the cows but next year she must try for a good harvest of her own. Meg also wanted to buy pigs and young turkeys, for it was important that they be as self-sufficient as possible. And there was still the problem of labour to be resolved. She didn't just want to take on anyone, not living here alone as they did.

But that was all in the future. For now she was thankful to be well fed and happy in her work. Effie was settling into school now that she looked the same as everybody else, and starting to learn her letters.

Then, best of all, Meg heard from Jack. He was staying for a few days at Connie's house in Grange. And would she come and spend a day there with him? Would she!

'What about the cows?'

'I'll get Mr Davies to do them for once,' Effie said. 'Oh, but how can I leave you here, all alone?'

'I'll be all right. I can stay with Sal, I don't mind. Go on, go and see him, you know you want to.'

1940

Chapter Seventeen

Meg was up hours before dawn to get all the necessary chores done, a lift to the bus stop in the Co-op van, a long cold bus ride, but it was all worth it. Now here she was wrapped warmly in Jack's arms, not noticing the bitter cold north wind that blew straight across the estuary into their shelter beneath the trees. Nothing would prise her from his arms.

His kisses were everything she could remember and Meg basked in her need of him. 'Oh, I wish I could stay here for ever like this.'

Jack tickled her ear with the tip of his tongue. 'It would get a mite draughty at night.'

'Stop it, you fool. You know what I mean.'

'I'm sorry Connie is so, well, you know, a bit funny with you. She'll come round, in time.'

'She's still mad about the farm, I suppose?'

'Mad as hell if you want to know. She thinks Dad should have left it to me, as his only son. She does have a point.'

Meg tucked herself inside his greatcoat, her arms tight about him, and giggled. 'Yes, but he knew you'd sell it, if left to your own devices, so he has in a way, hasn't he? Since we're going to be man and wife.'

'The farm would still be yours, whether we marry or not. Connie checked that out with Mr Capstick.'

'Oh.' Meg was silent for a moment. 'Does that bother you?'

'I can see why he did it. Never thought much of my efforts at farming. While with you, he thought the sun shone out of you. But I don't mean to be tied to farming all my life, whatever you say.'

Meg closed her mind to the warning in his words. She was too happy to be here, cuddled in his arms. 'Lanky was kind to me, and I loved him as if he were my own father.' She thought it politic to change the subject. 'Have you heard anything more about going abroad?'

Jack shook his head. 'I don't want to talk about the war. Or the farm. I get enough of all of that from Connie. Come here, let me warm my hands on you.' And he made her gasp in an agony of delight as he slid his cold hand beneath her jumper and over her breasts. When he put his mouth to hers, Meg forgot all about her worries about being accepted by his family, and about Jack's very natural jealousy over the ownership of Broombank. What did it matter? What did anything matter so long as they could be together, like this?

All too soon they went dutifully back to Connie's house for a cold tea of fish paste sandwiches and tinned peaches, then Jack walked her to the bus stop for her ride home.

This was to be Meg's last day out for some time as Broombank became locked into a hard, cold winter. Snow filled the leaden skies for days and weeks on end. It piled four and five feet thick against the walls of the farmhouse and smothered the hen arks so thoroughly that digging them out and making space for the hens to peck about became a back-breaking morning chore. Wads of glistening white snow lay so heavily upon the oldest barn roof that it finally gave up the battle and fell in.

'Let's be thankful we have other barns,' said Meg, determined not be cast down by this expensive catastrophe.

So many of the local quarrymen were called up that only the old men were left and the quarry had to be closed. Those who were able worked instead on the roads, shovelling the snow out of the narrow lanes only to have the fierce winds blow it all back in again the next day.

For weeks they'd seen not a living soul and even the little school had closed until the thaw. Their only source of contact with the outside world were the broadcasts on their battery wireless, listening to how the weather was creating nationwide misery, blocking roads, stopping trains, freezing lakes and rivers. It depressed everyone so much there was talk that there would be no end to the war, at least not until Hitler died.

Most of the time they sat in darkness, except for a wood fire, to save lamp fuel as the snow continued to fall relentlessly.

The sheep on the high fells would survive well enough but most of Meg's day was spent searching for those who wandered lower, digging them out of the huge drifts that piled against the dry stone walls. Wet through and exhausted much of the time, never had she been more thankful for the help of the dogs, particularly the faithful Rust, as they spent almost every waking hour walking the snow-laden fells together. She would push her crook deep into the drifts, the collies would sniff and roam about then suddenly start to bark with excitement or claw at the snow with their paws, nose pointing to the spot where a sheep was buried.

'Good dog,' Meg would say, and she and Effie would start to dig, pulling another half-senseless animal out from the depths to drag it on the sledge back down to the intake field where it could recover. Then they would climb back up the fells and start the search all over again.

If Meg got depressed she only had to listen to Churchill, who always managed to raise spirits, once by announcing the rescue of 300 British seamen from a German prison ship, the Altmark, in a Norwegian fjord. But it didn't last long. By March, Finland fell and complacency vanished.

But the snow finally melted into a cool spring, the waters gushed in the becks, and life became a little easier.

Effie was a willing worker for all she was only a skinny child, wanting to take an active part in the running of the farm. Once they spent an entire day building up one long wall over which the sheep kept jumping to reach the new green grass in the intake field.

'We must stop them getting in or we'll have none left for the new mothers and weaker lambs,' Meg said.

'Just look at that grey-faced one,' Effie pointed out. 'Hasn't missed a move we've made all morning. I wonder what she's thinking.'

'How she can reach this delectable meal.' Puffing for breath, Meg heaved yet another stone in place. The walls really were in a sorry state of repair.

At about three o'clock they stopped for a rest and a snack. 'Another two or three hours and we should be done,' Meg said, sighing with relief.

The words were no sooner out of her mouth than the grey-faced sheep Effie had pointed out earlier started to trot alongside the wall, seeming to sniff at it curiously.

'She's checking to see whether we've done a good job,' Effie chuckled, but the laughter faded as the sheep discovered the limits of their efforts, finding the next broken section they had still not mended and leapt over it with nonchalant ease. And where she went, her comrades quickly followed.

Meg jumped to her feet. 'Oh, no, now we have a dozen sheep to get out of the field before we can start the wall again. Oh, Effie, we shouldn't have stopped.'

But she was rolling on the ground with laughter, holding her aching sides, the tears sliding down her thin cheeks. 'You have to hand it to her, she's sharp that one. Who says sheep are stupid?'

Meg found herself laughing too. That was the good thing about Effie. She never let you take life too seriously.

It had been arranged for Broombank and Ashlea sheep to be brought down from the fells together. The sheep from both farms would be compacted into one moving, seething mass, and, following the whistled instructions of the shepherds, the dogs would drive them from the heaf down the incline to be closer to the farm where they could more easily be sorted and supervised at lambing time.

Meg had arrived early at Ashlea in good time for the gather, but Sally Ann seemed anxious to talk, for all it was scarcely four in the morning. The reason was soon made clear.

'I'm expecting again.'

'Oh, Sal, I'm so pleased.' Meg hugged her sister-in-law. 'You must take special care this time. I hope that brother of mine is looking after you.'

'Oh, he is, he is.' Sally Ann's eyes grew soft. 'He'll hardly let me lift a finger. Always telling me to sit down and put me feet up. He even washed up for me the other day.'

Meg's eyes grew wide. 'Is the end of the world nigh?' Both girls laughed and hugged each other.

'Is Dan ready for the gather?'

Sally Ann let out a heavy sigh. 'Joe insisted they leave earlier than usual, in case the weather should worsen. They set off an hour ago.'

'But they said I was to be here early, four at the latest, and I am. It's barely dawn.'

'You know what Joe's like when he gets an idea in his head.'

Meg uttered a silent oath. Now she would have to climb up the fells and find them all by herself. Trust her father to make things difficult. She'd so wanted to be fully involved, show her worth, on this her first gather. As she walked she gazed at the wilderness stretching ahead. At the lonely, empty fells where silence could be felt, like a presence. At the colours smudged together by a dampening morning drizzle, grey crags poking like dry bones through a green baize cloth. She loved this country, even when, like today, the sky was heavy with cloud and a thick swirl of mist was collecting on the tops. Only slightly paler than the rocky outcrops were the clusters of sheep compacted together by bright-eyed collies, without whose skill the task would be impossible.

It was not a good day for a gather.

'Will we call it off?' she asked her father when she finally achieved the top of Dundale Knott, leaning on a dry stone wall to catch her breath.

Joe and Dan had already made a start on collecting the ewes from the high fells.

'Not chickening out already, are we?'

Dan chuckled. 'She's happen wet and tired and didn't want to leave her bed.'

'Shepherds don't have time to sleep at lambing time, as she well knows,' Joe said, speaking about Meg as if she weren't standing right next to him.

She clenched her hands and forced herself not to react. Meg had promised Sally Ann she wouldn't fall out with her father and brother today. Besides, she couldn't bring down the sheep on her own. Trouble was, Joe knew that.

'What would you like me to do then?'

'Keep out o'road, that's what. I've told thee afore, shepherding is not for women. It's hard work.'

Meg smiled, holding fast to her patience, wanting so much to get it right. 'I'm not afraid of hard work, and I'm here now, so tell me what to do.' Still Joe ignored her, his eyes intent on the sheep. 'What's that young cur doing now?' He put a small flat whistle to his lips which he'd been forced to adopt since he got his false teeth. He gave two sharp blasts upon it. One dog shot smartly to the left and rounded up a few stragglers. 'Away by,' he shouted.

Meg watched, impressed, as Ashlea dogs went about their work with professional expertise. A fell dog needed to be strong and have considerable stamina as well as absolute obedience, for he could cover anything from thirty to forty miles in a day. He'd be soaked and muddied by the peat, snagged by the spikes of heather and bracken. The sheep would be quick to take advantage of any sign of weakness and it was not uncommon for a ewe to charge a dog and butt it if she thought she could get away with it, so a dog's personality too had to be strong.

Joe walked away and followed his sheep, leaving his daughter to the buffeting wind.

'I see you fetched yon dog,' said Dan, pointing his crook in the direction of Rust who was standing, legs foursquare beside her, eager to be off.

'I've brought three dogs, as you can see,' she said, closer to tears than she dared to admit.

'Aye. Is that the young daft one that Lanky gave you last year? Has he done a gather afore?'

'No, Will Davies brought the sheep down for me last backend, as you well know. But Rust is a good dog. He's ready for work. Strong, intelligent and quick-thinking, as he's supposed to be.' As I am, she wanted to add.

'Aye, well, I hope he doesn't take it into his head to run off home when the going gets tough, as his mistress seems keen to do.'

'He won't. Nor will I. We're both ready. Let's get on with it, shall we?'

As they set off walking together, Dan seemed to consider. 'Did you see Sally Ann?'

'Yes. She told me about the baby. I'm so pleased for her, Dan, and for you.' She put a hand on her brother's arm. 'Take care of her. Don't let Father bully her as he does me. Stand up to him for a change.'

For once Dan didn't argue but seemed seriously to consider what Meg was saying. 'He's not an easy man to defy.'

'I know, but it has to be done if we're to survive, and if Sally Ann is to stay well. He thinks he can dictate our lives to us and we mustn't let him. You're a married man now, Dan, with a wife and coming family to consider.'

'Try telling him that. It's all right for you, you have Broombank and can please yourself. I have only what he gives me.' The resentment in his tone was bitter.

'Let's get on with the job in hand, shall we?' Meg said, wishing to avoid an argument.

'Right, take your dogs round that knob. Remember, some of the ewes will be hiding in t'bracken. So see your dogs don't just slink about. They should speak up and tell you if they find one.'

'They will,' Meg assured him, feeling her confidence strengthening bit by bit as Dan issued his instructions. Even so her gaze took in the enormity of the task. All the sheep seemed to have disappeared, or were distant blobs on the horizon.

Tess and her son Ben were more used to Lanky's commands and were only slowly getting used to hers. Meg could only hope that she'd remember what the signals were that Lanky had taught her. She gave two quiet whistles and at once the dogs moved softly forward, eyes bright, ears alert. Meg's nervousness instantly began to ease. She could do it. She would show her father that a woman could make a good shepherd.

–

It had been a long, hard, wet day and Meg was dropping on her feet. The weather, if anything, had worsened. Grey clouds were lying heavily over the peaks, rolling slowly down after them, gobbling up the heaf almost faster than the sheep could move across it. The whistles seemed to come from all directions as the dogs gathered the flock ready for the main drive down.

One ewe broke away and Meg gave a slow rounded whistle. Rust, who hardly needed to wait for the signals now, got there almost before she'd made a sound.

'Good boy.' She liked to praise him, to show her appreciation. The sheep started to move forward with Rust at one side, Ben at the other and Tess behind, stalking them. Not too close, keeping wide.

The drive down was not as straightforward as she'd expected. Meg constantly had to urge the dogs to correct the wandering line as the animals persistently sought any gap to dash through. Sometimes a whole bunch would break free then a dog would be sent off to run wide and round them up to bring them back, adding miles to the journey.

Up, down, right, left, forward, stop, forward again. Sometimes Meg wondered if they were making any progress at all. But the challenge was fascinating, engrossing her completely.

Ahead of them in the valley below was the enclosure. Getting the sheep through the open gate and into the field would be the easiest part of the manoeuvre. The sheep knew well that the grass beyond was always better and more lush than that they'd left behind. They'd learned this when they were in-by at lambing time and never forgot it.

Meg stepped out purposefully, for she knew what needed to be done and was proud to be a part of it.

Afterwards there would be a soak in a hot tub and supper by a blazing fire. She felt exhilarated, alight with an inner glow at having accomplished so difficult a task. Her dogs had more than pulled their weight in gathering the ewes today. And Dan, perhaps even Joe, seemed to have accepted her as a useful part of the team which added to her sense of satisfaction. Of course Joe had shouted at her from time to time, and Dan had shown scant patience, but they hadn't packed her off home which she'd been half afraid they would do.

Then suddenly she saw it was all about to go wrong. She looked in dire danger of blotting her copy book good and proper.

Maybe she'd given the wrong signal, or perhaps Rust had been a touch over enthusiastic. Whatever the reason, he had three sheep pinned out on a ledge and there seemed no way of getting round him to fetch them on to safe ground. They stood hesitant, poised to run if Rust came at them too fast or made one wrong move. If they fell, they would slide down the lethally slippery slope of stony scree, bounce off jagged rocks and not stop till they reached the valley bottom, several hundred feet below.

Meg tried edging forward, but every time she moved the sheep panicked, compacted closer together and backed right to the lip of the precipice.

'Wait, boy. Steady, steady.'

She chewed on her lower lip, agonising over how best to deal with the problem. Meg could almost read the dog's thoughts, as frustrated as herself. High above them on the fells, coming closer every minute, were her father and Dan, ready to see her mistake and judge her.

A buzzard swept past, the wind whistling through its outstretched wings. Leave the sheep here too long and the crows and ravens would peck their eyes out where they stood.

Then suddenly Rust was away, running up the fellside away from the ledge. Meg watched him reach the top of the knob overlooking the crag where he stopped and lay down in the bracken. Following his lead, Meg moved quietly away too. Several achingly long moments later the sheep jostled each other, looked about them, then seeing the way was clear, darted forward, struggled through a narrow gap in the rocks and pelted off down the hillside to join their companions.

Meg laughed out loud. 'Well done, boy. Well done! You did it. You've taught me a lesson there.'

'Daft dog. Didn't I say you'd make nowt of him?' The figure of Dan loomed suddenly above them. 'Too eager. He could have killed them ewes.' And lashing out with his feet, he kicked at the dog. Rust yelped, failing to avoid the toe of that great boot.

'No!' Meg cried, and leapt forward just too late to stop Rust slithering right over the edge of the precipice.

–

Kath tugged at the sheet to drape it over the huge rollers, sweat pouring from her. Why had she ever complained about the old mangle at Southview Villas? The steaming hot rollers of this one were a thousand times worse.

Polly, who was the nearest she had to a friend at Greenlawns, urged caution, as always. 'Take your time. You can't hurry.'

Kath recklessly yanked at the wet sagging cloth which had wrapped itself into a proper tangle. 'Drat the thing.' But her efforts only made the situation worse.

There was the most terrible grinding sound as gears locked and then oil was spurting out, soaking a treacherous, sticky path over the white cloth.

Both girls struggled to free the fabric, glancing fearfully over their shoulders, anticipating trouble. They were not mistaken. Bearing down upon them came Miss Blake, her expression so sour you'd think she'd been sucking lemons.

'Don't say anything,' warned Polly. 'Leave it to me.'

Polly had been put in Greenlawns for stealing a loaf of bread. The fact that she had been starving at the time because her mother had abandoned her was not taken into account. She was fourteen years old and considered herself lucky that she hadn't been sent to prison. Kath had no such consolation. In her estimation she had done nothing wrong and it was perfectly ludicrous for her to be here at all. A Home for Wayward Girls indeed?

But then Polly was an exception. Most of the other girls were in Greenlawns for the same reason Kath was. Yet others, simply because they might become pregnant. Their crime, since that was how it was viewed, had been to 'entice' some young man into an 'immoral act', or even the threat of one.

At first she had protested vigorously at the very idea of Katherine Ellis, darling daughter of Larkrigg Hall, being incarcerated in such a place.

'There must be some mistake,' she'd said, over and over. 'There is absolutely no reason for my being here.' Not that anyone listened, and those that did only laughed.

'Do you mean that bump isn't a baby growing in your belly?' asked one particularly coarse warden, making even Kath blush.

'I don't see that has anything to do with you. I'm leaving this very minute.' But all the doors were locked. And remained so, morning and night.

'There's no way out, once you're in,' one old hag told her. 'I came in as a girl for the same reason you've been sent here. By my loving, caring family. Ashamed of me they were, as yours are of you. That was so long ago now I can scarcely remember when it was.'

Kath stared in horror at the grey bedraggled locks of hair and the wrinkled skin. 'I don't believe it. My family have no idea where I am. It's a mistake, I tell you. I thought I'd come here for a job.'

The old hag had cackled with laughter as if Kath had made a joke.

The most humiliating part had been the shockingly intimate examination she'd been subjected to on the day she was admitted. For venereal disease, the wardens had told her. If she'd been infected she wouldn't have been accepted. Kath had wondered since if that would have been so terrible.

Gradually her panic and temper were forced to subside as the awful reality that dear Aunt Ruby had known exactly what was wrong with her niece, and where she was sending her. But Kath refused to believe that her mother knew of her fate. Let alone her lovely, kind, adoring daddy. She refused to believe that they would ever condone locking her in such a place.

'I shall write home at once and they'll come for me, you'll see.'

She had indeed written, countless times. Rules permitted one letter home per week, though all were carefully vetted. Any sign of criticism and the letter was instantly destroyed. Kath made that mistake only once. The letter had been destroyed and she wasn't permitted to send any more for the next two weeks.

Nevertheless Christmas had come and gone, treated as any ordinary work day with no sign of a celebration. Up at six, work all day, watched the entire time by the sharp-eyed wardens. The midday meal taken at one. Stew, always stew. Half an hour was allowed for this followed by a walk around the cold yard then back to work. A similar walk was permitted in the evening but there was no hope of escape. The walls were high, the great iron gates kept permanently locked. Nobody outside knew what lay behind them, nor bothered to ask.

'This is as bad as a Victorian workhouse,' Kath protested, half in disbelief, half in fear.

'Aye,' Polly agreed. 'Only worse, because you generally died quicker in them days.'

January passed in an agony of bitter weather, getting colder as the snows filled the February skies, with still no sign of release, no reply to her letters. She was trapped, abandoned by those who claimed to love her, for the sin of carrying a child that would be born with the dreadful label of illegitimate, using one of the kinder words for it.

The pregnancy grew daily into a heavier burden.

To think that not so long ago she had refused Richard Harper and turned her nose up at the very idea of marrying Jack Lawson. The thought made Kath feel ill.

Sometimes, on a Sunday after church, they were permitted to read books. Kath had fallen upon this small pleasure with relief at first, until she found that so many sentences were blacked out, even whole pages removed, that the story was rendered senseless. Or they might be shown a film only to find that that too had been given the same treatment. The wardens considered some passages inflammatory to a young girl's passions, be it only a simple kiss or word of affection, they were obliterated.

Knitting socks for servicemen, chopping and tying up bundles of firewood and endless mending were the only recreations considered safe.

The regime at Greenlawns must, in Kath's hotly held opinion, be far worse than any soldier's at the front.

'What is it you've done this time, madam?' Miss Blake was eyeing the ruined fabric, glaring fiercely at Kath.

'Bit of an accident, Miss Blake,' explained the cheerful Polly. 'My fault, not hers.'

'Don't you argue with me, you little brat.'

'I didn't, I only said...'

'*Silence.*' Grabbing hold of the girl's arm, Blake twisted it painfully behind her back, making Polly gasp and sink to her knees. Tears filled the girl's eyes as the arm, looking as if it might come off if it were moved another half inch, was held in a merciless grip by Miss Blake, the familiar smirk upon her face.

'Very well, if you wish to take the blame, you can spend your recreation time this evening scrubbing that sheet until it is as white as snow. See that you show it to me before you go to bed. Is that clear? I'll teach you to recklessly ruin perfectly good linen.' She gave the arm a final tweak before dropping it. Polly fell to the ground on a low moan.

Kath was incensed. 'For God's sake, we don't finish work till gone eight and we have to eat the loathsome stew you give us after that. How will she have time to wash your damn sheet? It'll need to soak all night at least. It's stupid to expect otherwise.'

There was the most awful silence, the only sound that of the swish and grind of the rollers, the thump of wet fabric being scrubbed and beaten clean, scouring away the sins of the wicked, or so the girls were told.

Not a soul in the laundry glanced in their direction. No one moved to lift the sobbing Polly, whose arm hung at a dreadful angle. Kath understood everyone's desire not to get involved in case worse trouble should fall upon them, but it infuriated her all the same.

'What did you say, girl?'

'I said, leave her alone, you great bully,' Kath repeated, and pushed at Miss Blake with the flat of her two hands. Perhaps she used more force than she intended, or the woman's heels caught on something, but she fell backwards on to the giant rollers.

The hem of her skirt got caught between the chewing rollers, winding her in like a rag doll. The breadth of her flat hips soon brought it to a halt but not before the flailing fingers of her right hand had been crushed to pulp.

The machine was switched off instantly by a quick-thinking girl but Miss Blake's screams echoed on and on.

Kath was marched off into solitary confinement. She went quietly enough, her moment of rebellion spent, frightened by the consequences of her temper. There she remained for seven days and seven nights on nothing but bread and water.

The fingers, except for the tip of one which had to be removed, were saved, though they would never grip a girl's arm quite so savagely again, nor knit another pair of socks. Kath couldn't help but hope that the disability would be a constant reminder to Miss Blake of her lack of charity.

Polly was 'removed' to another home. Friendships were not encouraged in Greenlawns and Kath's days seemed longer as a result. By the end of March she was close to her time and exhausted. The callous treatment and the loss of Polly, the unrelieved treadmill of work, brought a grinding ache to her lower back which seemed never to leave her. The inadequate diet and the sense of hopelessness that permeated the place had quenched even Kath's sense of rebellion. And still there had been no letter from home.

She longed for the day when her baby would be born. 'Then I can leave,' she insisted, refusing to heed the dour words of the old hag, that there were a hundred other girls in Greenlawns who had already given birth and remained, for their own 'safety', locked up.

Their babies were sent for adoption or to the orphanage, name and identity quickly changed to avoid the lifetime's stigma that accompanied such a birth.

'That won't happen to me,' Kath insisted. 'My family will come for me any day. You'll see.'

She went into labour on a freezing morning at the end of March. 'I want Meg,' Kath cried as the full impact of the first pain seared its scorching path across her back. Nobody took the slightest notice. Miss Blake's leering face grinned down at her, her whining voice grating in Kath's ear.

'Don't waste any sympathy on this one. Hard-hearted little madam she is, and a troublemaker to boot.'

They put her in an empty room and left her to get on with it.

—

Tam O'Cleary was not normally one to make a fuss, let alone get involved with other people. He'd left a perfectly good home at the age of sixteen when he'd realised that America was not the land of milk and honey his family had hoped for. An Irishman living in the Bronx in New York did not have an easy time of it. Tam didn't want to struggle, as his father had done for years, trying to find work to feed a growing family. Besides, much as Tam loved his family, and there was no doubt that he did, every last one of them, he was young and could feel the blood pulsing through his veins, telling him to get out there and discover whatever there was to be discovered about life.

He'd packed his bags and gone off to seek his own fortune, not wishing to be a burden to anyone.

Since then he'd had more jobs than he cared to count, spent years exploring Europe at a time when it was safe to do so. Considered himself, at twenty-seven, a man of reasonable intelligence, a raconteur and wit even, on his better days. He'd come to enjoy his footloose existence and considered possessions and people an unnecessary encumbrance. Keep himself to himself, that was Tam O'Cleary's motto.

Hadn't he once tried to save a fellow traveller from certain death as he'd hung over the edge of a schooner? Only to have the man beat the living daylights out of him for his trouble. How was Tam to know the man had wanted to die anyway because of some broken love affair? People. You never knew where you were with them, unlike horses.

He'd nursed two broken ribs and a sore jaw for weeks as a result of that good deed, and vowed never to be involved in other people's problems ever again.

Nor was wartime the moment to change that philosophy. He was Irish. His old country, and his new, were both neutral, and that was the way he liked to live his life, safe behind a screen of neutrality.

Yet here he was, breaking all those principles, over one young girl. Katherine Ellis was not even his type, and he'd known her only a few weeks. Yet he couldn't help thinking how his own mother would react if Mary or Jo or Sarah got into similar trouble. She'd open her heart and her home to them with no recriminations. Tam believed that Kath's family had failed her when she needed them most.

So how could he, her only friend, fail her too? He knocked again, louder this time.

It was the thought of that unwanted baby she carried, and the fact that she had disappeared, without warning, without even a goodbye. He'd thought nothing of it at first, but as the weeks passed by it had struck him as odd. He was not the melodramatic sort, never had been. But Katherine Ellis seemed to have vanished off the face of the earth.

For no reason he could justify to himself, he started hanging about outside Southview Villas, and seen no sign of her. Now, quite against his better judgement, he'd walked up the scrubbed path and lifted the polished door knocker.

A plain-faced girl of about fifteen came to the door. He raised his cap.

'Good morning to ye. I wonder if I could be speaking with Miss Ellis? The name is O'Cleary, would you tell her?'

'Miss Who?'

'Ellis.'

'I'll have to ask Madam. Wait here.' So saying, the girl closed the door in his face and Tam was forced to kick his heels and wait. When the girl came back she was again alone. 'The mistress says as how Miss Ellis is no longer with us.'

'No longer with you? Lord above!'

The round cheeks flushed scarlet. 'Oh no, I don't mean that. The mistress says she's gone, that's all.'

'Gone? Gone where? Home?'

'Ooh, I wouldn't know.'

'I'd be obliged if you'd ask.'

'Ooh, I can't do that.' And she again closed the door.

Tam walked away. He'd try again mebbe, in a day or two. Or mebbe not. What a fool I am to be worrying over her. 'She'll have gone home to her mammy and daddy, you great soft ejit. Hasn't she the right to go where she pleases, if she has a mind, without consultation with you?' He muttered to himself, determined to put the matter out of his mind forthwith.

When the next pain came Kath was certain she was about to die. The world seemed to be swamped by it. The pain lashed itself around her back and plunged down into her groin as if a devil was dragging all the innards from her body. If she survived this ordeal, she thought, gasping for breath, she could survive anything.

When the wave eased for a moment, she tried to sit up. Maybe if she walked about a bit. She struggled from the bed and started to pace the room, but soon found the pain returning. A mile or more from the bed, Kath clung to a nearby washbasin. It was so loosely attached to the wall the thought flashed through her mind that she was not the first girl to cling to it as if it were a life support.

Back on the bed she vowed never to leave it again, but that didn't help either. In the end all her inhibitions deserted her and she screamed.

'Now we'll have none of that,' warned the stern-faced woman who bustled in, deputed to care for her in the last throes of labour. 'We don't want you frightening the other young girls.'

Those who have still to go through this terrible torture, Kath thought.

'Keep moving, and keep quiet.'

Walking, standing, sitting, lying. Now clinging to the bed rail, now kneeling on the floor, now desperately trying, and failing, to find the energy to will the pain away. Kath longed for darkness, for insensibility, for someone to tear this wicked blockage from her. She didn't care how, but it had to be done.

'Lie down, lie down now,' the voice urged. 'Time to push.'

You have to be joking, Kath thought, too exhausted to move.

A white face floated above her as if in a mist. Every muscle and nerve in her body strained against the pain. She would lose this battle, she would, if somebody didn't make it stop.

'I-I c-can't do it,' she tried to protest, shaking her head. Couldn't the woman see that she needed to rest for a while first? How could she summon up the effort necessary for pushing a child out of a body that was already weak and exhausted from overwork. 'Let me rest. Let me alone.'

The woman, Dorothy Parkins, was not without compassion. She had seen too many girls in this situation to break her heart over them, but she cared nonetheless, and this one was well bred by the looks of her, beautiful probably at one time. Dorothy blamed society for its callous treatment of girls 'in trouble'. For all this was the twentieth century, the poor creatures were outcasts just as surely as if old Queen Victoria herself were still upon the throne. Where was the girl's family when she needed them? Hiding behind a veneer of respectability, no doubt, terrified a neighbour might discover that their precious darling had 'fallen'. Places like Greenlawns were left to pick up the pieces.

'Don't talk foolish, girl. Push. I can see its head. Come on, Katherine, push!'

Perhaps it was this use of her given name, the one her mother used for her, that gave Kath the energy needed for one last essential effort. She shouted some obscenity as the world burst apart and a wet, slithering mass was sucked from her body, followed by a gush of warm liquid that ran over her legs and soaked the bed.

'I've wet myself,' she cried, shamed. 'Like a child.'

Then she was crying and laughing all at the same time. The tiny blue and red streaked object that was laid across her stomach was crying too.

'It's a girl. You have a fine, healthy daughter.'

The woman was cutting the cord that attached the baby to her, paddling a flat palm into Kath's juddering belly to make the afterbirth come. Kath reached down and stroked the soft dark down of surprisingly glossy curls on the baby's head with one tentative finger. She could feel a pulse beating and the reality of this new life she had brought into the world suddenly astounded her.

'Is she all right?'

'Perfect,' said Dorothy. The door opened and Miss Blake swooped in. 'Are we done yet?'

'Just about.'

'Good.'

Wrapping the baby quickly in a towel, Miss Blake tucked the child under her arm.

'My baby!' Kath cried. 'I want my baby.'

Miss Blake looked down her thin nose and handed the child over to the other woman. 'Don't be foolish, girl. It would do no good to hold her.'

Kath leaned up on her elbow, trying to catch a glimpse of the child. 'I suppose not.' The cries had stilled as the woman rocked her and Kath felt a sudden urge to be the one to soothe her own child. 'But she is *my* daughter.'

'Not for long. Think of this as the end of a problem and the beginning of redemption. You will be washed and fed shortly,' said Miss Blake coldly. 'Then get a good night's sleep. I shall expect you back at work first thing in the morning.'

Kath gasped. 'So soon?' This was to be Miss Blake's revenge, was it? Treated worse than a cow that had calved. 'Can't I even feed her?'

As Miss Blake strode from the room, Dorothy smiled sympathetically at Kath, cuddling the baby close.

'It's best if you put her from your mind. Don't think about the baby. That's the only way. I'll give you something to make the milk go away.'

Not think about her. Kath sank back upon the bed. Perhaps it was the intense tiredness she felt that made the tears roll down her cheeks. It wasn't as if she'd ever wanted to keep the child. She'd given no proper thought to the baby itself in these long painful months, only to her own survival. Now that it was born, Kath knew she should feel relief. Soon she would be free, out in the fresh bright spring morning.

'I'll be back in a minute to clean you up, then you can sleep,' Dorothy told her, bustling away.

The door was almost closed when Kath called out, 'Her name is Melissa.'

–

'I was wondering if you had a room to let?' Tam O'Cleary was again standing on the doorstep of Southview Villas, smiling down into the dreaded Aunt Ruby's face with all the Celtic charm he could so easily muster, when he had a mind to. She was quite unmoved.

'I'm afraid I do not take in young men, particularly strangers.'

'I assure you I am perfectly respectable and can provide references.'

She remained unconvinced but Tam persisted. 'My employer will vouch for me. I worked for a time on the Kilgerran Estate. You could ring there.' Once he knew that Kath and the baby were safe, he'd be content. Until then… He smiled at the look of keen interest that came into the watching eyes.

'Lord Kilgerran, you say?'

'In Southern Ireland.'

'You don't sound very Irish.'

'I've spent a good deal of time in America but I'm told we southerners have a softer lilt to our tongue.' He thought for a moment that he had won but the eyes narrowed and she stepped closer.

'I've seen you before, haven't I?'

'Now I'm sure I'd be remembering if you had.' Tam took an instinctive step back, but it was too late. He saw the recognition dawn in her eyes.

'You're that friend of my niece, aren't you? The one that's been hanging about week after week. Well, she's gone, so be off with you. I'll not be pestered by Irish scum here. Lord Kilgerran my eye!' She waved a fist at Tam. 'And if you come round here again, I'll set the police on you.' The echo of the door slamming sounded all along the street.

But if Ruby Nelson thought that would be the end of the matter, she'd mistaken her man. Tam thought that had she invited him in and chatted with him in a respectable fashion, told him some tale to satisfy his curiosity, he would have smiled and nodded politely and gone on his way. Instead, she'd succeeded in annoying and insulting him. Tam did not take kindly to either.

'So, you old dragon,' he said to the closed door. 'You think to ignore me, do you? Well, there's more ways than one of cracking a nut than stamping on it. I'll crack the mystery of this one, be sure if I don't.'

He spun on his heel and strode off in the direction of the sea and the stable yard where he worked. He'd collect the money that was owed him, pack his belongings, then he'd be off to Westmorland and see what he could discover there. He could remember the descriptions and details that Kath had given him. That would do for a start. Oh, yes, he'd find the answer to this puzzle, Aunt Ruby or no Aunt Ruby. For all he knew, she might have tipped the girl into the River Mersey.

Meg pushed open the solid oak door and stumbled into her own kitchen, already calling out to Effie when she was confronted

264

by the broad back of a man. Her heart leapt into her throat until she saw he was not Jack.

The stranger sitting at the table was laughing at something Effie had said. But where Jack's hair was near black, the dark mahogany of this man's glinted red in the light from the Tilly lamp and when he turned his face towards her at the sound of the opening door it wasn't the violet of Jack's eyes that met hers, but the softest moss green. To her shame she flushed, for as he offered her a smile Meg was for some reason reminded that under all of her wet clothing, the mud and the grime, she was still a woman.

Effie was beside her in a moment. 'Oh, Meg, you're soaking wet through. Let me take your coat.'

Meg tried to form her lips into the word, the one word that echoed in her head, but for some reason they seemed paralysed with the shock and cold, even as her teeth wouldn't stop knocking against each other. The sound of Rust's body scraping and bouncing over the rough stones of the scree still rang in her ears. She'd been shaking as she faced her brother, the rage in her running so hard and fast and furious that had she possessed the strength she would have kicked him off the crag too, right after her lovely dog.

'I never meant him to go over. He shouldn't have jumped the wrong away,' Dan had shouted at her.

Meg couldn't believe what she was hearing. 'Don't try to lie your way out of this, or blame the dog. You kicked him. Why must you always try to appear tough? Isn't one bully in the family enough?'

Dan had put on his sulky look. 'He'll come home with his tail between his legs tomorrow.'

'If he comes home at all,' she'd shouted, beside herself with rage. Meg refused to even consider that Rust might be dead. He must be found, and quickly. A night out on the fells and he would be.

Now she finally found the words. 'It's Rust. I need a rope.' Then her knees buckled beneath her.

Meg had a vague impression of big rough hands, a lilting cry of concern, and the wonderful sensation of warm strength wrapped around her body as she was lifted and carried to the big chair by the fire. Then a cup was rattling against her teeth and Effie's voice was urging her to drink. She turned her head away.

'There isn't t-time,' she murmured. 'I-I m-must get back.'

'You're going nowhere.'

'I have to find Rust.'

'I'll see to him,' said Effie calmly. 'I've got all the dogs' dinners ready and waiting.'

Meg pushed the cloying warmth away from her. They didn't understand. They weren't listening. Not even Effie.

'He's g-gone,' she gasped. 'He fell over the edge.'

Someone swore softly but Meg couldn't find the strength to chastise Effie for breaking her promise not to use bad language. She was too busy struggling to get into a dry raincoat, wrapping a scarf around her hair, but now she'd started talking, she couldn't seem to stop.

'It'll be dark soon. I have to find him. He fell off the knob on Dundale Knott, or rather Dan kicked him over, though he denies it. I think I can guess where he'll have ended up. We've must have some rope somewhere, a blanket. What else?'

She started searching for the things she would need for the rescue.

'I've got everything.' The stranger's voice was firm, assured. In his hand he held a coil of rope, a sack and a torch. 'Let's get going.'

Chapter Eighteen

As they strode out together across the fells, Meg couldn't help but notice that the stranger moved easily, as if he were used to walking long distances, and in all weathers judging by his tanned face, weathered and creased by the sun and the wind. Glancing sideways at him she decided the face held a certain arrogance, for all the bluntness of the jawline was softened by a lurking twist of what might be good humour at the corners of the wide mouth.

With a start she found he'd turned his head to meet her curious gaze and there was downright mischief in the eyes half hidden beneath the lowered eyelids.

He's formed an opinion of me already, she thought, and wondered if there was any way she could find out what it was. She gave a half smile, embarrassed at being caught out in her scrutiny, and turned away.

The sheep were almost down now and Meg waved to Dan, indicating that she had help already to find Rust. Dan nodded, acknowledging the wave but did not return it.

The stranger didn't speak until they had climbed a hundred or so feet.

'You're Meg Turner, right?'

'I am.'

'Have you lived here long?'

'All my life in this area, less than a year at Broombank.'

He nodded, satisfied, as if she had solved a problem, and said no more.

A part of her was glad of the silence, as she worried over her lovely dog and if she would find him alive. But another, less disciplined part experienced an urge to learn more about this man who had so unexpectedly appeared in her home, starting with his name. But he did not offer it and this was not the moment to ask.

After they had climbed to a good height they edged their way along a rake, a diagonal groove that cut into the hill. They found Rust lying, as she had hoped, on a ledge halfway down the scree. It had undoubtedly saved his life and they approached with care, anxious not to slide down to the scree themselves.

He lay on the ledge, much as he had learned to do on the threshing floor of the old barn, his obedience training and instinctive patience paying off in these dangerous conditions. He lifted his head at the sound of her voice, thumped his tail on the rock and whimpered, telling Meg how glad he was to see her, how he'd known all along that she would come.

She fell to her knees beside him and put her face against his. He was alive. Dear God, thank you for that. As the tears ran unchecked down her cheeks she could hear him breathing little gusts of love into her ear. If he'd been a cat he would have purred.

'Let me look at him.' Tam ran knowledgeable hands over the dog's limbs. 'He's broken a leg, and possibly his shoulder.'

Meg swallowed carefully. 'We have to get him down. Take him to the vet somehow.'

The stranger was tying birch sticks across the dog to hold his legs still. 'These will have to do as splints.' Then he tore open the sack to form a hammock. 'Help me lift him on to this, easy does it. I can carry him on my back, across my shoulders.'

Meg winced and cringed as she lifted Rust into position, but if the movement hurt the dog he gave no sign. Velvet brown eyes gazed trustingly into hers, his brown ear was torn and a great patch of his coat had been grazed down to the flesh. But he knew he had nothing to fear now. Meg would take care of him.

Miss Shaw, Effie's teacher, had called in to bring her some books, and kindly drove them to the veterinary in her little car. Rust was to stay at the surgery overnight to have plaster put on his fractures and be carefully checked over. Now Meg and the stranger were sitting in Broombank kitchen, gratefully enjoying one of Effie's home-made soups.

'I owe you,' Meg announced, not looking at him. Whenever she did she was half afraid her cheeks would flush under his oddly appraising gaze. 'You haven't yet told me your name.'

'Thomas O'Cleary. At your service.'

'Irish?'

'Irish-American-Liverpool you might say, and goodness knows what else besides.'

Meg smiled. 'Don't you know which?'

'I'm a mongrel. Like your dog.'

She was outraged. 'Rust isn't a mongrel, he has an excellent pedigree. I also own his mother and brother.'

The green eyes twinkled. ''Tis awful fond you are of that creature. Wouldn't a man give his eye-teeth to be so adored?'

A stillness came upon Meg and she heard Effie titter. She turned at once to the child. 'You ought to be in bed. You have school tomorrow.'

'Aw, Meg.'

'Go on. No messing.'

Dragging her heels and taking as long as humanly possible without risk of inciting more stern words, Effie went to bed. When she'd gone, Meg realised her mistake. She was alone now, with a stranger, and night was coming on.

Tam grinned. 'Do you have a barn?'

Meg hid a smile at his uncanny ability to read her thoughts. She shook her head. 'We have several but none fit to sleep in, if that's what you're thinking.'

'Ah.' Tam glanced across at the window. The shutters were closed, but the rain could be clearly heard beating upon the glass. 'Now that's a pity, to be sure. 'Tis not a night for a lonely, unemployed male to be prowling about.'

Meg found her lips twitching upwards at the corners. 'If ever I heard a load of soft-soaping bunkum, that just about takes the biscuit!'

The strange, soft green eyes which reminded her so much of Kath, opened wide in false innocence. 'So what would you be meaning by that remark?'

Meg got up and removed the empty dishes to the sink. 'You can sleep here, on cushions by the fire.' Then more sternly, 'Any prowling about in my house and you'll find I have other, more fierce dogs to protect me.' The thought of young Ben and quiet Tess setting upon this man almost made her laugh but she managed to keep her face perfectly serious. He didn't know how soft they were.

'I'll bear it in mind, to be sure.' His gaze held hers for a moment, boldly challenging, as if saying it might be worth trying anyway.

Meg brought him a pillow and a blanket and placed them on the chair by the fire, hoping that she'd made her point. As she started up the stairs he spoke in his quiet, lilting voice.

'I'm glad to have made your acquaintance, Meg Turner. I hope as how we are going to be friends and you'll call me Tam.'

For some foolish reason, Meg's heartbeat quickened as she looked down upon him. 'I think it's time you closed those Irish eyes of yours and got some sleep.'

She called at the surgery first thing the next morning. Rust had spent a comfortable night but was still drowsy from a minor operation he'd had to set his shoulder.

'He'll live. You can take him home later,' the vet said. 'When he wakes.'

'He will be all right?'

'He'll never work again, I'm afraid. A quiet life in future for this young man. If you decide to keep him, that is.'

'I'm not having him put down.'

The vet smiled. 'I didn't think for a minute you would, Meg. Nasty accident though. How did it happen?'

Meg hesitated. 'Just one of those things.'

She went straight from the surgery back on her bike up to Ashlea. She had it in mind to give a piece of her mind to Dan but found herself being interrogated by Sally Ann instead. Her sister-in-law was busy knitting khaki socks for her soldier brothers but was willing enough to put down her knitting for a minute and hear about the stranger who had helped to rescue Rust.

'You let a man sleep all night in your house?' Sally Ann gazed at her in astonishment. 'I wonder what Jack would make of that?'

'Oh, don't. I daren't even think. He's Irish and behaved most properly.'

'He's good-looking then?'

Meg dropped the ball of wool she was winding for Sally Ann, so surprised was she by this question, and had to chase it under the table. 'Why do you think so?'

'I can see it in the flush on your pretty cheeks,' Sally Ann said, making the rosy hue deepen as a result.

'What else could I do but offer him a night's accommodation? Him having helped with the rescue.'

Sally Ann's grin faded. 'How is the dog?'

'He'll live, the vet says.'

'That's grand news. He'll be out on the fells again before you know it.'

Meg swallowed. She wouldn't cry at the damage done to her good friend, she wouldn't. 'He'll never be up to working again, but maybe he won't mind so much. He always has had a fancy for the easy life.'

'Dan is real sorry about the accident. Could hardly sleep last night. He likes dogs.'

Meg was aware of her sister-in-law glancing anxiously at her and tried to smile but her skin felt all tight and stiff. 'I'm sure he is,' was all she managed.

'He didn't think. Oh, I know, that's Dan all over, you've said so a dozen times. But he is doing his best to change. He does try, if not often enough mind, to be his own man. But Joe goes on at him so much it's as if Dan has to prove how tough he is, even when he doesn't feel it.'

Meg reached out and squeezed Sal's hand. 'My father has a way of getting under anyone's skin and turning them into monsters. The dog will be fine. And it's true he did behave a bit daft. Rust has a nervous streak in him, as collies often have. Remember how he ran away that time? I don't think he likes Dan's booming voice.'

'I can sympathise with that,' chuckled Sal. 'Here, have a piece of curd tart while I put on a brew of tea. It's freshly made.'

They sat companionably for some moments before Meg spoke again.

'I hope you don't mind my calling here so often. But I always enjoy our little chats, as well as your delicious cooking.' Meg grinned and took a bite out of the wedge of tart.

Shrewd eyes regarded her in silence for a moment. 'You miss someone to talk to up there, don't you?'

A flash of guilt crossed Meg's face before she could stop it. 'I do, yes. Effie's lovely but she's still a child. I forget that sometimes. I miss Kath, and oh, Jack of course, so very much. But that isn't the only reason I come here. I hope you and I can be friends.'

'Course we can. I know Kath is special to you. Sometimes, I used to think, a bit too special.'

Meg looked at her sister-in-law in surprise. 'What do you mean by that?'

Now it was Sally Ann's turn to flush beetroot red. It clashed alarmingly with her hair. 'Trust me to put my big foot in it. I didn't mean anything, except, well, she did push in between you and Jack, didn't she?'

'Push in?'

'Yes. Going out with you on picnics and swims and such like. Wasn't natural, I thought, for a beautiful girl like her to

272

want to be with you two all the time, just as if you were sisters and always had to be together.'

'I suppose we felt like sisters sometimes.'

'Why didn't she find a fella of her own?'

Meg sat and listened to the clock ticking out in the hall while she considered this. 'She was a friend. Still is. Therefore always welcome with Jack and me. We didn't mind.'

The sharpness in Meg's voice caused an awkwardness to fall between them, one that might have continued indefinitely had it not been broken by the arrival of Joe.

'Is that cur of yours still going strong then?'

'Yes, no thanks to your son.'

'Don't look at me so fierce. I didn't kick him down the scree.'

'No. But you put it into Dan's head to try and make it as difficult as possible for me to run Broombank.' Meg spoke quietly but her tone said she wasn't to be made a fool of. 'You've taken my hay, my tups, my cows, and now damaged my dog, but you'll not make me give up. I'll tell you that for nothing.'

Joe sat down in his chair, took off his cap and rubbed one hand over his thinning hair. He was quite calm, infuriatingly so in Meg's opinion. 'I've allus had a fancy for Broombank.'

'You can buy land as good anywhere.'

'Aye, but not cheek by jowl with me own place. Anyhow, it has more usable acres than I have as well as good access to the heaf.'

Meg steadied her breathing and sat down opposite her father. Sally Ann excused herself swiftly, and went off to find something that didn't need doing.

'This is about Mum and Lanky, isn't it?'

The question was quietly asked but it was as if she had lit a match to touch paper. She watched his face turn red, then white as it drained of all colour, his mouth screwing into a tight knot of rage.

''Oo told you?'

'Does it matter? Isn't it all very old hat now? Does it really matter if Mum once loved Lanky? Who knows if anything would have come of it? It mightn't have lasted, they were only young.' Like me and Jack, came the unbidden thought, but Meg quickly squashed it. Her love for Jack was absolute, not here today and gone tomorrow.

'Aye, she used to say that.' Joe reached for his pipe as he always did in times of stress and emotion. 'She spent half her life up there at Broombank, even when Mary was alive. After Mary was gone Annie still kept going. She was never away. How do I know what was going on?'

It hurt Meg more than she could bear to hear her mother's memory so defiled. 'You nasty old man! Mum, Mary and Lanky were good friends. That's all. They're all dead now, let them rest in peace. Why you always have to see the worst in people, I don't know.'

'Because it's generally the way things are. I don't trust women. Never have, never will.'

For the first time she began to feel truly sorry for her father. He lied and cheated to get Annie to marry him but had never felt secure with her. Because of that he'd kept her close to the house, and her daughter too in the fullness of time. He'd bullied his two sons, each for different reasons, but he hadn't managed to make any of them love him. It was really very sad.

Meg went to kneel by his chair and Joe looked directly into her eyes, surprise in his own at seeing her beside him thus.

'Why do you have to be pushing and shoving all the time, ordering people about? Why can't you just let things be? Maybe, if you gave me the chance, you might find something in me that you like. Would that be so terrible? Would it really damage you, or Ashlea, if I managed to be as good a farmer as you?' She didn't say better, that wouldn't have done at all.

Joe made no reply.

When he made no move towards her, Meg got wearily to her feet and stood before him. 'I don't want to fight you, but

I will if I have to. Every time you knock me back it makes me a little bit stronger, gives me a little more confidence to cope. If Mum hadn't the courage to stand up to you, and escaped at every opportunity to a place where there was friendship and love, you've only yourself to blame. As I have escaped. And Charlie. If you don't watch out, Dan will do the same.

'But I'm still your daughter, Joe Turner, and I'm certainly not going to deny that fact, nor give in to your bullying. Nor will I fail in this enterprise. In fact, I intend to be a success. Have you ever considered that I might want to be like you, and not my mother?' Then, bidden by some instinct she could not at that moment define, Meg leaned over and kissed her father on the cheek. She left the kitchen quickly before he had time to reply.

-

'Walk with me up the lane for a bit,' she said to Sally Ann.

'You haven't had another falling out?'

Meg shook her head, tears welling in the grey eyes. 'I don't want to talk about it, all right?'

Sally Ann nodded in silent misery and Meg could see her sister-in-law wishing life with the Turner family could be a lot less complicated. So did she.

'You've not taken the hump, have you? About what I said earlier, about Kath?'

Meg shook her head. 'Course not. It's always hard to understand other people's friendships. Forget it, I have.' Meg was trying not to think too much about what Sally Ann had said about Kath pushing in. Weren't they a trio, like the three musketeers? But the silence from her best friend was deeply worrying. Jack's letters too were few and far between, and not exactly romantic. It hurt to remember their vow that snowy Christmas night. Had they forgotten it so quickly?

The two girls paused to smile at the hectic toing and froing of a pair of hedge sparrows, busily preparing their nests. 'I feel like that sometimes,' Sally Ann said. 'Allus rushing back and forth. It's good to escape the chores for a minute and catch a breath of fresh air after all this rain and mist.'

Meg glanced at her sister-in-law anxiously. 'You are all right? The baby and everything?'

Sally Ann smiled a contented smile. 'Oh, yes, never better.'

Meg relaxed. 'I'll be getting more than enough fresh air now with the sheep to sort and the lambing about to start.'

'You enjoy it though.'

'I love it.'

'Will you keep him on?'

'Who?'

'The Irishman. Whatever he's called.'

Meg jerked up her head and looked at Sal, the idea new to her. 'I hadn't thought.'

'Well, I would if I were you. Things aren't always going to be this quiet, are they? I keep expecting the skies to be filled with aeroplanes and parachutes, but nothing's happening. Except that everyone you see has faces as long as a wet fortnight, thinking of their loved ones going overseas.'

Meg too looked suddenly glum. 'Jack will be going soon. I can't bear to think of it. I don't see much of him but at least I know he's safe.'

'Do you think we'll be safe, up here?'

Meg tucked her arm into Sally Ann's. 'Of course. It's a bit shaming really, to be so far away from the action. I intend to work extra hard on the farm. People are going to need food, it's an important job too.' She laughed, rather self-consciously. 'That's what I tell myself, anyway.'

'You're right. All I seem to do is start babies.'

'Well, you're going to finish this one. A real beauty it will be, with a cheerful smile just like its mother. Take care now.'

As Meg strolled away, Sal called after her, 'What was it he wanted, this Irishman?'

Meg stopped in her tracks. 'O'Cleary. His name is Thomas O'Cleary. Known as Tam.'

'Tam, is it?' Sally Ann's lips twitched with teasing good humour. 'Maybe you won't miss your Jack as much as you might think.'

'Sal!'

'You said he was waiting in your kitchen. What was he doing there?'

Meg blinked. 'Do you know, I haven't the first idea.'

—

Tam O'Cleary declared himself in no hurry to depart and seemed willing enough to help with the sorting. Meg picked out the ewes that appeared weakened by the hard winter and put them closest to the farm where she could keep a better eye on them. The rest were divided up into their likely lambing weeks and enclosed in-by accordingly.

'Have you worked with sheep before?'

Tam shook his head. 'Horses. Cows.'

'I need a sheep man.' She wasn't sure she wanted Tam O'Cleary about the place, though Meg couldn't rightly say why. 'I've too much to learn myself to try to teach you. Green as they come, that's me.'

'Not quite,' said Tam softly. 'You were born and raised on a farm.'

'Yes, but not allowed to work with the sheep.' She lifted her chin a notch. 'But it's what I want to do, so don't you start telling me how hard it is and not women's work.'

He checked the mark on a ewe, shifted a hurdle and let it scamper through, then closed it again. 'But you need help, that much is certain. Where else would ye find a fine strong man like meself with a war on?'

Meg couldn't help but smile at the deliberate use of the Irish accent, finding herself warming to this man though really she shouldn't. 'How you can turn on the charm, Tam O'Cleary.'

And they both laughed, eyes meeting, shifting, dancing away. She decided to be entirely businesslike.

'We don't dip the ewes in the spring. But the hoggs, they're the first-year lambs that have spent the winter at farms on lower ground to give them a good start, will be returning on the fifth of April. That's Hogg Day, and they will require dipping and marking up before we let them back on to the fell.'

'You'd want that done before the lambing starts?'

Meg agreed that would be for the best. 'Though it doesn't always work out that way, or so I'm told.' She screwed up her eyes as she gazed over her stock, wishing Lanky was here to pass judgement on them, and help with the weeks of lambing she now faced. 'When the hoggs have been dipped,' she continued, aware that Tam was watching her, 'they always go back to the part of the fell where they spent the first summer with their mothers. It's a wonderful homing instinct that keeps them safe on their own ground, which is vitally important on these vast areas of high fell.'

'You're the same. Safe on your own ground.'

Meg smiled, unaware how it lit up her face, golden curls streaming in the wind. 'Something of the sort.' She saw the pensive expression in Tam O'Cleary's face and it confused her. He was a man, after all, and had a way of reminding her that she was a woman just by the look in his eye.

'No more talk. There's work to be done,' she said crisply, and tried not to watch his smile.

Later, when the work was over for the day and they'd all enjoyed one of Effie's cheese bake suppers, the question that had been teasing her for so long finally came out.

'Why did you come?'

Meg had meant to ease into the question politely, in a roundabout way, a method in which her father was an expert. But as ever she was too frank and straight, and the question came out boldly, tactlessly even, making her blush. 'I'm sorry, I didn't mean to sound so blunt. Only you never said what you were doing in my kitchen that day?'

'I came because of Katherine.'

'What?' It was the last thing she'd expected to hear. 'How do you know Kath?'

Tam told the tale of how he first met Kath and her subsequent disappearance. He showed not a trace of his usual teasing humour, nor made any mention of the pregnancy. He wanted to tread warily, for no reason beyond instinct.

'Are you saying the old girl has done her in?' asked Effie, eyes like saucers.

Meg's glance quelled her into silence. 'Don't be silly. All this reading is doing your imagination no good at all, Effie Putnam.' Turning back to Tam, she said, 'Where could she be? Why do you think there's anything wrong at all? She might just have taken it into her head to leave. Kath has always maintained that she wanted to go to London. I can't think why she didn't go there in the first place.'

So here it was. 'She was short of money, her family not understanding her problem. Perhaps she was nervous there might be bombing, with the war about to start.'

Meg pooh-poohed this idea at once. 'Kath isn't a weak weed. She isn't afraid of anything, and certainly wouldn't let the rumour of bombing, which might or might not happen, stop her doing what she wanted.'

'Maybe not, in the normal course of events. But then there was the child to consider.'

'Child?' Meg frowned. 'What child? I don't understand.'

Tam glanced sideways at Effie's face, avid with interest. Meg took the message.

'Good heavens, it's past six. Effie, be a dear and feed the hens, will you? I forgot at lunchtime with being so busy.'

'Aw,' Effie groaned, realising she was about to miss some glorious tidbit. As if there was anything they could say that would shock her? Not that she dare admit as much.

'Perhaps you'd rather do the milking? I have to do that too in a minute.'

Effie was convinced. When she had gone, on feet so rapid it was a wonder she didn't fall over them, Meg turned back to Tam. 'Best make it quick, whatever you have to say. She'll be back before you can shake a lamb's tail.'

'Kath was pregnant when I last saw her. So far as I know she hadn't told anyone else besides me. Probably only told me because I was a stranger. I wondered if mebbe her aunt discovered it.'

'Kath? Pregnant? I don't believe it.'

'I'm afraid it's true. And no, she isn't married, if that's what you were wondering.'

An odd little pang of disappointment pinched at Meg. Why should Kath tell this man, this stranger, about her problems and not herself, her one best friend? But she mustn't show that it mattered. It would be foolish. Only Kath's health and well-being was important. 'Poor Kath, suffering this terrible ordeal all on her own. So that's why she went off abruptly to Southport, to hide from the disgrace. I wonder if she's told her parents?'

'She said not.'

Meg looked solemn. 'No, I can understand that. Mr and Mrs Ellis are very proper. Doctor and magistrate Mr Ellis is, and Rosemary organises the flower rota at the church. Oh dear, how dreadful. Poor Kath. And you think that this Aunt Ruby threw her out?'

'Or took her somewhere. The point is, where?'

Chapter Nineteen

'I don't believe a word of it.' Twin spots of outraged colour burned high on Rosemary Ellis's cheekbones but Meg was more interested in the fingers pleating and unpleating the linen skirt to take too much notice. It was the sign of a nervous woman, rather than an angry one.

They sat politely either side of the marble fireplace in the aquamarine and white drawing room and Meg had never felt more uncomfortable in all her life. Rosemary Ellis preferred not to associate herself with the common-or-garden dalesfolk, linking herself instead to the fringes of the upper echelons of Lakeland society. She used as her model such notables as the Bagots of Levens, the Hornyold-Stricklands of Sizergh, and the Lonsdales.

'I'm sorry to have to be the one to break this news, Mrs Ellis, but there it is, these things happen in the best of families. Better you hear it from me than from a stranger.' The effect of these simple words, meant in a kindly way, was electric. Rosemary Ellis was on her feet in a second, looking as if her knees might buckle under her at any moment.

'A stranger? What do you mean? Who else could possibly know?'

Meg wondered whether she ought to involve Tam, but saw no help for it. She would have to offer some explanation for her learning the truth. Sighing softly, she told of Tam's arrival at Broombank and how he had been concerned for Kath. She even told the story about Rust, and how well he was doing now, the leg mending nicely, just to give Rosemary time to collect herself.

'He asked after me at the Co-op and they directed him up to Broombank.'

Rosemary was white to the lips. 'Is he the father? Because if he is…'

That idea had not, until this moment, occurred to Meg. Oddly enough, she felt a pang of anguish at the thought, then realised it was impossible. 'No, no, he couldn't be. They've only just met. They are just good friends, Tam says. Both lonely people, away from home, I suppose. Look, would you like me to make you a fresh pot of tea?'

Rosemary dropped back on to her sofa with the movements of a woman twice her age. 'No, thank you, I'm perfectly all right.' The fact that she didn't at once offer to make a fresh pot for Meg proved the opposite to this brave declaration. Rosemary Ellis, the hostess *par excellence*, would never have committed such a breach of good manners.

Meg cleared her throat. Sorry as she was for Mrs Ellis, she felt more compassion right now for Kath. 'You wouldn't have any idea where she might be?'

'Me? How should I know?'

Meg might have reminded Rosemary that she was the girl's mother but thought better of it. 'I just thought that perhaps Kath might have written, told you where she was staying.'

'I haven't the faintest idea what my daughter has chosen to get up to.' The sharp edge to her tone surprised Meg. Had she perhaps outstayed her welcome? She got up at once to go.

'I'm sorry to have caused you any distress.'

Meg found herself being shown to the door with a speed quite unlike Rosemary's usual politeness. She gave the older woman a reassuring pat on the hand. 'I shouldn't let it bother you too much. Kath isn't the first, nor will she be the last, to find herself in this situation, particularly now, with a war on. She'll cope.'

'I'm sure she will,' said the icy voice. 'She always was wilful.' The door was held open, Rosemary clearly anxious for her to depart, and Meg only too ready to obey, when stubbornness gripped her. 'I've written to Southview Villas so many times and got no answer but I won't give up. I want to see her, write to her at least. If you hear where she's moved to, you'll let me know? I worry she might be ill or something.'

'Katherine is perfectly well, I tell you,' snapped Rosemary, and Meg couldn't stop her eyebrows rising in surprise. Very quietly, she pushed the door closed again and stood facing Mrs Ellis.

'You do know where she is, don't you? I wish you'd tell me.'

Rosemary Ellis's eyes held sudden panic then a plea for understanding and all her confidence seemed to seep away. 'I had to do it. Her father would have been devastated if he'd found out. Once the baby is born Katherine may live where she chooses but no one, most of all Jeffrey, must find out about her condition.'

'Where is she?' Meg quietly persisted.

Rosemary ignored the question. 'Jeffrey hasn't been at all well. On top of everything he's recovering from a severe bout of influenza. It would quite ruin his health if word were to get out about that Katherine. You must promise me that you will say nothing, not a word to a soul? Promise!'

Meg grasped the hands that Rosemary was wringing with such anguish and squeezed them gently. 'I will say nothing if that's what you want, but you must tell me where she is. I am her best friend and surely have a right to know. I'm worried about her.'

Jeffrey Ellis chose this moment to walk into the sitting room. He was wearing a blue checked dressing gown though it was past eleven o'clock in the morning. He seemed pleased to see Meg. 'Hello. How is the farm doing?'

'Very well, thank you.'

Meg had always thought he was a man who carried a sort of quiet dignity about him, as all good medical men do. Now he seemed thinner, more tired, with an air of resignation or defeat about him. 'Have you heard from Katherine?' he asked, a pleading in his face, and Meg shook her head, unable to trust herself to speak as she watched the light of hope die in faded eyes so like Kath's own. 'I was hoping you might have. She's adventuring somewhere. That's my daughter, never still for a minute.'

Meg caught the expression in Rosemary's eyes, begging her to leave. 'I must go. Work to do, I'm afraid.'

Mr Ellis grasped her hand as she reached for the door handle. The grip was surprisingly firm. 'You'd let me know if you did hear, wouldn't you?' It made her shiver to hear her own words of a moment ago echoed back to her. She smiled and nodded. Somehow she couldn't see this gentle man as the censorious creature Rosemary made him out to be.

'Of course.'

'If she writes to anyone it will be to you.' Which gave Meg pause for Kath had done no such thing. Why was that? Shame perhaps? How very silly.

At the front door she tried one last time. 'I'll write to her aunt once more then, just in case. Miss Ruby Nelson, isn't it, Southview Villas? Perhaps she might have heard where Kath is by now.'

But Rosemary was pushing something into her hand, a scrap of paper, crisp and rustling, whispering feverishly as she glanced back over her shoulder, half an eye on her husband wandering like a lost soul into the drawing room. 'You can check if she's all right, if you like. Don't come again. I don't want her here. Not till she's got rid of it. Then she can come home as if nothing had happened.' The door closed firmly in Meg's face.

Standing on the empty driveway Meg read the address. *Greenlawns Home for Wayward Girls.*

'I can't go. Not yet, much as I'd like to. I'll write and tell her that I'll come as soon as the lambing is over.'

'She's your best friend,' Effie pointed out.

'The sheep are my livelihood, I can't neglect them. It would take days to go to Liverpool, find this place and come home again. I'd have to stay overnight, maybe longer with the trains the way they are. She might refuse to see me.' Meg wanted to drop everything that very minute and go and find Kath, but how could she? She simply daren't risk leaving her flock at this important time.

'What can I offer anyway? Her own mother won't have her home.'

'You could let her come here,' Tam suggested.

'I will. Oh, I will. There's nothing I'd like better. I'll bring her to Broombank where she can have all the love and care she needs. But I must be sensible.' She looked from one to the other of them, begging them to understand. 'The next weeks are the busiest in the farming calendar. I can't leave now.'

There was no one else to stand in for her. Effie certainly couldn't deal with the lambing, nor could Tam manage on his own, since he said himself that he was more used to horses. 'I'm sorry, but it has to be. Mrs Ellis says she is being taken care of. We'll just have to believe that.'

'She also said that she hadn't the first idea where Kath was,' Tam reminded her, in his quiet, lilting voice.

Meg turned on him at once, upset by the implied criticism. 'You go then. You find her if you think I'm so wrong.'

'I didn't say you were.' He sighed. 'This is your first lambing season. I don't suppose another week or two will make much difference and I rather think you're going to need all the help Effie and I can give.'

Effie puffed out her flat chest, pleased at being included. 'I'll keep you all fed, anyroad,' she volunteered, just to make sure they understood that she wasn't having anything to do with the underparts of sheep.

Tam grinned. 'I'd like to see how it all pans out, so I'll stay on if you don't mind?'

Meg was surprised, alarmed by the offer and strangely relieved all at the same time. 'I can't pay you. Not yet anyway. Not till I sell the lambs in the backend probably.'

'Did I ask for payment?'

'Nobody works for nothing these days.'

'I like to be different.'

'You know nothing about sheep. What use would you be?'

'I don't think you can afford to be choosy. I'll work for my keep to begin with. Let's at least make sure you have some lambs to sell.'

He was far too sure of himself in Meg's opinion. Whenever he stood about, watching her, she felt strangely inadequate and came over all ham-fisted and clumsy. And Thomas O'Cleary was too good-looking for his own good, certainly for hers. She daren't think what Jack would have to say about this man staying here. Yet she needed help, very badly. Reluctantly, and with a strange excitement in her heart, she agreed.

'All right. You can stay till the autumn sales. We'll see how we get on.'

Tam smiled, as if he had known all along that she would agree.

Effie simply giggled.

'Now that's settled, perhaps we should work out a shift system. Them sheep will need watching round the clock, presumably,' he said.

And so will you, came the unbidden thought.

The first lamb died. The failure was such a devastating blow that Meg redoubled her efforts to shepherd them more carefully. It was important that she had a good crop of lambs this year if she was to build up the flock. She set an alarm clock by her bed. Every two hours it woke her and she would pull on her boots and raincoat, usually with her eyes still half-closed, pick up her torch, and walk out into the bitter cold night to check her precious flock. Her successes were sweet but every time a lamb died she blamed herself, whether justifiably or not.

The ewes were not in their best condition. They'd had a hard time of it through the frost and snow, so mortality was bound to be high. Broombank did better than some places lower in the dales and Meg knew she shouldn't complain.

Then came the day when she had to skin a dead one and pull its skin over a live orphaned lamb so that the bereaved mother would accept it as her own. Meg performed the task but then went and vomited her breakfast into the hedge.

Could Joe have been right? Was farming too tough for a woman? Determined to prove herself, she refused help from anyone. Out every morning before dawn she spent all day amongst her flock, missing meals and far too much sleep.

'I have me pride, for God's sake,' Tam said. 'If I can birth a mare surely a ewe isn't all that different? You can trust me to do a shift on me own, surely? You'll be no good to anyone if you collapse.'

Shame-faced, feeling oddly light-headed, Meg allowed Tam and Effie to chase her off to bed for a proper night's sleep at last.

It was Effie's task to feed the orphan lambs that a ewe rejected or had insufficient milk for.

Meg came down to the kitchen one morning to find them all gathered, bleating madly, about Effie's legs.

'They're driving me crackers,' Effie mourned. She was holding two bottles at once to a pair of fiercely sucking lambs while the others desperately nuzzled her hand wanting their own share. Meg watched as she got herself a mug of tea, a smile on her face.

'How do you know which ones you've fed?'

Effie gave her an anguished look. 'You might well ask.' The two bottles were now empty and Effie dabbed a blob of milk on the top of each head to identify the two fed lambs then went to refill the bottles with fresh mixture. The moment her back was turned the other lambs leapt upon the first two and quickly licked off the delicious fluid. Meg burst into laughter.

'I don't think your system is working.' She explained what she'd just seen.

Effie stared at the milling lambs in despair. 'Drat! No wonder some get fat while the others stay skinny.'

Effie met Meg's gaze, brimming with laughter, and burst into giggles. Then they were both laughing so much Meg was clutching her sides in agony. 'Oh, the thought of them licking up the milk as fast as you mark them.' They were off again and it was some moments before the two of them could wipe away tears and bring themselves back under control.

'Well, come on, what do you suggest?' Effie asked.

'How about some sort of label?'

So luggage labels were found, one attached to each lamb and duly numbered.

'Now you start at one, mark it, and keep going, in order, till they're all fed. Easy.'

'Let's hope they don't eat labels,' chuckled Effie. But the system did seem to work and the lambs started to thrive better after that.

It was the middle of May before Meg felt it safe to take time off from her duties. A familiar twittering warble told her that Broombank's swallows had returned to take up summer residence and there were five blue eggs in the dunnock's nest by the gate.

The lambing season had been longer and harder than Meg could ever have imagined. But her first crop of lambs were safely delivered, smaller than she would have liked, but it was a start.

Oh, and how she had loved watching them grow, seeing them play 'I'm the King of the Castle' each evening as they gambolled and frolicked on the knolls of grass about the farm, as lambs are supposed to do. It filled her with such pride to watch them that it took her twice as long to get her chores done. She had survived her first winter, and the knowledge seemed to give her fresh courage, ready to face anything, even this sour-faced woman who was taking an age to answer a simple question.

She tried to imagine Kath sitting here in this green painted room in exactly the same way. Though not quite the same, for Kath's mind would no doubt have been a turmoil of misery and confusion, worrying over her baby and her future. How long had she been in this place? Six, seven months? Maybe longer.

Meg had disliked Miss Blake on sight. There was a smell about the place, rather like the paraffin and sand they used to spread over 'accidents' in infant school. It made her feel uneasy.

'She probably came at the end of last year,' Meg helpfully pointed out. 'A pretty girl, with fair hair worn in a bob.'

The woman sniffed. 'They're all pretty, or so they think.'

Meg watched as she leafed painstakingly through a long slim book, wishing she would hurry up. Meg wanted to get this mission done with and be back on the train before nightfall. This was not a time to linger in Liverpool.

The wisdom of her coming had been debated long and hard for some weeks. They'd listened to the news every night, horrified by what was happening. The phoney war was turning into a real one as Hitler occupied Denmark, Norway, Holland, and swept on through Belgium to France. Mr Chamberlain had gone and Winston Churchill was now Prime Minister, promising them nothing but 'blood, sweat, toil and tears'.

'What if you get bombed?' Effie had asked, panic in her voice. Tam calmly told her that nothing of the sort had yet happened so why should they choose to drop one on Meg the moment she set foot in the city. Tam O'Cleary was good at easing tension, Meg had discovered. But then he was good at a lot of things.

She'd taken the train to Southport and been forced practically to bully the directions to Greenlawns out of Ruby Nelson. It was as well she had since nobody in Liverpool seemed to have heard of the place.

Miss Blake paused at a page in her large blue book, peering through narrow rimmed spectacles. 'Ah, here we are. Yes, we did take in a girl by that name: Katherine Margaret Ellis, aged twenty. She came to us in November last. Yes, I remember her now.'

Meg felt a flood of relief. 'Is she still here?'

The pale eyes regarded her in vaguely troubled surprise. 'She has not been a particularly good influence upon our other, er, residents. Something of a trouble-maker is our Miss Ellis.'

Meg's lips twitched. 'May I see her, please?'

'That is rather irregular. It can be most unsettling for our girls to have visitors from the outside.'

'From the outside?' Meg echoed the words in amazement.

Miss Blake leaned forward. 'Are her family ready to reclaim her?'

Reclaim her? Meg was horrified by such language, but was forced to admit that they weren't. Miss Blake sniffed, almost with pleased satisfaction.

'You must appreciate that most of our girls have been abandoned, by their family, by their friends, by society. There is nowhere for them to go. The charity of Greenlawns is all they have to depend on.'

'Kath – Katherine – has not been abandoned. She still has friends. Me, for instance.' Meg smiled sweetly, grey eyes issuing a challenge.

'Are you wishing to take her with you today?'

Meg winced at the implication that Kath was no more than a parcel to be collected or abandoned as if in a left luggage office. 'That is my intention.'

'If you do so, you must undertake to be completely responsible for her health and well-being. She has not been – well, and of course, she may sin again.'

'I will gladly undertake to care for her.'

A long pause, then a small bell was lifted and rung, sounding loud in the still room. An even longer pause followed it. Finally, steps were heard hurrying along the corridor outside, a rapid knock and a figure appeared, slightly breathless.

'Sorry, ma'am, I'd just gone out for a moment.' Instructions were given to bring Katherine Ellis to the office. As the heels clacked away again, Meg cleared her throat. 'I understand that there was a child?'

Miss Blake adjusted her spectacles and returned her piercing gaze to the book, reading the reports written by each name, giving details of each girl's history and behaviour. Katherine Ellis had a long string of convictions for temper and the inciting of rebellion. If this young woman planned to take her away with her, Miss Blake would not object. 'A female child,' she read and Meg cringed at a baby being so described. 'Born 27 March, weighing six pounds, seven ounces.' She closed the book, as if the matter were dealt with.

'And?'

'I beg your pardon?'

'Where is it – she?'

'In the orphanage, awaiting adoption, of course. We are not a children's home, Miss Turner. We offer no provision for infants here.'

'I see. Have any adoptive parents been found for her?' Meg held her breath, wondering what answer she hoped for.

'Indeed it is difficult at present, to find adoptive parents, with the war. People have enough to worry about without taking on other people's by-blows.'

The word was so offensive to Meg that she had to bite her lip very hard to keep her good manners in check. Then came the familiar tap of heels, the rap upon the door, and the woman was there again. 'Katherine Ellis, ma'am.'

Meg gazed upon a stranger.

'Kath?' Not a vestige of girlhood remained in the narrow planes of the sunken cheeks. The lovely swinging bob had been cut close to the finely shaped head. The porcelain skin was ashen, almost grey, the hazel eyes rimmed by the red of exhaustion. And the hands, those beautiful tapering white fingers with pearl shaped nails that Meg had always envied, now picked restlessly at the cotton of her green overall. Workworn, blistered, the nails bitten down to the quick, they looked red raw, as if they'd recently been bleeding. 'Dear God, what have you done to her?'

At the sound of Meg's voice the heavy lids lifted, revealing a blankness in the eyes, and a terrible despair. The sight brought such pain to Meg's heart she had to fight hard not to burst into tears as emotion thickened her throat.

'Meg?' There was wonder in the question, and disbelief.

Then Meg opened her arms and Kath stepped into them with a quiet sob.

—

Lime Street railway station was thronged with people, many of them in uniform, most were crying. Meg felt like crying too, though not for the same reason. She wasn't seeing someone she loved off to the war. That had been done months ago and not a day had passed since when she hadn't thought of Jack. Now she thought of him for a different reason.

When Kath's baby had been put into her arms, Meg had gazed down upon the small bright face, the halo of glossy black curls, the violet blue eyes, and had known instantly whose child she was. Everything seemed to come clear in that moment. It was all so obvious, so stupidly plain.

She wondered now how she had managed to remain so calm. There had been no doubt in her mind, and if there had, one glance at Kath's face confirmed her worst fears.

'Jack?' Meg had whispered, and Kath had put her hands to her lips to stop the sob that escaped.

'I'm so sorry.'

That was all that had been said. All that needed to be said. They had signed the necessary papers, collected the child's documentation and walked out onto the bustling streets into the sunshine of a perfectly ordinary spring day. But Meg felt it would never be ordinary for her again. *Life* would never be the same again. That simple happiness she'd found was now gone. Vanished for ever. She felt numb inside.

The strange sensation around her heart must be pain, though it was difficult to describe it as such. Her body continued to function although it did so of its own accord. She could walk, count the money out of her purse to pay the bus fare, hand in her ticket at the station. But for these things no thought was required. Her mind was not in any way engaged. It existed now in another universe, another time, lost in some far distant place. Let it rest there for a while, instinct warned. There would be time enough later to waken it and use it to examine the problem.

Doors were banging, a hiss of steam, the sound of desperate sobbing from the mass of people facing separation from their loved ones. Bags were flung into compartments, windows dropped open, hands reached out. Meg tried not to watch.

A whistle sounded.

'I can't come with you.'

Meg struggled to focus her gaze upon Kath. 'What did you say?'

'I can't come with you. I can't go home. Not now. Not like this.'

'Where will you go then?'

'Somewhere. Anywhere.'

'Oh, Kath. Have you any money?'

'Some. Enough for a day or two. I'll get a job, join up perhaps.' Kath opened a carriage door and pushed Meg inside, the child still in her arms. 'Can't you see? I'd be no good as a mother. I don't know her. I don't even love her.'

Meg was shocked, annoyed suddenly at Kath's lack of responsibility. 'How can you say such a thing about your own child?'

A small sob sounded, quickly stifled. 'I've never held her in my arms, not even when she was born. They wouldn't let me. Now it's too late.'

293

'Kath, this is madness. You must come home. We need you. You need us. Look at you, you're like a walking skeleton.' Again a whistle sounded and the guard was moving along the platform, slamming doors, telling people to stand back. 'You can't just abandon her like this.'

'I'm not. She's got you, and Jack. I'm sorry if we hurt you. We didn't mean to. Don't blame him. It was a game, that's all, a kind of madness during that last lovely hot summer when we believed, hoped, that war wouldn't come. Love her for me. You're much better at that than me. Look how I've treated *you*, my best friend, my *only* friend! I don't deserve either of you.' The tears were spilling over, then she turned abruptly and hurried away.

The last sight Meg had of Kath was her little tan hat with the silly veil disappearing into the crowd.

The train gave a sudden lurch and as it started to move out of the station, Meg sat and held Jack's child on her lap and the tears ran unchecked down her cheeks and dripped on to the baby's shawl.

–

Meg walked into the farmhouse like a sleepwalker. She'd taken a taxi from Kendal Station to Broombank, extravagant but necessary, she'd decided, with the baby and her bag. She'd no recollection of the journey, thankful only that it was over and – and now what? Where did she go from here? Without Jack. Without Kath. The shock was easing and in its wake came pain. Pain so terrible it didn't seem possible to bear it.

'Meg?'

Effie, dear Effie, standing in the doorway, her arms outstretched. 'Oh, Meg.'

Meg fought to hold on to her self control, laid the baby in Effie's arms and watched as the girl, little more than a child herself, drew her close and whispered love into her ear. Love.

What was that? Not something to rely on, not if it brought this much pain.

She would go upstairs, lie down for a bit, think over this terrible thing that had happened to her and sort out how she felt about it. Meg thought she only needed to rest and it would all come right in her head.

Tam, who had evidently been sitting at the table, taking supper, stood up, blocking her way. Big and patient, saying nothing, asking no questions. But something drove her to look up into his eyes. No sparkling, glinting green challenge in them today. Only a gentle wash of jade, like rain on glass.

'Kath is all right,' she said, and as he nodded he opened his arms and this time, unable to prevent herself, Meg walked into them. She laid her head against the broad strength of his chest, felt his arms wrap her in their warmth and let the tears come. Great wet globs that rolled down her cheek and into the neck of her best blue blouse. Not a sound came from her throat, only the silent anguish of a woman betrayed.

Chapter Twenty

It was all around the close-knit community in no time at all that Meg Turner had a baby. Even the thrill of Dunkirk failed to distract the gossips for long. In no time they were back to worrying over whose baby it was, and how it had appeared, out of the blue, in Meg Turner's house.

Effie was shocked to see how quick everyone was to condemn. 'Sanctimonious old biddies,' she muttered as she stood in a queue for new ration books and overheard a snippet of tittle-tattle she wouldn't repeat to her worst enemy, let alone her lovely Meg. Though she supposed the long hard weeks of winter had something to do with it, what with keeping them all indoors so long, and then Meg being busy with the lambing and disappearing off to Liverpool so soon after that. There were plenty ready to think she'd emerged from the winter with a babe in her arms. Folk being folk would naturally assume the worst. But if they stopped to think about it, they'd see it was a daft idea. Not unless they believed in immaculate conception.

This last phrase had been learned in the Scripture lessons at school, explained by a blushing Miss Shaw. Not that she need have worried where Effie was concerned. You'd have to get up early to make me blush, Effie thought, with some pride. But she enjoyed new words and struggled with the newspaper every morning in her efforts to improve her reading.

The woman's voice rose and carried on the morning breeze and the people in the queue heaved forward so as not to miss a scrap. 'Who would have thought it of her? So well brought up, and her father quite a big man in the chapel.'

'Indeed, I admit to being quite shocked myself when I heard,' said Hetty Davies, quite put out that she'd not been aware a baby was even expected, in all of her regular visits to Broombank. 'How she kept it hidden I cannot imagine.'

'We mustn't jump to conclusions,' warned the less excitable Miss Shaw, privately thinking with joy of yet another child for her school, in the fullness of time. 'It's true there has been no sign that a baby was on the way, and Meg is not at all the sort of girl one would expect to do such a thing.'

'No smoke without fire,' chimed in another.

'She was seen driving through town in a taxi. No doubt went away somewhere private to have the baby, tried to hide the fact, and then couldn't get it adopted because of the war, so had to fetch it home again.'

Another added the titillating information that Meg had a man staying in her house. 'Irish. Been living there for some time, I believe, and not in the barn neither. Now what is that, if not blatant disregard for what is right and proper? Doesn't it just go to show?'

'Tch. You never do know about people, unless you live with them.'

'Oh, dear me, no.'

Effie had heard enough. 'You bad-mouthed old besoms,' she shouted, making them all jump as no one had seen her small figure hiding behind large bosoms and baskets. 'How dare you condemn her when you don't know nowt about it? A saint, that's what my Meg is, and if you knew the truth you'd chop your lying tongues off.' Then to her complete mortification, Effie burst into tears and had to turn and run from the queue and the shocked, questioning eyes. She'd reached the Shambles before she realised she still hadn't got the new ration books after near an hour of queuing and would have to go back and start all over again.

Yet the rumours persisted, and, as expected, Joe came.

'What's all this then?' he began, mildly enough. Meg lifted her chin a fraction and tightened her lips to something very like a button, saying nothing. 'Where's this child you're supposed to have? Or is it all daft talk?'

'No, I do have a baby living here,' Meg admitted. 'But nor is there any truth in what you're thinking and everyone is saying.'

Joe took a seat by the fire and glared accusingly at his daughter, still far too wilful in his opinion. 'Where is she then?'

'Upstairs asleep, and I'll not have her disturbed.'

Meg was glad, for once, that they were alone. Effie was upstairs with Melissa, and Tam was out seeing to the cows. It would give her time to calm her father down, explain something of the truth. 'She isn't mine. I brought her from Liverpool. She's – she's an orphan.'

'Orphan my eye! What were you doing in Liverpool?'

Not for a moment did Meg consider telling him about Kath. 'I'll not have anyone say different. How can she be mine anyway? Don't talk soft.'

'It's not that long since that lad o'yourn left. It could easily be yours.'

Meg swallowed carefully, painfully aware that he spoke the truth. She wasn't a virgin, after all. That one moment of madness in the barn with Jack could very easily have resulted in a child. But that had been more than a year ago and they'd never repeated it, not once since. But Kath had.

Oh, but how different things would have been if Meg herself hadn't denied him the love he clearly wanted. Maybe he wouldn't have bothered with Kath then. She couldn't help wondering if it was all her own fault.

Meg would have written to Jack with joy if the baby had been hers, eager to tell him he was to become a father. They would quickly have married and everyone would have counted a little on their fingers and smiled and said, 'Ah, yes, but they're young and there is a war on.' But that was not the way it had gone. Melissa was Kath's baby. Kath's and Jack's. And it was all too terrible to think of.

She was spared from answering Joe's direct accusation by the arrival of Tam. Joe took one look at the tall, well-set Irishman, got to his feet and stood glowering before him.

'So this is how the land lies. Mebbe you're the one who has caused this trouble.'

Tam's brows lifted very slightly in surprise. At any other time Meg might have laughed at the comical sight of her father trying to outface a man a good six inches taller than himself. But this wasn't the moment.

'Dad, leave Tam alone. Don't make a bigger fool of yourself than you already have.'

'A fool am I? And there's me thinking it's my daughter who's the laughing stock around here. I can see why. I think thee'd best leave, son.'

'Leave?' Tam smiled down at Joe. 'Now why would I be doing that?'

'Pack your bags, or whatever it is you roving Irish carry your chattels in, and go.'

Tam lifted his eyes slowly to Meg and held them for a long moment before returning them to Joe. There was some message in it, one she couldn't quite read, or perhaps didn't wish to. 'I'll go when I'm good and ready, or when Meg tells me to. I don't think you have any say in the matter.'

'Have I not? We'll see about that.' Joe was beside himself with fury, almost spitting with rage. 'Nobody gainsays me without being sorry for it,' he roared. 'I'll not have my daughter preyed upon by strangers. Foreigners at that.'

Meg took a quick step forward to lay a calming hand upon Joe's shoulder. 'Dad, stop it. Tam is right. This is *my* house, *my* farm, and you are the visitor here.'

'*What?*'

'I'd be obliged if you left without any bother. Tam has nothing to do with any of this. He is my employee and, I hope, my friend. I'll not have him tainted by your nastiness.'

'Thee has a funny way o' choosing thy friends.'

'The choice is mine, not yours.'

Joe glared furiously at her. 'Then don't expect me to come and bail you out when nobody will lift a finger to help thee, because of him and what he's done to you.'

Meg almost laughed. 'When have you ever bailed me out of anything? Never. More likely the very opposite. Everything I have here has been achieved in spite of you, not because of your help which has been non-existent. Now get out, before I forget I'm still your daughter and thump you one.'

So startled was Joe by this spirited response that he glowered once more at each of them before storming out, slamming the door behind him just to show who was boss.

'You stood up for me, against your own father. I'm flattered.'

'Don't be. I'll not have Joe telling me what to do. Nor you neither.' She turned from him and walked from the room, but his soft chuckle had a strange effect upon her all the same.

—

The small Austin car left the rough cart track and started along the lane. It drove past a cluster of whitewashed cottages around a former bobbin mill and on over a humped bridge. Ahead lay the wild grandeur of mountains and the rugged outline of Goat Scar and Raven Crag.

'I hear you have a baby staying with you?' Rosemary Ellis had stopped to offer Meg a lift into town and she put the question briskly, as if the answer were of no consequence. Meg felt her heart quicken.

'I have.'

Mrs Ellis did not take her eyes from the road as she shifted the gear lever and eased the car forward. 'Is it Kath's?'

A slight pause while Meg thought through her line of approach. 'Everyone thinks she's mine.'

'She?'

'Melissa. Effie has started calling her Lissa and I'm afraid we've all picked it up. But it seems to suit her.' Meg cast the older woman a sidelong glance, then stared out at the passing scenery, achingly beautiful on this September morning, the bracken aflame to a rich russet red. Here there was freedom and solitude. Space to breathe and feel. She could scarcely imagine Kath's despair, living in that dreadful home. How thin and desperate she had looked. Yet Rosemary Ellis, her own mother, had known where she was. 'Kath has gone. I don't know where.'

'I rather thought she might run.'

'Isn't that what you wanted? For her to disappear?'

The question was very nearly impertinent and Meg heard the sharp intake of breath. 'I don't know what I wanted,' Rosemary admitted. 'For it not to have happened, I suppose. The scandal was too dreadful to contemplate.'

Meg wanted to feel sorry for this woman who'd lost her daughter, but somehow couldn't quite manage it. 'Did you send her money when she was in that place, in Greenlawns?'

Mrs Ellis fell silent as they drove on beside the tumbling waters of the beck, a worked-out quarry and an old farmhouse with a medieval pele tower. She was quiet for so long Meg thought she'd decided not to answer the question, which had been cheeky anyway.

'We were asked to provide what we could towards her keep though the girls were expected largely to work for it themselves. I considered myself fortunate that Ruby had found somewhere to take her, somewhere the baby could be born and cared for.'

'What did Mr Ellis think?'

The car swerved slightly and Meg grabbed the door strap, heart in mouth. But the road was empty as usual, so no harm was done. They came out of the narrow lane on to the main road.

'Jeffrey doesn't know anything about it. He mustn't. His heart, you know. He isn't as strong as he likes to think.'

Meg had no trouble in feeling sorry for Mr Ellis. 'He misses her. Doesn't he ever wonder why she doesn't write?'

The silence lasted so long this time, they had almost reached the bridge that led into Kendal before Rosemary answered.

'I pretended once that she had. I read him a letter that was supposed to have come from her, saying she was going to be away for a long time, somewhere secret, and she couldn't write again for ages. It seemed to satisfy him. He thinks she's doing her bit for the war.'

Meg gasped. To shuffle off one's pregnant daughter to avoid a scandal was bad enough; to lie to one's husband about her welfare was altogether more terrible. The words burst out of her before she could prevent them. 'How could you do such a thing? Kath loved you. She still loves you. Both of you. All right, so she made a mistake but she paid too high a price for it. It's not a criminal offence for God's sake. Lissa is just a baby and she's beautiful. She's very dark, and sitting up nice as ninepence. Kath's child. Don't you want to see her? Aren't you even going to tell Mr Ellis that he has a granddaughter?'

'No.'

'Stop the car here, please.' Meg had to get away before she said something truly unforgivable.

'Just as well Lissa has me then,' she announced to the retreating vehicle as it sped away, Rosemary Ellis sitting stiffly at the wheel.

–

Later, in Melissa's bedroom, Meg gazed down upon the sleeping child. Effie had made a bed for her out of a large drawer and she knelt beside it. The sound of the baby's breathing was oddly calming and Meg felt a fierce need to protect her from cruel gossip, from the war, from all the problems she might meet as she grew. Meg stroked the back of one finger over the soft down of the baby's cheek. So tiny. Such a frail scrap of humanity. A bubble of milk dribbled out upon the rosily pouted lips and Meg smiled.

'It's not your fault, little one. You didn't ask to be born, nor to be abandoned. Kath, your mum, didn't mean to be heartless. It's the way she is, a bit reckless and impulsive. Never gives a thought to anyone but herself, and look what a mess she's got herself into. Things are difficult for her right now, what with being thrown out by her ma and pa, and not having any job. Things aren't too good between her and me either. Not like they used to be, nor ever will be again, I don't suppose.' Meg smiled sadly down at the baby. 'Still, given the chance, she might have loved you.'

She bent over, about to gather the sleeping baby in her arms, so deliciously sweet did she look, then stopped as a new thought entered her head. As I might come to love you.

It jolted her and Meg became very still, aware, in that moment, of a new risk. The possibility of fresh pain in the future if she came to care too much for Kath's child.

She took a step back, away from the sleeping baby. No, that wouldn't do at all. She must think very carefully about this. What would happen when the war ended, and Kath and Jack returned?

In the meantime Melissa must be fed and given a home, as was only right and proper, until her mother came to claim her. But that was all she could give her. 'You're not mine, do you see, so I can't love you as a real mother would. That wouldn't be right. Or safe. For either of us.'

Being responsible for a baby on top of all her other chores would cause endless complications. Admittedly it was pleasant sometimes simply to sit and watch her gurgling happily, but Meg dare not allow herself too many such treats. Nor did she feel she could ask Sally Ann for any help since her sister-in-law gave birth to a baby herself in June. A boy, Nicholas David Turner, much to Joe's delight. Both mother and child were doing well, Dan walking about as if he had performed the entire miracle single-handed.

Meg was relieved when the school term ended and Effie took over, leaving her free to concentrate on the farm, and to avoid too much contact with the baby. Making a living for them all was all that mattered now.

In the days and weeks that followed, Meg buried her pain in work. She was glad of it, welcomed it. Up before dawn each day she laboured, blotting all thought from her mind. She concentrated entirely upon seeing to her flock, milking her two cows, seeking ways to make her farm pay. Her heart wasn't in the task, the work feeling little more than drudgery but it got her through each day. Come the evening she would eat one of Effie's suppers, though it might be sawdust for all she noticed half the time, and fall into bed praying for oblivion. Rarely did she find it. More often than not that was when the thoughts started, turning over and over, replaying the events that had led to this pain. Seeing Kath dancing in Jack's arms, laughing up at him with her lovely hazel eyes.

Why hadn't she realised what was going on? How blind and naïve she must have been. So much in love she hadn't seen because she hadn't wanted to see.

'Will you take the bairn for a walk?' Effie would ask her each day. 'Will you give Lissa her bottle?'

Requests that became a constant thorn to stab into her heart.

'I don't think so. I have work to do.' Meg would hurry from the kitchen back to the peace and sanctuary of the heaf and her sheep, aware of Effie's troubled gaze upon her.

But the thorns kept on stabbing her.

What had she done to deserve such treatment?

Wasn't Kath her best friend, and Jack much more? The thoughts whirled and burned, images to torment and torture. *Where* had he loved Kath? In the barn where he'd made love to her? How? Why? Till Meg felt insanity threaten and prayed for exhaustion to bring relief.

At first she expected a letter from Kath any day, an enquiry about Melissa at least, or word that she'd found a job. When summer followed spring and still Meg heard nothing she put the thought from her mind. In any case, she wasn't ready to face

Kath yet, wasn't even able to think about the effect her betrayal would have upon their friendship. Betrayal was the only word for it.

Their threesome had become dangerous, she could see that now. A mistake had been made, boundaries had been crossed from which there was no retreat.

But she continued, despite Tam's and Effie's protests, to write to Jack as if nothing had happened.

'He's gone to fight for his country, perhaps even die for it. I can't just abandon him.'

'I would,' declared the less complicated Effie, who had learned the whole sorry tale by this time.

Once, in the depth of her despair, Meg wrote to Jack, based now in Southampton, to say that perhaps it would be best if they called off their engagement, in view of the war, and go their own way. It was a coward's way out but she felt short on strength.

He replied almost by return, saying he needed to be able to think of her waiting for him at home, and whatever was bothering her could surely wait until Christmas by which time the war would be over and they could sort it out. The rest of the letter was about how hard the training was and how he was expecting to be sailing any week now, so that might liven things up a bit.

'Wish I could get up to see you before I go, but it's so far I might not manage it. Thinking of you, Jack.'

Ashamed that she was fussing over a spoiled love affair when he might lose his life in this terrible war, Meg never again suggested they break their engagement. It seemed only fair to wait, as he suggested, for Christmas when the war would be over. That would be soon enough. As for telling him about Melissa, that was for Kath to do, when the time was right. Nothing to do with her.

'You're a fool,' Tam told her. 'Why concern yourself with Jack's feelings, after what he's done to you? Or Kath.'

'I can't help it. Kath and I have been friends all our lives, it's hard to reject her even now. I'm sure she never meant it to happen. We were all too close, that's all.'

Tam raised one eyebrow in disbelief. 'What about Jack? How do you feel about him now?'

Meg dipped her head, not wanting to answer or even consider the question too closely, yet even that simple gesture seemed to exasperate him.

'Don't hang your head like that, Meg. The shame is not yours.'

Deep down she knew that worrying over Kath and Jack was all tangled up with her own self-pity. So long as she centred her thoughts upon feeling sorry for them, she didn't have to think of her own pain, or the future and how she would cope without Jack. She knew it was over between them, that she must learn to face life without him, but the prospect was bleak and daily brought fresh pain to her heart. What did she care about the farm now, without Jack? What did she care about anything?

–

During the long hot summer everyone feared the south of England was about to be invaded but September dawned and though the battles still raged over London, here in Westmorland the quietness of the coming autumn hung in the air, an almost guilty peace. In the woodlands the red squirrels were busily burying their nuts, constantly chittering reminders to them-selves not to forget. Even the youngest stags wore their hard antlers as they cleared the after grass following the hay harvest, and sleek young foxes learned to hunt alone.

In the first week of September, Effie handed Mrs Davies a basket of fruit and vegetables with a satisfied flourish. 'All home grown,' she said.

The scent of fresh fruit rose tantalisingly to Hetty Davies's nostrils, seeming to fill the small church. She looked at the girl before her and laid aside the bronze chrysanthemums she was arranging in a vase on the altar table. Chrysanths were always lovely at this time of year, and Will had quite a talent for growing them, something not everyone had. 'You do realise we're not having a harvest festival as such this year?'

'I hear folk are bringing stuff, all the same.'

'Those who can afford it. But nothing like we usually have, not with the war and the shortages, oh dear me, no.' Mrs Davies offered a kindly, if slightly embarrassed, smile to Effie. She was sorry they'd got this trouble at Broombank. Hetty had always liked Meg and had felt a keen disappointment that she'd turned out to be, well, just as silly-headed as all the rest, as you might say. She hadn't felt it right to call, since she'd heard.

But Effie was still talking. 'Sending the produce to a children's home, I heard. That right?'

'Perfectly correct.'

'Then I'll leave them, if it's all the same to you. And Mrs D, I'd just like to say as how I'm right sorry my tongue ran away with me in the queue that time. I were that mad, I don't know what come over me. Only it didn't seem fair, what people were saying about Meg.'

Mrs Davies cleared her throat and a well of pity rose in her ample breast. Who was she to cast the first stone, even if it were all true? What she wouldn't give for a baby half so delightful as this one was said to be, from those who'd been lucky enough to catch a glimpse. Hadn't she and Will longed for just such a child? Once upon a time.

'There's no need to apologise. No need at all. Perhaps I should be the one to apologise to you. Gossiping is a dreadful sin, and I should have known better than to think such things about our poor, dear Meg.' Her round cheeks were crimson with embarrassment.

Effie smiled. 'It don't do Meg no good, no good at all, to have everyone taking sides against her when she's only doing her best to make a go of things. Hasn't she enough trouble, with Joe Turner on her back?'

'Oh, indeed, yes. A most dreadful man.' Appalled by what she had just said, Hetty cleared her throat. 'I mean…'

'It's all right. I know exactly what you mean. I agree with yer. I wondered if happen you could let it get round like, about the baby coming from just such a children's home in Liverpool? Greenlawns, it were called.' So there, said the tone, as if adding a name gave truth to the tale of an orphan child plucked from the jaws of almost certain death and uncaring deprivation by Meg's caring hand.

'I will indeed, Effie. I will indeed.' Mrs Davies's flushed face became very still. Perhaps they might have other babies needing a home? No, she shook the idea away. She was far too old now for sleepless nights, and she and Will were comfortable enough as they were. But she could at least help Meg, try to make up for her own unkind remarks.

Effie was anxious to go, but there was one other matter needing to be settled. 'Meg says as how you can call and see our Lissa any time. Mebbe you might like to take her for a walk.'

Hetty's cheeks now went quite pink with pleasure. 'Oh, that would be lovely. I'll be round tomorrow, if that's all right?'

'I was wondering if you might feel able to do a bit more than that, Mrs Davies.' Dark eyes, large and beseeching, gazed up into the woman's enquiring gaze.

'Oh?'

'Well, the thing is I have to be in school much of the day. Meg's busy about the farm, proper thrang she calls it; Sally Ann is up to her ears with her own bairn, not to mention looking after that lot at Ashlea. It might be a bit cheeky to ask, but it crossed my mind like, that you'd happen be willing to have our Lissa for an hour or two each morning? Just to give Meg a chance to get on. She could manage her in the afternoons, till I got home.'

'Oh,' Mrs Davies breathed, too stunned to speak for a moment. 'Oh, yes. I would like that. I would like that very much.'

Effie beamed and stuck out a hand, rather grubby and stained red from the blackberry picking. 'It's a deal then?'

Mrs Davies regarded the hand rather cautiously for a second, then shook it firmly. 'It's a deal. Oh, my word, yes, it is indeed. And thank you for the fruit,' she called as Effie departed, flourishing an airy wave.

Hetty Davies returned, quite flustered, to her flowers, but her mind was no longer on the beauty of the chrysanths. 'Now I wonder if Will ever threw that big old black pram away that we kept up in the loft all those years.' She'd look it out, the moment she got home.

It was Rust, strangely enough, who helped turn the tide of Meg's depression. The dog was making a good recovery, thanks to the services of the veterinary and the care he received at home afterwards, fussed and spoiled by everyone. He now managed to lollop about the farmyard on three legs, rarely putting down the fourth, which poked out at an odd angle, not entirely under control. By her side at all times, he was ever her comfort and her joy.

Then one morning Meg collected the other farm dogs ready to go up the high fells to check on the sheep. 'Don't let him out for an hour at least, till I'm long gone.' She rubbed his head affectionately. 'You're retired now, old friend, no longer a working dog. Rest easy.'

Meg set off, the other dogs at her heels, reaching the flock on the high fells some forty minutes later. She stood, crook in hand, as the dogs ran, or waited at her command. But then some movement in the distance caught her eye, and there he was: a streak of black and tan racing up the hillside, running in his own odd and peculiar way.

Rust barely paused long enough to greet her before getting down to work, as he had always done. But then how could she possibly manage without him?

Meg shook her head in disbelief. 'Would you look at that? Never say die, eh, lad?'

Oh, but she was glad of his courage, for she needed his solid friendship by her. It came to her then that if a dog could bravely put injury behind him and soldier on, couldn't she summon up the same fighting spirit? Easier said than done perhaps, but she could at least try.

That day as she worked her flock, Meg realised that no matter what the cost she would find the strength to build her life again and put the past behind her. She had lost her best friend, and the man she had loved and hoped to marry, but she still had a life to be lived. She still had Effie, and Rust. Most of all she still had the farm and her sheep.

She still had her dream.

She would focus now on turning Broombank into the best sheep farm in the district. In spite of the war, her bully of a father, and a jealous brother. She'd do it or die in the attempt.

This decision brought such a blinding delight, such a joy to her heart, that Meg knew, in that moment, she would indeed survive.

On a beautiful morning like this with puffs of white cloud marching over Striding Edge, she knew this was the best place in the world to be. She did indeed have a future, here at Broombank. No matter what pain and hurt Jack and Kath had caused her in their youthful carelessness, she could overcome it. She might, one day, even find someone to share it with her.

–

'Were you wanting a permanent job?' Meg asked Tam, and waited, stomach muscles clenched, for his response.

Tam stopped scraping grass from the mower long enough to glance up at Meg. The harvest was in, not as good as it might have been because of the drought at just the wrong time, but at least there would be oats and hay for the stock this winter. It had crossed his mind that it was time to move on, but hadn't yet fixed on a date. He continued steadily with his task. 'I don't generally make permanent arrangements. I come and go when I choose.'

Meg sat on a stone wall, smoothing the yellow lichen with her fingers, trying to organise her thoughts so that she might find the most persuasive words. She needed Tam to stay. He was a good worker, and strong. There was no denying she needed some muscle about the place. She'd little hope of carrying out her plan without some form of male assistance, much as she might balk at the idea. And labour was hard to come by just now. Besides all of that, she trusted him and that counted for a great deal these days.

She also liked him, rather a lot, although Meg didn't care to consider at this stage quite what an effect his presence in the house made upon her. Enough to say that he was cheerful, kind and friendly. Good for morale, as the government posters would say. And she really didn't want him to leave.

Meg cleared her throat. 'I wouldn't normally push you for a decision, only it's been such a hard year, one way and another, and I have to make plans, d'you see, to survive.' Then in case this wasn't quite positive enough, she added, 'I mean to do well, but I'm not so stupid I don't realise I need help.'

Now the teasing laughter was back in his eyes. 'Well, isn't that something for the proud Meg Turner to admit she needs help?'

Meg felt her mouth twitch at the corners. It was going to be all right, she just knew it. 'I might even be able to pay you soon. Though not much, I'm afraid.'

'That'd make a welcome change, to be sure. This is to be your way of coping then, is it? Your personal battle.'

'Don't tease me, I'm serious.' Meg blinked rapidly. 'I can't bear to think of Charlie being taught to fight in the skies. I can't do anything to help him, or any of the others up there. But I can do my bit here for the war effort. This is my place. My home. My way of life.'

Meg dipped her head, not wanting him to see her vulnerability. 'I miss Lanky, badly. He knew everything there was to know about sheep farming, and about Broombank. His family has worked this land for generations. I owe it to him not to give up. I have to make a go of it because if I don't it will be as if I'd flung his generosity back in his face, and that would be terrible. I look at my Luckpenny every night and remember his faith in me.

'He couldn't go on because he was too ill, but he thought I could. He handed his good fortune on to me. Lanky believed in me, you see so I must believe in myself. No one else ever has.'

She lifted her face to his and Tam quite forgot he was supposed to be cleaning and oiling the mower, preparatory to putting it away for the winter. 'I believe in you.' Where had those words come from? Tam was astonished that they'd popped out of his mouth without even a thought. 'I believe you can do anything you want to do. But if you're serious about making a go of this place there'll be no room for sentiment.'

'I realise that.'

'Farming is a hard business. Are you tough enough?'

Her lips curved into a smile, tremulous, sensual, beguiling, and a sudden need raged through him, leaving his hands shaking so that he felt obliged to put down the oil can he was holding and pay excessive attention to wiping them on an old rag.

'I don't know, but I'm learning. How can anyone know if they are up to a job until they try? I want to try. Besides how I feel about Lanky leaving me Broombank, I have Effie to think about, and now Melissa, but also I want – need – to do this for myself. I've always felt the desire to be independent, to prove myself. This is my opportunity and I mustn't give up just because life is tough.'

'There'll be no medals at the end of it.'

'I know that.' She smiled. 'Grinding hard work in all weathers with little cash in hand. What I want to know is, does it bother you?'

'Bother me?'

'Working for a woman?'

Tam fought his thoughts back into order. He'd never worked for a woman before, let alone one as entrancing as this one. But if he was to stay, and there were worse places to spend the war, this relationship must be strictly business. Meg Turner might look homely enough at first glance, childlike almost with her hair all tied up with string and herself dressed in scruffy overalls much of the time. But a second glance, a smile from those lovely lips, and a man could forget his manners in a moment. 'So long as you realise I'm as independent as yourself.'

'I realise that.'

A long pause, then, 'We could start by getting rid of these damn rabbits, not to mention the foxes. Since the hunt has been called up, the place is overrun with them.'

Meg laughed, her heart soaring. 'We could sell the rabbits for two or three shillings a brace on Kendal market.'

'Three shillings?' Tam grinned at her. 'Then I'll clean the gun next. If we get enough it'll help pay next quarter's rent.'

Suddenly excited, Meg knelt on the grass beside him. It had been decided. He would stay. 'I mean to fatten more turkeys for this Christmas. I'm taking orders already. I've nearly paid Will Davies for those two cows and then I'll buy one or two more. The Co-op will take the extra milk off me, or I could get a hand-buggy and take it round myself. It'll give a regular income till I've time to build up the flock.'

Tam was watching her face, wondering how it was he hadn't noticed before how beautiful she was. He'd seen her as a young girl playing at farming, content to ride out life in the quietness of her own home in an unquestionably safe area. But there was much more to Meg Turner than that. She was exciting, ambitious, beguiling. Very likely passionate. He blanked that thought from his mind. It wouldn't be wise to consider taking his employer to bed, tempting as it might be.

'So? Are you with me?'

'I'm with you,' he said, without even a pause. Meg smiled her thanks, openly, and with delight in her grey eyes. Tam knew then he would stay with Meg Turner for the entire war. Longer, were she to ask.